**HARD TO FIND BOOKS ON BREEDING, RACING
AND MARKETING THOROUGHBREDS**

**THE RUSSELL MEERDINK COMPANY, LTD.**

P.O. Box 485
Menasha, WI 54952
(800) 635-6499 in the USA & Canada
(414) 725-0955 Worldwide
FAX: (414) 739-4322

# Thoroughbred Stallions

# Thoroughbred STALLIONS

Tony Morris

THE CROWOOD PRESS

First published in 1990 by
THE CROWOOD PRESS
Gipsy Lane
Swindon
Wiltshire SN2 6DQ

*British Library Cataloguing in Publication Data*

Morris, Tony 1944-
   Thoroughbred Stallions.
   1. Thoroughbred horses: Stallions
   I. Title
   636.132

ISBN 1-85223-331-1

Typesetting by Goodfellow & Egan,
French's Mill, French's Road, Cambridge.
Graphic work by Zig Zag Graphics,
319-320 Long Lane, Halesowen, West Midlands.
Printed by Butler & Tanner,
Frome and London

# Contents

# Preface

THE aim of this book is to provide a background to the Thoroughbred racing and breeding industries of the modern era with particular reference to the role played by leading stallions. It examines the key events in the racing and stud lives of 75 horses, each notable for some reason or other.

The most common qualification for selection was the impact a horse has made as a sire on current or recent racing in Britain and Ireland, while others were chosen on account of their own high profiles as runners and their – supposed – potential influence on future racing. A few of those included are not, and are not likely to become, important sires; they figure primarily to illustrate some of the reasons why some racehorses of great distinction fail to make the grade at stud.

The selection of horses for inclusion was entirely my own. It was made in the summer of 1989 and took account of no stallions who retired to stud later than 1988. In the case of horses who had yet to be represented on the racecourse at the time of selection, it should be emphasized that racing merit, rather than my assessment of possible stud achievements, was the chief criterion for inclusion. Worthy individuals were undoubtedly omitted.

One of the most widely employed methods for measuring the merit of both racehorse and sire these days is by successes achieved in Pattern Races or their American equivalent, Graded Stakes. There are numerous references to both throughout the book. The European Pattern system was instituted in 1971, with the aim of identifying the principal races contested in Britain, Ireland, France and Italy, and classifying them into three Groups; Group 1 races were reckoned to be the most important. Germany joined the scheme in 1972. The composition of the Pattern has been subject to relatively few modifications over the years and it is universally accepted as a worthwhile gauge of merit. The most noticeable changes in the European Pattern have been those to the names of races, generally to accommodate the interests of a sponsor; in this book, in the interests of consistency and in order to facilitate comprehension and comparisons, only the basic elements of race names appear.

Since 1971 most countries have adopted their own versions of the European Pattern. The North American Graded Stakes scheme was initiated in 1973 with the same basic objectives, but for various reasons has never achieved the credibility of its European counterpart. Since 1980 numerous changes have been made to its composition every year, with the number of races included advancing from 276 to 450 in the course of a decade. Many of the horses who are able to win Graded Stakes now, particularly those in Grade 3, would not have done so ten years ago. That inconsistency is worthy of note when it comes to assessing the relative achievements of runners and/or sires in America in the 1970s and 1980s.

There is Thoroughbred racing on every day of the year in the northern hemisphere, and every event has the potential to change perceptions in the industry. The records and reputations of racehorses and their sires tend to fluctuate rather like shares on the stock market - often with similar consequences - and events would not stand still to make this book a definitive account. Had it been written six months earlier or six months later, it would necessarily have been different in many material respects, reflecting the changes in perceptions caused by the changes in the data to hand. This book – apart from a few minor subsequent amendments – was written in February 1990, and its contents are an expression of how I assessed the data available then. The records of sires' progeny in Pattern and Graded races were cut off at 10 June 1990. The facts should stand the test of time, but some of the interpretations I put on them may have been wrong then and may have become exposed as serious errors of judgment between composition and publication. I can but hope that my fallibility will not shine forth on every page.

I would also stress that this is a work devoted to the highest class – or perceived highest class – of Thoroughbred. The horses examined in it are judged by the highest standards, effectively their merit as producers of top-level performers. All stallions – except the very worst – get winners. Many who disappoint by failing to get athletes of superior quality are quite capable of getting – and do get – plenty of worthwhile racehorses. Several who are the subject of critical comment here are sires of real consequence below the top level.

Several people gave me assistance, generally at very short notice, during the writing of this book. I would particularly like to thank bloodstock agents Richard Galpin, James Delahooke, Jill Lamb and Tote Cherry-Downes for the benefit of their expertise, which in numerous instances helped me to make more considered judgments of featured horses. David Dink, of the *Thoroughbred Times,* and Sue Cameron, of Sagittarius Bloodstock, came up with instant answers to factual queries in dire emergencies caused by brain seizure and library failure.

Tony Morris
Newmarket, 1990

The author and publishers are grateful to the following for permission to reproduce photographs:

MICHAEL BURNS: Northern Dancer (155).

ED BYRNE: Ballad Rock (30), Lord Gayle (125), The Minstrel (239).

GERRY CRANHAM: *Black and white* – Alzao (25), Blakeney (36), Bustino (50), Caro (56), Ela-Mana-Mou (70), Grundy (81), Ile de Bourbon (106), Known Fact (111), Mill Reef (133), Nijinsky (147), Rainbow Quest (170), Seattle Slew (190), Thatching (236), Top Ville (243). *Colour* (in order of appearance) – Mill Reef (head), Shirley Heights, Kris (head), Shergar, Nashwan, Shahrastani, Teenoso, Slip Anchor, Dancing Brave, Sadler's Wells (head), El Gran Senor, Lomond, Shareef Dancer, Known Fact, Busted, Nijinsky, Shardari, Ajdal, Ahonoora, Last Tycoon, Brigadier Gerard, Mill Reef (at sunset).

JOHN CROFTS: *Black and white* – Ahonoora (12), Ajdal (14, 15), Ardross (27), Assert (28), Busted (49), Caerleon (53), Dancing Brave (61, 62), Darshaan (67), El Gran Senor (73), Green Desert (86, 87), High Top (104), Kalaglow (109), Kris (114), Last Tycoon (116), Law Society (119), Lomond (122), Niniski (152), Nureyev (161), Petoski (168), Quest for Fame (171), Reference Point (173, 174), Rousillon (185),Sadler's Wells (187), Shadeed (200), Shahrastani (202), Shardari (204), Shareef Dancer (206), Shernazar (211, 212), Silver Hawk (219), Slip Anchor (225, 226), Storm Bird (229), Sure Blade (231), Teenoso (233). *Colour* – Secreto, Rousillon, Shadeed, Sure Blade, Sadler's Wells (action), Rainbow Quest, Nureyev, Ardross.

GRANGEWILLIAM STUD: Habitat (92).

DELL HANCOCK: Danzig (65), Mr Prospector (139).

TIM HANNAN: Persian Bold (165).

TONY LEONARD: *Black and white* – Blushing Groom (41), Green Dancer (83), Lyphard (129), Riverman (177), Sharpen Up (209), Vaguely Noble (246). *Colour* – Sharpen Up, Blushing Groom.

JOHN NOYE: Alydar (21), Chief's Crown (59), Forli (76), Halo (96), Roberto (181), Secretariat (195), Secreto (197), Sir Ivor (222).

ALEC RUSSELL: *Colour* – Kris (action).

GEORGE SELWYN: *Black and white* – Alleged (17), Be My Guest (33), Great Nephew (79), Green Forest (89), Shirley Heights (215). *Colour* – Great Nephew, Green Forest.

SPORT & GENERAL: Brigadier Gerard (45), Mummy's Pet (143).

GUY WILMOT: High Line (100).

# Introduction

THE Thoroughbred racehorse has often been described as one of the most remarkable products of the English genius. The development, within an amazingly short space of time, of a type of horse which could run appreciably faster than any of its forbears was planned and executed by a relatively small group of Englishmen, utilizing a select group of imported stallions and native-bred mares from obscure and diverse backgrounds. The difference was phenomenal, the experiment a total success.

It is a moot point, though, whether 'genius' is the right term to apply to those who created the Thoroughbred. Given that there was a desire on the part of England's nobility and gentry to up-grade the standard of the nation's racing stock – and of that there can be no doubt – it was natural that they should look to such places as Turkey and Arabia for the quality horses who might effect that improvement. The resources, financial and military, were available for the purchase or capture of those fine specimens, long admired in the west for their beauty and stamina. What those pioneers – buccaneers, some of them – could never have imagined was that the mares waiting at home for the Turks, Arabs and Barbs who were imported by the score would prove their ideal match, the crosses instantly establishing a hybrid of distinctive heritable qualities perfectly suited to the demands of England's racing system.

In a sense, the Thoroughbred was made to happen by the circumstances of the era. King Charles II, who bred, raced and often rode horses in competition after the Restoration (1660), did much to popularize racing. It was his favourite pastime, indulged to the extent of sometimes removing his entire Court to Newmarket, the town established under his patronage as the Headquarters of the Turf. That royal seal of approval for a sport which for centuries had provided just occasional amusement for the masses was the spur for the growth and regulation of racing and for the quest for horses better adapted to the purpose. Charles was still on the throne when breeders first raided the east for the stallions who were to create the Thoroughbred.

Nearly two centuries before Darwin's *Origin of Species* and Gregor Mendel's effective founding of the science of genetics, those innovators could not fully comprehend what they had achieved. However, they knew enough to recognize that the importation of those stallions from the east had made a crucial difference to the quality of racing stock they were able to produce. It was not long before they also cottoned on to the fact that what they had developed was essentially a new, distinct breed, incapable of further improvement for the purpose of racing by crossing either with other breeds or with fresh imports from the east.

Logic told those innovators that as this astonishing progress had been instigated and the new breed established as a result of the achievements of the first wave of imported horses, the real credit for the advances belonged to those stallions. As racing and breeding developed and detailed records began to be kept, it seemed that three horses in particular, the Byerley Turk (imported 1689), the Darley Arabian (1704) and the Godolphin Arabian (1730), had been crucially influential in the evolution of the breed. By the end of the 18th century, it was already evident that only those three stallions had established enduring male lines in the Thoroughbred population. It seemed only right to refer to them as the founding fathers of the breed.

The myth has persisted to the end of the 20th century, for all our modern knowledge of the workings of heredity. It remains a fascinating curiosity that every Thoroughbred in the world today can be traced back in the direct male line to one or other of the Byerley Turk, the Darley Arabian or the Godolphin Arabian; that fact is still retailed in every reference to the origins of the breed, always to be interpreted (and often expressed) with undue significance. There can be no denying that all three horses were important stallions in their day, but in our more enlightened era there should surely be no excuse for failing to appraise events more realistically.

It was essentially the crossing of the imported stallions from the east with the English native-bred mares which produced the Thoroughbred. Both made vital contributions; the one could not have done it without the other. The much-glorified "great triumvirate" were not the only successful imported sires of their era, and the fact that their male-line descendants flourished more obviously than those of some others does not mean that those whose female descendants excelled were not equally, perhaps even more, significant. In the male line, the Darley Arabian is now far and away the most widely represented of the three in the world's Thoroughbred population, but recent analysis has shown that the Godolphin Arabian figures much more commonly in pedigrees. Studies have also indicated that a hitherto unsung hero, the Curwen Bay Barb, is more numerously represented than the Byerley Turk.

Before Mendel and the sweet pea experiments which provided the first real clues about genetic inheritance, it was excusable for civilized Man to believe in male dominance. Brought up on Biblical listings of who begat whom, on the succession of kings and peers, and on numerous social and legal conventions which emphasized the father-son connection while effectively treating the female as a mere receptacle for the male's seed, it was anything but surprising that 18th and 19th century Thoroughbred breeders should set great store by male lines. Genetics (and to some extent, the women's movement) has taught us differently in recent times, but progress in that respect has not yet reached the stage where breeders are ready to recognize that the sole factor invariably transmitted only from father to son is the male sex chromosome, a factor not known to be linked with any other inherited characteristic which might be associated with racing merit.

The myth of male supremacy lives on in Thoroughbred breeding for numerous reasons – chiefly of a biological, environmental or financial nature. The most obvious difference between the sexes, on the score of their capacity to influence the breed, is that the mare's gestation period of 11 months permits her to have but one foal a year, whereas a normally virile and fertile horse can easily become a sire 60 or 70 times over in the same time. The average broodmare will produce about eight foals in a lifetime; a popular stallion may get 600. Opportunity favours the male to an overwhelming degree.

On the other hand, that old canard about the female being merely a receptacle for the male's seed is still very much alive. It is expressed, now as from the dawn of the Thoroughbred, in the fact that the lip-service paid to the hifalutin notion that "the purpose of racing is the improvement of the breed" (another canard) extends only to the male. Generally speaking, a colt must display racing merit of a superior order before he is granted the opportunity to become a sire.

A filly need not earn her right to breed by racing successfully; whether she can run or not, she is recognized as a prospective parent by dint of her ownership of ovaries rather than testicles.

It follows that the breeding population is made up, for the most part, of stallions with good racing form and mares with poor racing form. It also follows that the racing population is made up, for the most part, of horses who have a good sire and a poor dam (in terms of racing ability), though genuine believers in male supremacy and those with vested interests in stallions tend to allude to it only in connection with runners of distinction. The fact is that sire and dam make equal genetic contributions to their offspring, and nobody can predict at the time of conception which will dominate in terms of any factors which affect racing merit. It must also be said that it is rarely possible to make categorical attributions about the source of merit (or lack of merit) in the product of any mating.

It is, of course, the unpredictability of Thoroughbred breeding which accounts for much of its fascination. That, though, is an outsider's allowable objective view, not the way the industry perceives it or promotes it. The unpredictability of racing itself is all part of the fun, but that is something which owners pay for, generally suffering it with an equanimity founded on the knowledge that they came into the game with their eyes open, aware of the pitfalls, and prepared to squander their spare cash enjoyably. Breeding – and breeders – are different.

Breeders are not reconciled to the unpredictability of their business. As a group they behave, alternately or even simultaneously, like ostriches, like sheep, like lemmings. They would prefer to remain ignorant about the latest developments in the science of genetics, which might give them ideas about how to mate their mares more advantageously. The only science they want to know about is veterinary science, most specifically that branch of it which gives them some assurance that their mares will get in foal instead of proving barren, as nature may have intended.

They feel compelled to employ expediency rather than flair or imagination. They are dedicated followers of fashion, never daring to risk anything uncommercial, and they pursue that route even insofar as it may entail adhering to one of the many crackpot, long-discredited theories which abound in breeding lore. They commonly feel bound to act against their better judgment, through the simple fear that it may cost them dear to step out of line. They make many wrong decisions, and feel better about them because most of their fellows do exactly the same.

Of course, there are exceptions to the rule, principally those owner-breeders with sufficient funds to stand the risks of acting regardless of market forces. It may be no coincidence that, throughout the history of the Thoroughbred, horses who raced for their breeders have tended to be better than those produced for sale. However, the days when racing was dominated by a relatively large group of owner-breeders have gone; there has lately been a revival in Europe, though concentrated in fewer hands, marked by a resurgence in the fortunes of the Aga Khan's studs, and a powerful challenge has developed out of the massive investment of a small party of Arabs, but in the modern era, Thoroughbred breeding is more typically all about producing horses for the market, to be sold either as foals or as yearlings.

In that context, it is easier to see why breeders behave as they do. By definition a breeder is a mare-owner, who, in the time-honoured manner, sends his mare, complete with dowry, for an arranged marriage with a stallion. Not so many years ago, he could have done that quite cheaply, the fees for stallions then being more closely aligned to the price of yearlings, which in turn bore some relation to the amount of prizemoney in racing. Things have changed dramatically, with the result that commercial breeders, always an unadventurous, careful group of fellows, have become ever more circumspect in the conduct of their business. There is a certain method in their collective madness, it must be said.

Where Europe is concerned, the changes may be traced to the developments in racing in the late 1960s. Over a long period it had been evident that the quality of Thoroughbreds produced by the principal owner-breeders in America was quite up to the standard of the best in England and France. American breeders raced extensively in both countries with considerable success from the 1920s, and because they did so on a relatively modest scale, for the laudable reason that they enjoyed the ambience of European racing, we tended to rejoice over their occasional notable triumphs. Europe never really envisaged a time when America would become a large-scale competitor on its own territory.

The rude awakening came when men like Charles Engelhard (with such as Habitat and Nijinsky) and Raymond Guest (with Sir Ivor) brought products of American commercial studs, purchased at American auctions, and carried off the most coveted prizes on the European Turf. In fact, only the want of such enterprise, and the modern phenomenon of easy horse transportation, had delayed the shocking realization of American superiority in Thoroughbred production so long, but when it hit home, Europe was powerless to respond. American markets, bolstered by a significantly stronger prizemoney structure for their product, were far higher than those in Europe, and while we now knew where we should go for the champions of tomorrow, few European-based owners and breeders dared to take the necessary risks. Of those who ventured, early in the piece, Tim Rogers came home with Lyphard, and sold him at a loss. Alec Head returned with Riverman, and also relieved Rogers of Lyphard, at auction in Newmarket.

With the floodgates open, and American stock successful wherever there was kudos to be gained in Europe, the panic response was to purchase stallions from the States. Predictably, the Americans off-loaded the worst they had on to the eager and unsuspecting English, Irish and French. This, clearly, was not the answer, but it was not long before the vision and enterprise of Robert Sangster became embodied in an altogether different and more coherent approach.

Sangster, at that time heir to the Vernons football pools fortune, conceived a strategy which involved substantial financial risk, yet offered potentially vast profits. The risk he endeavoured to minimize by employing the services of a number of Europe's outstanding horsemen, most notably Irish-based trainer Vincent O'Brien. The plan was to raid the principal U.S. yearling markets at Keeneland and Saratoga for choicely-bred colts, with the intention of developing them into champions on European courses and re-selling them as prospective stallions back into America. Success would make the scheme self-financing, and continued success would have knock-on effects, leading to a time when the necessity to sell back to the States would not be an imperative; the champions produced could then be based for their stud careers in Ireland, where Sangster joined forces with O'Brien and John Magnier with a view to establishing Coolmore Stud as Europe's number one stallion station.

The timing of Sangster's initiative was right. American breeders revelled in the knowledge that they had extended their sphere of influence – and dominance – to Europe. Their successes in English, French and Irish classic and championship events had inevitably added strength to their yearling markets and they were already consciously attempting to produce stock more obviously suited to racing in Europe. In addition, the fact that top European races were now patently contested by leading representatives of studs on two continents, instead of one, had enhanced their prestige and put substantial additional value on their winners.

The first concerted efforts of Sangster and his team succeeded beyond their wildest dreams. Among their auction purchases in the summer of 1975 and spring of 1976 were The Minstrel and Alleged, who were to prove the outstanding three-year-olds in Europe in 1977. The Minstrel, purchased for $200,000, was re-sold to the States for $9 million after having won the Derby, the Irish Derby and the King George VI & Queen Elizabeth Stakes. Alleged, who cost $175,000, won consecutive runnings of the Prix de l'Arc de Triomphe and was traded back to Kentucky with a stud valuation of $16 million. Inevitably, the repercussions were dramatic and wide-ranging.

The message seemed to be that those who gambled with high stakes stood to yield enormous dividends. Markets soared higher than ever in America and rose appreciably in Europe, with fresh money attracted into an industry that promised vast profits fast. The average price for a yearling at the 1975 Keeneland Summer Sale (in which The Minstrel was purchased) was $53,000; by 1980 it was $160,000. At the principal yearling sale in England, the average rocketed from under 10,000gns in 1976 to more than 42,000gns in 1981. Further staggering increases followed, with individual records for a yearling reaching the ludicrous level of $13.1 million in America in 1985 and IR3.1 million gns in Europe in 1984.

Initially, the Sangster ploy had seemed to work perfectly. He had obtained the champions he set out to develop, re-sold them at huge profits and re-invested to repeat the process. He kept making the scheme work while others who jumped on the bandwagon failed for lack of his resources and/or the quality of expertise he had hired. Soon enough he was able to embark on phase two of his project, standing some of the champions developed in O'Brien's stable at Coolmore. Effectively, what Sangster had done was to drive markets higher on both sides of the Atlantic, and because he had a few years' start on anyone else in Europe, he was uniquely placed to take advantage of the situation. For a brief period, it seemed to some that he and his partners had done enough to establish an enduring dominant role for themselves on the European scene.

There were others, though, who felt all along that the success of the Sangster initiative was, at best, a mixed blessing. There was always a danger that short-term benefits to the breeding industry in the form of higher prices for its product would swiftly disappear through the vastly increased production

costs which had followed as a matter of course. The upward revaluation of all racing and breeding stock was irrational, because only comparable increases in the level of European prizemoney could have underpinned the market, and they did not – indeed, could not – come. Breeders in Europe were never going to be able to sell untried stock into America, which already demonstrably produced higher-quality horses, and there was surely a limit to what Europeans could be induced to spend on yearlings destined for racing here. The market had forsaken reality for fantasy, and before long painful adjustments would inevitably have to be made.

The next development, which changed the face of the industry on both sides of the Atlantic, prolonged the fantasy and, for some, has delayed the return to reality indefinitely. The arrival of the Arabs, most conspicuously the Maktoum family from Dubai and Khalid Abdullah from Saudi Arabia, was understandably welcomed by the Sangster party and by others who had become dependent on the maintenance of a market divorced from real values. Nobody could have foreseen, however, the far-reaching consequences of what initially appeared to represent no more and no less than a tremendous stimulus to the market.

The Arabs' determination to involve themselves in European racing, with England as their principal base, came with a wholehearted commitment to the pursuit of excellence, backed by a level of investment which went far beyond the bounds set by any previous patrons of the Turf. Their simple target was to race, and ultimately to breed, the best horses, and money really was no object in the furtherance of those aims. They attended all the major auctions, commonly sending prices through the roof as they competed with – and generally outbid – the Sangster group and all other rivals for possession of the choicest lots. Throughout the eighties the Maktoums were the heaviest spenders at the select Keeneland yearling sales (where their investment ran into nine figures over the period), and their dominance was inevitable, as their operation was at no time subject to the purely commercial considerations which necessarily restricted the scale of everyone else's involvement.

The impact of the Maktoums was phenomenal in every aspect of the business. They spent lavishly, not just on horses, but also on property (often established studs and stables which they refurbished to the highest standards), on race sponsorship, on the provision of better training facilities for all at Newmarket, and on endowments for veterinary research. They gave employment to many, and, not least of their accomplishments, were largely responsible for the improvement of the quality of racing in Europe, through their large-scale and long-term importations of the best available untried stock from America. They were also prepared to stand their horses at stud in Europe, most especially in England and Ireland, rather than sell back into the American market, so the benefits of their involvement were, potentially at least, available to other European breeders. Inevitably, however, not all of their influence was for the general good.

The most obvious result of their insatiable acquisitiveness was that they began to dominate at the races as surely as in the auction markets. The scale of their operation became a deterrent to others who saw no point in attempting to compete with them. In the marketplace, prices for top-grade stock continued to rule at an irrationally high level because of their involvement, and became so strong that even Robert Sangster, who had precipitated the drive for upward revaluations, himself became a casualty of his own enterprise. He was rarely able to buy the horses he wanted at auction from the early 1980s onwards; he could not establish the stallion prospects as before; and the funds for re-investment were no longer available. The Maktoums, the only players who were not dependent for their survival on their return from investment in bloodstock, were also the only players geared to thrive in the prevailing financial climate.

The basic problem in Europe was that the level of prizemoney was too low, and rising too slowly, to encourage wider ownership of Thoroughbreds. The only surefire way to make money out of a yearling colt was to have him develop into a high-class racehorse who could be sold for stud duty, and, realistically, the odds against that were remote. The incentives to purchase yearling fillies were negligible. Like most acquisitive buyers, the Arabs also proved to be reluctant sellers, which meant that they could rarely be induced to part with stallion prospects who had earned racing distinction in their colours. Fewer such horses were available for purchase, while demand for them remained keen, in line with the popular belief that the real money in the bloodstock business was to be made in stallions. The upshot was that the cost of buying horses out of training remained unrealistically high, and the fees charged for the stud services of such horses (geared to producing a profit for investors over a four- or five-year period) were just as unrealistically high for breeders.

By the mid-1980s it was already apparent that production costs were making life difficult for breeders on both sides of the Atlantic. Stallion fees had reached a point where they had lost any kind of relationship to the available returns in the yearling market. When the going had been good, stallion-owning syndicates had been able to hold breeders to ransom while making vast profits; they set the prices which breeders had to pay to enable them to participate in a thriving industry. When breeders found that their products had become less attractive to buyers, to the point where there was little or no profit to be made, pressure was put on stallion owners to reduce prices. Inevitably, they met with considerable reluctance on the part of a group who had enjoyed making substantial sums. Moreover, many stallion shares were now in the ownership of individuals and companies with neither interest in nor experience of the Thoroughbred business, having been attracted to it solely on the grounds that it seemed to have become a highly profitable enterprise.

The Americans had more justification for a high stud fee policy than Europe, because they could at least sell their best products into two markets and they did have the 'cushion' of a soundly-based prizemoney structure at home. There was no American demand for European-bred yearlings, whose destiny could only be to race for the modest sums available in their own neck of the woods. Yet it was in America where the first steps were taken towards giving breeders a fairer crack of the whip, and as the eighties gave way to the nineties, the outlook for European breeders remained somewhat grimmer.

Between 1985 and 1990 stud fees in America declined by around 50 per cent overall, the horses at the top of the market being those most drastically reduced. The reductions came later in Europe, and for the most part were much less dramatic; horses at every level of the 1990 market still seemed overpriced, in relation to the earning potential of their offspring either in the sale-ring or on the racecourse. Another interesting development was that in the States a trend against the syndication of racehorses had set in; several of the very best runners of 1988 went to stud in the following spring as the property of those who had raced them, their fees set on the basis of what breeders regarded as realistic and subject to revision in accordance with future market conditions, most obviously when the performances of their offspring on the track gave indication of their merit.

By contrast, with the market for horses out of training in Europe still irrationally high, prospective stallions continued to be syndicated, with their fees determined according to the projected return to shareholders over a period. Moreover, the trend was for stallions to cover more mares, and the practice of maximizing income potential by standing horses in Europe during the northern hemisphere spring and in Australia or New Zealand in the southern hemisphere spring became prevalent. Experiments with dual-season covering had been undertaken in the early 1970s and all had failed lamentably, but the lessons learned then were fast forgotten when opportunities to exact more income from money-generating stallions re-presented themselves.

The Thoroughbred breeding industry of 1990 is scarcely recognizable from that of the late sixties, when Europe was shaken out of its complacency by the 'American invasion'. Developments since that epoch-making event have, for one reason or another, merely confirmed American supremacy, a situation which current trends can only accentuate. The American industry is much more broadly-based, supported by a prizemoney structure in racing which offers real incentives and ensures a realistic market for young stock. Americans have also been swifter to react to every positive and negative factor which has had an impact on their business, and they are heading into the last decade of the century with confidence, having made the necessary corrections and adjustments to restore stability and provide the base for progress.

Fears that their having sold so many of their supposed best mares and fillies to the Maktoum brothers would cause the quality of their production to suffer have not been realized, and in 1989 the Maktoums bought nearly half of the yearlings offered in the select portion of the Keeneland July catalogue. One matter which still causes some concern is that most of the stallions who have been identified with American success over the last decade have died, retired or have simply aged without obvious replacements having come to the fore. That is a situation which may well be remedied by the industry's recent release from the self-imposed shackles of a syndication system which had so lent itself to abuse in the 1980s that it had come to militate against the development of stallions on the basis of merit while concentrating on establishing them as money-making commodities, regardless of their real worth as sires. Even so, it will be crucially important to American breeders that buyers for Europe rapidly identify the potential successors to the star stallions of the '80s and obtain good results from them. A sudden halt in the supply of high-quality stock from the States at this juncture would not benefit a Europe by no means ready to meet its demands at home.

The current scene in Europe is bleak. Racing is dominated by a small group of Arabs whose only goal is success, at whatever price, and who are not governed by the profit motive which rules everyone else's actions. The Arabs do not make money, are not attempting to make money – as either breeders or owners - and are meeting with much of their success on the racecourse because other owners are powerless to compete with them. Commercial breeders are finding it increasingly difficult to make money for several reasons, none of which seems likely to go away in the foreseeable future. The prizemoney fund in racing is insufficient to encourage a broader base of ownership, for which the Maktoum dominance is already a deterrent in any case. The continuing successes of American-bred runners in Europe effectively advertise the shortcomings of European stock and limit its international appeal. Most significantly, production costs remain inordinately high, their usually most substantial element, the stallion fee, being set with little or no regard to the eventual market value of the product.

There never was sufficient money in European racing to sustain a high stud fee policy in the breeding industry, and much of what has gone wrong here in recent years dates from the Coolmore-inspired canard that there was. The annals of Thoroughbred breeding show that 95 per cent of all stallions are failures, comparative or complete, assessed in terms of the racecourse performances of their progeny. Hype cannot alter that ratio, nor yet ensure that the horses who are hyped figure among the successful five per cent. At the height of the market, when prospective stallions were syndicated for astronomical valuations, it became an imperative to form a different judgment of success, and all that really mattered then was that a horse should make money for the shareholders. In order to make money for people who had invested with borrowed money and were subject to high interest charges, stallions had to cover more mares at higher fees. Breeders were easily exploited in the furtherance of that aim, as their predilection for young and unproven stallions had the force of a tradition, and they were induced to spend unwarrantably large ums in the support of horses whose 'management' was all about servicing bank loans and making short-term profit, and not all about using the time-honoured industry skills designed to develop horses into stallions who produced long-term benefits for both shareholder and breeder through commercial success based on solid racecourse achievement. If a stallion became a sire of good racehorses, that was a bonus; it was never really the plan. The paths of the stallion man and the breeder diverged.

This, of course, was precisely what had occurred in America, but it could not be made to last even in the stronger markets there. Breeders declined to continue subsidizing the mistakes of stallion syndicates, and the much healthier trading conditions which now obtain were instituted. Here the breeding business is still controlled by the stallion owners, who remain convinced that breeders owe them a living and are all too capable of ensuring that they provide it. Breeders feel compelled to do what is supposedly fashionable in order to minimize their risk in a high-cost business, only to find, as often as not, that their only 'achievement' is to have contributed, at high cost, to the over-supply of stock by a stallion doomed to market failure.

It is no coincidence that since the abortive mid-seventies attempt to drive the European bloodstock market closer to that in America, few stallions of any import have been established in Europe. New horses are hyped, over-used for the benefit of share-holders, then discarded and replaced as soon as the market turns against them. That process is frequently complete before a stallion's stock has been properly tested on the racecourse, and there have been numerous instances of horses whose reputations as sires have become significantly enhanced after their sales abroad.

There has been a marked reluctance on the part of stallion owners to introduce horses at realistic fees and allow the racecourse achievements of their progeny to establish their proper market level in the fullness of time. When there is big money involved, shareholders understandably prefer to shift the risk to breeders, and breeders, blackmailed into believing that the only way they can remain in business is to play according to the rules set by the stallion owners, fall meekly into line. The syndication of high-class horses for stud, once regarded as something akin to a sacred trust for the protection and promotion of a valuable property, has become a sham. The old notion of a band of breeders clubbing together with a view to supporting and furthering the interests of a potentially successful sire has gone by the board. Proper syndications, with horses split up into (usually) 40 equal parts among almost as many shareholders, no longer exist. In countless instances less than half the horse is sold, a bogus valuation formed on the basis of 40 equal shares having changed hands, and a stud fee devised from those mythical figures which aims to yield profit for the few investors, regardless of the stallion's eventual success or failure. No thought is given to the profitability, or otherwise, of outside breeders whose money is expected to finance the enterprise.

The abuse of the syndication system is to some extent a product of the age and society in which we live. It is a microcosm of a world funded on credit bought at extortionate rates of interest. In the old days nobody in his right mind ever bought anything as vulnerable and unpredictable as a Thoroughbred other than with his own money, and spare money at that. Buying horses with borrowed money is exceedingly unwise at the best of times, insane when it is conducted on such a large scale that it represents a built-in inflationary factor defeating – or at least obstructing the ends of all in the industry except those at the top with huge incomes and no debts to service.

# The Stallions

# Ahonoora

BREEDERS, like punters, act on the basis that results are predictable; both groups live lives that are full of shocks and surprises. The notion that like begets like is fundamental to every breeder's philosophy, its consummation devoutly wished at every mating, but nature scorns such simplistic ideas, constantly providing examples which contradict them, occasionally producing a specimen which spends a lifetime refuting them.

Ahonoora was one such horse. His sire Lorenzaccio was a gifted athlete in the 8-11 furlongs range who compiled an impressive record over a four-season career and was most famous – or notorious – for his remarkable victory over a jaded Nijinsky in the 1970 Champion Stakes. He was never a better racehorse than the wonderful Nijinsky, of course, but his racing record and his pedigree seemed good enough to raise hopes of his developing into a successful sire. Instead, he proved incapable of getting anything of his own class, and in 1977 he was despatched to Australia, having not a single winner of an English Pattern race to his name. Ahonoora was a two-year-old in training with Brian Swift at the time of his departure.

A 7600gns yearling purchase on behalf of Sheikh Essa Alkhalifa, Ahonoora came from a female background noted for speed and usually short on class. His dam Helen Nichols had won five races over five furlongs, his grand-dam twice over the same distance. Swift, always a trainer to exploit speed and precocity when he found it, soon surmised that Ahonoora was not destined to stay the distances favoured by his sire, but did have the makings of a smart sprinter. At the second time of asking the rangy chesnut bore out that view, taking a six-furlong maiden at Newbury in a field of 22. Next time out he was beaten a length at Salisbury, and then came a blessing in disguise – a split pastern which put him out of action for the rest of the season.

The enforced rest was exactly what the growing colt needed, and as a three-year-old he was able to establish himself as a useful performer in sprint handicaps. He won two of nine races that season, his best moment coming in a 50/1 triumph in the Stewards' Cup at Goodwood. There he got home by half a length from another three-year-old, Double

Form, who had been trying to concede him 19lb, and the exceptional early speed he showed that day convinced his trainer that his natural distance was five furlongs rather than six. The point was proved when he won a handicap under 10st over the minimum trip at Newbury.

Ahonoora changed stables during the winter, resuming in another Newbury handicap for new trainer Frankie Durr. By winning it in good style he earned the right to try his luck in Pattern company. The gulf he was required to bridge in the Group 3 Temple Stakes at Sandown was enormous, as he now met Double Form at level weights, but he led that rival most of the way, then rallied gamely to be beaten only a length. He had clearly made abnormal improvement and was patently of Pattern calibre; subsequent events earned him recognition as the third-best sprinter of his crop. He won the Group 3 King George Stakes at Goodwood, and he had the good fortune to be awarded the Group 2 York Sprint Championship on the disqualification of Thatching, who had beaten him fair and square into second place, but had hampered the third finisher, Abdu. Double Form was behind him that day, but on two other occasions, in the Group 1 King's Stand Stakes and the Group 2 Haydock Sprint, Ahonoora came off second best.

Ahonoora was at no time a great sprinter. It could be said, though, that he plied that trade honestly and consistently, displaying admirable early pace and an evident zest for competition. He had qualities which breeders seek to reproduce, and that gave him some sort of chance as a stallion. On the other hand, as a son of the otherwise disappointing Lorenzaccio, from a family which generally lacked class, he seemed at best to represent what the Americans call 'cheap speed'. If he were to make a name as a sire – and few would have bet on it – it would happen courtesy of a profusion of ordinary sprinters. Things did not work out like that.

There can be no doubt that Ahonoora was fortunate to find a home at the Irish National Stud, an establishment which traditionally has concentrated on providing a base for good physical types likely to attract a wide range of commercial breeders, rather than high-priced horses who might get classic-quality stock, but could be afforded only by a limited clientele. Advertised to cover at a fee of IR£2250, with a live foal concession, Ahonoora suited plenty of pockets and seemed a reasonable risk, for all his want of pedigree. The early tests were passed when the first foals and yearlings – almost all active, athletic types – brought healthy profits in the sale-ring, taking the eyes of trainers.

Ahonoora soon began to get winners. At first they were generally of modest enough character, but when allowance was made for the lack of class in the mares he had covered, there seemed to be genuine merit in his achievements. Before long there were better winners; in 1984 two fillies from his first crop, Ahohoney in France and Princess Tracy in Ireland, collected in Pattern company, and one from his second crop, Park Appeal, excelled them by scoring twice in Group 1. Indeed, Park Appeal's display in Newmarket's Cheveley Park Stakes was regarded by many as the outstanding performance of the season by any two-year-old. She was named champion of her sex in both Ireland and England; her sire was suddenly fashionable, and his fee was hoisted to IR£12,000.

The idea that Ahonoora was primarily a 'filly sire' gained strength when Park Express developed into a high-class performer in 1986, with a Group 1 victory in the Phoenix Champion Stakes marking the pinnacle of her career. However, Don't Forget Me was soon to correct that impression. The product of an undistinguished mare, he paraded his speed and battling qualities with telling effect as a two-year-old, when his best win came in the Group 2 Champagne Stakes at Doncaster, and in the following spring he scored a rare classic double, taking the Newmarket and Curragh 2000 Guineas with almost identical displays of resolute front-running.

Those performances prompted the last significant change in Ahonoora's circumstances as a stallion. He had stood at a fee of IR£20,000 in 1987, making him easily the highest-priced horse ever at the Irish National Stud, and when Don't Forget Me elevated him to the status of a classic sire, offers poured in for him. The one which succeeded valued him at around IR£7 million, and it came from a partnership comprising Coolmore and Segenhoe, the latter being a progressive stud in New South Wales. It was at first denied that the deal would involve Ahonoora's departure from Ireland, but it soon emerged that he would be employed in both hemispheres, covering at Coolmore at IR45,000gns and at Segenhoe at A$50,000.

The deal meant that, in Ireland at least, Ahonoora was exposed to a higher class of mare, though it was

*Ahonoora defeats Abdu in the King George Stakes at Goodwood.*

debatable whether his record would improve on account of it. In the past, other 'chance-bred' stallions had fared worse when upgraded to cover supposedly better mares. As the first of Ahonoora's Coolmore-conceived progeny are not due to race until 1991, the effect on him remains to be seen. Meanwhile, the best of his stock conceived at Tully continued to do well, headed by a prominent 1989 sprinter in Indian Ridge and Negligent, who emulated Park Appeal as champion two-year-old filly in England.

Sadly, Negligent's victory in the Group 3 Rockfel Stakes, which made her the early favourite for 1990's filly classics, came as a posthumous credit for her sire. The breeding industries of both Ireland and Australia were shocked by the news that Ahonoora, still only 14, had been destroyed after a simple paddock accident at Segenhoe, where he slipped and broke his near-hind pastern. The extent of the loss, at a time when there were so many untried – and unborn – foals still 'in the pipeline', could not immediately be gauged. It was possible that the best was yet to come.

On the basis of what he had achieved by the time of his death, Ahonoora was a distinctly above-average sire. He was at times over-estimated, and his keenest advocates could never explain away the fact that his ratio of winners to runners was never very good. On the other hand, he was undoubtedly capable of getting really high-class performers, sometimes without much obvious help from his mates. A number excelled him in racing distinction and showed aptitudes to which he never aspired. As a rule, he tended to get sprinters out of mares from sprinting backgrounds (such as Indian Ridge and Statoblest), milers out of mares by milers (Don't Forget Me) and longer-distance performers from mares with prominent staying influences in their backgrounds (Ahohoney, Park Express). The natural inference from that rule is that Ahonoora did not have much impact on the staying capacity of his stock, but he certainly supplied a touch of class where it had been lacking in some of his mates.

Typically, the Ahonooras did not have the best of forelegs as yearlings, but they tended to 'harden into them', as horsemen say. It is strange – and quite without logic – that his stock who did not share his colour tended to be better than the rest, to such a degree that some horsemen automatically rejected his chesnuts. Irish trainer Jim Bolger, who has handled many of his progeny, admits to a prejudice in favour of the browns – and not entirely on account of Park Appeal. The most notable exception to the rule to date is Indian Ridge, who, as a product of a chesnut mare, could not have been any other colour.

## Racing record

| Year | Starts | Wins | 2nd | 3rd | 4th | £ |
|------|--------|------|-----|-----|-----|------|
| 1977 | 3 | 1 | 2 | - | - | 2,586 |
| 1978 | 9 | 2 | - | 1 | 2 | 19,164 |
| 1979 | 8 | 4 | 3 | - | - | 64,839 |
|      | 20 | 7 | 5 | 1 | 2 | 86,589 |

## Principal wins

1978  Stewards' Cup Handicap
1979  King George Stakes-Gr3
      York Sprint Championship Stakes-Gr2

## Principal progeny
### 1981
b f AHOHONEY (ex Honey Buzzard, by Sea Hawk)
   1984  Prix Fille de l'Air-Gr3
   1985  Prix Fille de l'Air-Gr3
b f PRINCESS TRACY (ex Princess Ru, by Princely Gift)
   1984  Ballyogan Stakes-Gr3
         Phoenix Sprint Stakes-Gr3

### 1982
b f NOORA ABU (ex Ishtar Abu, by St Chad)
   1989  Pretty Polly Stakes-Gr2
br f PARK APPEAL (ex Balidaress, by Balidar)
   1984  Moyglare Stud Stakes-Gr1
         Cheveley Park Stakes-Gr1

### 1983
ch f GINNY BINNY (ex Blue Gulf, by Gay Fandango)
   1987  Premio Melton-Gr2
b c NASHAMAA (ex Balidaress, by Balidar)
   1987  Ballymacoy Stakes-Gr3
br f PARK EXPRESS (ex Matcher, by Match)
   1986  Lancashire Oaks-Gr3
         Nassau Stakes-Gr2
         Phoenix Champion Stakes-Gr1

### 1984
b c DON'T FORGET ME (ex African Doll, by African Sky)
   1986  Vintage Stakes-Gr3
         Champagne Stakes-Gr2
   1987  2000 Guineas Stakes-Gr1
         Irish 2000 Guineas-Gr1

## AHONOORA                          (chesnut, 1975)

| | | Clarion | Djebel |
| | Klairon | | Columba |
| Lorenzaccio | | Kalmia | Kantar |
| (ch 1965) | | | Sweet Lavender |
| | | The Phoenix | Chateau Bouscaut |
| | Phoenissa | | Fille de Poete |
| | | Erica Fragrans | Big Game |
| | | | Jennydang |
| | | Hill Gail | Bull Lea |
| | Martial | | Jane Gail |
| Helen Nichols | | Discipliner | Court Martial |
| (ch 1966) | | | Edvina |
| | | Whistler | Panorama |
| | Quaker Girl | | Farthing Damages |
| | | Mayflower | Borealis |
| | | | Foliage |

### 1985
ch c INDIAN RIDGE (ex Hillbrow, by Swing Easy)
   1988  Jersey Stakes-Gr3
   1989  Duke of York Stakes-Gr3
         King's Stand Stakes-Gr2
b f PRINCESS ATHENA (ex Shopping Wise, by Floribunda)
   1987  Queen Mary Stakes-Gr3
br c PROJECT MANAGER (ex Beparoejojo, by Lord Gayle)
   1988  Gallinule Stakes-Gr2

### 1986
b c STATOBLEST (ex Statira, by Skymaster)
   1989  King George Stakes-Gr3
   1990  Palace House Stakes-Gr3

### 1987
br c ARMANASCO (ex For Going, by Balidar)
   1989  Railway Stakes-Gr3
gr f NEGLIGENT (ex Negligence, by Roan Rocket)
   1989  Rockfel Stakes-Gr3
gr f RUBY TIGER (ex Hayati, by Hotfoot)
   1989  Premio Dormello-Gr3

# Ajdal

FEW horses attract as much attention and controversy in a short life as Ajdal, who was seldom out of the news from the time of his first public appearance, as a sales yearling, to his premature death at stud little more than three years afterwards.

The circumstances surrounding Ajdal's date with the auctioneer at Keeneland on 23 July 1985 were bizarre. This striking, really handsome Northern Dancer colt, a bay with three white socks, stepped into the ring only five minutes after it had been vacated by a son of Nijinsky (Seattle Dancer) who had fetched a world-record $13.1 million. Many judges reckoned that the later colt was a finer specimen, and the atmosphere was electric as the bidding again exceeded the seven-figure mark. The process was inevitably long, and it was complicated by the fact that when the action became confined to two parties, one – Sheikh Mohammed – was clearly visible in his usual seat in the auditorium, while the other chose to bid from a point way behind the auctioneer's rostrum, unseen by most observers. Such was the protracted nature of the proceedings that one of the Sheikh's aides, who chanced to be standing at the back, had time to scurry around the arena and through the throng to inform his employer that his opponent was a representative of the colt's vendor. By that time the bidding had reached $7.5 million, and the Sheikh promptly dropped out. The most highly-priced 'buy-back' in auction history returned to breeder Ralph Wilson.

That was not the end of the story. Away from the public gaze a deal was discussed, and some days later it emerged that the Sheikh had bought the colt; the price was never disclosed, but was assumed to have been much less than the sum reached in the ring. Ajdal was handed over to Michael Stoute, who had previously saddled Shareef Dancer, another Northern Dancer colt, for a victory in the Irish Derby.

Ajdal won all three of his races as a two-year-old, impressing greatly in the first two against modest opposition, then getting mixed reviews over his performance in the Group 1 Dewhurst Stakes. The burst of speed which carried Ajdal to the front at Newmarket seemed to indicate superior class of a high order, but in the seventh and final furlong he failed to maintain his momentum and only narrowly held his advantage. While the debate over the reason for this lapse continued to rage, Reference Point wrested the title of champion two-year-old from his grasp.

In the following spring Ajdal won the Group 3 Craven Stakes, again in less than scintillating style, and his efforts in the Newmarket and Curragh 2000 Guineas proved disappointing. It had always been assumed that a mile would prove his optimum distance, but there were clearly better milers and it began to look as though Ajdal had been over-rated. Those who remained convinced of the colt's inherent class prescribed a change of distance, with as many believing he was really a sprinter as imagined him to be a stayer. Michael Stoute, who freely confessed his own uncertainty, kept all options open by pointing Ajdal at the Derby while also entering him for the July Cup, over half the Derby distance. Remarkably, the colt contested both.

Ajdal performed with abundant credit at Epsom, where he finished seven lengths behind the winner

*Ajdal cantering to the start before winning the Craven Stakes at Newmarket.*

*Ajdal draws clear of Sizzling Melody and Perion (right) to win the Sprint Championship at York.*

(Reference Point) and was found wanting only in the last quarter-mile. It was certainly the performance of a non-stayer, but it provided no inkling that he was a champion sprinter in the making. Within five weeks he was exactly that. He stormed home in the July Cup, beating established top sprinters; a month later he was even more impressive over five furlongs in the York Sprint Championship, and in September he completed a hat-trick of big sprint victories at Haydock. He failed to confirm his pre-eminence in the Prix de l'Abbaye de Longchamp, where he was badly drawn and made no show, but by then his rehabilitation was complete. A partial syndication, valuing him at £7.2 million, had already been effected, and after the French trip he retired to Dalham Hall as many people's idea of the most exciting stallion prospect recruited to an English stud in years.

There were numerous celebrated mares among the collection of 40 who visited Ajdal in 1988, when his fee was £35,000, and whenever the Dalham Hall stallions were paraded, he was the one who always caught the eye. Alas, like Shergar (though for a different reason), he was destined to have only one crop. A month after the end of the season, when being led out of his paddock, he broke free from his lad and ran into a fence, shattering a hind leg irreparably in two places. The one crumb of comfort to emerge after the disaster was that virtually all Ajdal's mates had conceived. There were 36 living foals, destined for the racecourse in 1991.

## AJDAL (bay, 1984)

| | | | |
|---|---|---|---|
| Northern Dancer (b 1961) | Nearctic | Nearco | Pharos / Nogara |
| | | Lady Angela | Hyperion / Sister Sarah |
| | Natalma | Native Dancer | Polynesian / Geisha |
| | | Almahmoud | Mahmoud / Arbitrator |
| Native Partner (b 1966) | Raise a Native | Native Dancer | Polynesian / Geisha |
| | | Raise You | Case Ace / Lady Glory |
| | Dinner Partner | Tom Fool | Menow / Gaga |
| | | Bluehaze | Blue Larkspur / Flaming Swords |

### Racing record

| Year | Starts | Wins | 2nd | 3rd | 4th | £ |
|---|---|---|---|---|---|---|
| 1986 | 3 | 3 | - | - | - | 49,803 |
| 1987 | 8 | 4 | - | - | 1 | 190,359 |
| | 11 | 7 | - | - | 1 | 240,162 |

### Principal wins

1986    Dewhurst Stakes-Gr1
1987    Craven Stakes-Gr3
        July Cup-Gr1
        York Sprint Championship Stakes-Gr1

# Alleged

A CYNIC might say that the rare feat of winning Europe's greatest prestige race, the Prix de l'Arc de Triomphe, in consecutive years is best assessed in the context of how many horses actually attempt it. It is generally the case that the horse who succeeds as a three-year-old does not return for a repeat bid in the following year, the prevailing attitude being that there is little to gain and much to lose by the risk. When the 'Arc' is won by a supposedly sub-standard horse, it is commonly assumed that the previous year's winner would have collected again, if he had bothered. On the other hand, there is nothing quite like proving a point, and the horse who comes back, laying his reputation on the line for a second time in the most competitive race of the year, and defies all-comers again is rightly reckoned to be something special. Since World War II, only three horses have earned that distinction – Tantième, Ribot and Alleged.

Of that trio, Alleged had the least active career, starting only ten times in all. In most of his races he did not even have worthy competition to test him. Yet on the two most important days of his racing life he was overwhelmingly the master of his foes, an extraordinarily gifted, natural 12-furlong performer who could lie up with – or set – a fast pace, then out-run the best of the rest through superiority of both speed and stamina. His type is rare on the modern Turf, and the revelation of his talents was to some degree the product of fortuitous circumstances.

Alleged was bred in Kentucky, a son of distinguished parents. His sire Hoist the Flag, a champion two-year-old, finished first in all of his six races and seemed to be on the verge of an outstanding career when he broke a leg in training. Pioneering surgery saved him for stud duty and he was to excel as a stallion before a second broken limb necessitated his destruction. Alleged came from his second crop and was the first living foal of his dam Princess Pout, a mare who did her best running as a five-year-old and wound up with earnings of $260,265 from 13 wins out of 31 starts. The pedigree read well enough, but the plain and backward individual who owned it did not impress onlookers at the 1975 Keeneland July yearling sale. The least expensive of the dozen summer sales

yearlings by Hoist the Flag sold that year fetched $35,000, and the highest-priced brought $172,000. The bidding on Alleged fell short of his reserve, stopping at $34,000, and breeder June McKnight was all set to take him home when Californian Monty Roberts sought her out and did a private deal with her at $40,000.

There are few horsemen in the world who command more respect than Roberts, who perfected a widely-acclaimed new technique for breaking young horses to saddle with a minimum of stress while also becoming America's foremost 'pinhooker' (a buyer of yearlings for re-sale as two-year-olds). Educated the Roberts way, Alleged made a much more impressive specimen when re-offered at auction in California in March 1976, and there he topped the sale, bringing $175,000 from agent Billy McDonald, who acted for partners Robert Fluor and Robert Sangster. The colt was promptly despatched to Ireland to be trained by Vincent O'Brien, and he duly made an auspicious winning debut at The Curragh in November, trouncing modest opponents by eight lengths and more over seven furlongs on soft ground.

Alleged began his second season as just a low-profile member of the 'second division' team in the Ballydoyle stable, supposedly inferior to such as The Minstrel, Godswalk, Padroug, Be My Guest and Valinsky, and it was a while before even his trainer recognized his full potential. He opened with a minor victory over ten furlongs, then turned out for the Group 3 Royal Whip at The Curragh as a 33/1 outsider and third-string representative of his team, ridden by a part-time jockey who had not had a winner in years. He won, entirely on merit, giving the first indication that he might yet prove a top-class performer. Two weeks later he took the Group 2 Gallinule Stakes in good style, and in nine years out of ten that would have earned him a place in a Derby line-up at either Epsom or The Curragh. In 1977, though, stable hopes for those classics rested with The Minstrel, and while that flashy chestnut collected all the major honours of the summer, Alleged was allowed an opportunity to grow and develop his strength away from the racecourse.

The Alleged who returned to competition after a three-month break in the Group 2 Great Voltigeur

Stakes at York was a revelation. He was opposed by several who had run The Minstrel close on previous outings, notably the runner-up in the Derby (Hot Grove) and the second (Lucky Sovereign), third (Classic Example) and fourth (Orchestra) in the Irish Derby, and he made hacks of them all, leading from the start, accelerating from three furlongs out, and winning, pulling up, by seven lengths. It was an awesome display, proof positive that a genuine new star had arrived on the scene. The inevitable immediate outcome was that Alleged was made a short-priced favourite for the St Leger, and he started at odds-on, but that was to be the one race he failed to win. He did nothing wrong, and left all but one for dead as he powered up the Doncaster straight, but he had never before been asked to contend with a battle-hardened rival of comparable class, trained to the minute and relishing the opportunity to race over her optimum distance. On that day the experience of Oaks heroine Dunfermline told, and she emerged the stronger by a little over a length.

Alleged lost no caste in defeat. Robert Sangster was sufficiently emboldened by the display to buy out his partner in the colt, Vincent O'Brien made plans

for the 'Arc', and Lester Piggott declared his eagerness to renew his partnership. The public took the hint, and though Dunfermline and the best French colt Crystal Palace were among 25 who opposed Alleged at Longchamp, there was only ever one possible favourite. As the race was run, there was also only ever going to be one winner, as Piggott took Alleged confidently to the front after three furlongs, settled the issue by opening a gap early in the straight, and left the rest to sort out the minor placings.

The Minstrel was already in America by St Leger day, having just beaten a temporary ban on the importation of Thoroughbreds to that country. The embargo, placed on account of a (then) mysterious disease found in some European-based breeding stock, was still in force at the end of the year, meaning that Alleged could not follow his former stable companion across the Atlantic. He really had no alternative to remaining a racehorse, and in any case he seemed just the type to make further progress as a four-year-old. He did just that, though his season consisted of only three races. He won the Royal Whip for a second time in the spring; he sat

*Alleged, twice winner of the Prix de l'Arc de Triomphe.*

out the summer with a virus; he came back in September to set a course record for 2000 metres in the Group 3 Prix du Prince d'Orange at Longchamp; and he closed his career with an emphatic repeat victory in the 'Arc'. Never out of the first three, never so much as shown the whip, he burst clear in the straight and won as he liked. Now he could be traded back to the States, and he went – to Walmac Farm in Kentucky – in a deal which valued him at $16 million.

As a late-maturing horse, and essentially a stayer, Alleged was not guaranteed to be ideally suited by his new environment. US owner-breeders could not be expected to enthuse over the prospect of producing horses of his type for racing in the States, although a number had fond memories of his great-grandsire, Ribot, and the results of his stud career in Lexington. More realistically, he would have to trade on his appeal to commercial breeders, the hope being that he would attract mares of high quality capable of producing stock which would find demand from the buyers for European racing, who were already beginning to dominate American yearling markets. He would need to be good – better than an ordinarily good sire – to sustain a high profile when the natural preference was for sires with a Northern Dancer connection.

Alleged has been good, and in line with most predictions he has obtained his best results with products campaigned in Europe. As a competitor with many fashionable Northern Dancer and Raise a Native horses, he has not managed to attract the quality mares in quantity with a consistency which might have advanced his cause, and in the light of that fact, his record is highly commendable. To the end of 1989, with eight crops of racing age, he had been represented by 26 individual winners of Pattern or Graded races, including two of the Irish Derby (Law Society and Sir Harry Lewis), one of the Prix du Jockey-Club (Hours After) and one of both the 1000 Guineas and Oaks (Midway Lady). He has even sired a pair of dual Grade 1 winners in the States in Fiesta Gal and Milesius.

A pure-breeding bay (he has got the odd grey, but never a chesnut), Alleged stamps his stock admirably. Characteristically, they are 'scopy', of the classical type, and while they are seldom real eye-catchers, they are hard to fault as physical specimens. Several have succeeded in good company as juveniles, none more notably than Midway Lady, but – like their sire – they do not want to be rushed, they repay patience, and they tend to be best at ten furlongs and beyond.

Alleged covered in 1990 at a fee of $50,000,

half what it was at the height of the market in the mid-80s. By all accounts he is a difficult horse to handle, and some have gone so far as to refer to him as savage; it has certainly long been the practice for him to be led out by two men. His virility has never been in doubt, as he has always covered large books of mares, and in each of two seasons (1984 and 1986) he got more than 60 live foals. His fertility has evidently not been so notably consistent, however, and from 72 mares covered in 1987 only 44 live foals resulted.

In the five seasons from 1985 to 1989, Alleged figured four times among the top seven sires in Britain and Ireland, a record second to none. His importance as a sire is well-established, and he stands now on the verge of greatness. The better mares who came his way after Law Society's three-year-old campaign, many of them bearing Northern Dancer's influence, may prove to be the means to that end.

## ALLEGED                                    (bay, 1974)

| | | | |
|---|---|---|---|
| Hoist the Flag (b 1968) | Tom Rolfe | Ribot | Tenerani / Romanella |
| | | Pocahontas | Roman / How |
| | Wavy Navy | War Admiral | Man o' War / Brushup |
| | | Triomphe | Tourbillon / Melibee |
| Princess Pout (b 1966) | Prince John | Princequillo | Prince Rose / Cosquilla |
| | | Not Afraid | Count Fleet / Banish Fear |
| | Determined Lady | Determine | Alibhai / Koubis |
| | | Tumbling | War Admiral / Up the Hill |

## Racing record

| Year | Starts | Wins | 2nd | 3rd | 4th | £ |
|---|---|---|---|---|---|---|
| 1976 | 1 | 1 | - | - | - | 1,092 |
| 1977 | 6 | 5 | 1 | - | - | 187,223 |
| 1978 | 3 | 3 | - | - | - | 150,299 |
| | 10 | 9 | 1 | - | - | 338,614 |

## Principal wins

| | |
|---|---|
| 1977 | Royal Whip Stakes-Gr3 |
| | Gallinule Stakes-Gr2 |
| | Great Voltigeur Stakes-Gr2 |
| | Prix de l'Arc de Triomphe-Gr1 |
| 1978 | Royal Whip Stakes-Gr3 |
| | Prix du Prince d'Orange-Gr3 |
| | Prix de l'Arc de Triomphe-Gr1 |

# Principal progeny

### 1980
b c HERON BAY (ex Foreign Missile, by Damascus)
  1982 Larkspur Stakes-Gr3
b f SYLPH (ex Society Column, by Sir Gaylord)
  1983 Princess Royal Stakes-Gr3

### 1981
b c MONTELIMAR (ex L'Extravagante, by Le Fabuleux)
  1984 Gallinule Stakes-Gr2
b f SURELY GEORGIE'S (ex Georgie, by Damascus)
  1983 Tempted Stakes-Gr3

### 1982
b f APRIL AGAIN (ex Reason for Truce, by Turn to Reason)
  1986 Queen Charlotte Handicap [Div.2]-Gr2
b c KAZAROUN (ex Korinetta, by Petingo)
  1985 Gordon Stakes-Gr3
  1986 Cumberland Lodge Stakes-Gr3
b c LAW SOCIETY (ex Bold Bikini, by Boldnesian)
  1984 Anglesey Stakes-Gr3
      National Stakes-Gr2
  1985 Chester Vase-Gr3
      Irish Derby-Gr1
b c LEADING COUNSEL (ex Society Column, by Sir Gaylord)
  1984 Ardenode Stud Stakes-Gr3
  1985 Irish St Leger-Gr1
br c NEMAIN (ex Gulls Cry, by Sea-Bird)
  1985 Blandford Stakes-Gr2
  1986 Blandford Stakes-Gr2
gr c PERFECT PARADE (ex Street's Glory, by Dr Fager)
  1987 Florida Turf Cup Handicap-Gr3

### 1983
b c JURADO (ex Champagne Ginny, by L'Enjoleur)
  1987 Premio Cascine-Gr3
  1988 Premio Emilio Turati-Gr2
      Premio Vittorio di Capua-Gr1
b f MIDWAY LADY (ex Smooth Bore, by His Majesty)
  1985 May Hill Stakes-Gr3
      Prix Marcel Boussac-Gr1
  1986 1000 Guineas Stakes-Gr1
      Oaks Stakes-Gr1
b c NOMROOD (ex Sweet Habit, by Habitat)
  1986 Chester Vase-Gr3
b f SHARANIYA (ex Shanizadeh, by Baldric)
  1986 Prix Minerve-Gr3
      Prix de Royallieu-Gr3
  1987 Grand Prix d'Evry-Gr2

b c WISE COUNSELLOR (ex Quarrel, by Raise a Native)
  1986 Desmond Stakes-Gr3

### 1984
b c FAIR JUDGMENT (ex Mystical Mood, by Roberto)
  1987 Whitehall Stakes-Gr2
  1988 Supreme Stakes-Gr3
  1989 Citation Handicap-Gr2
b f FIESTA GAL (ex Proud Pattie, by Noble Commander)
  1987 Mother Goose Stakes-Gr1
      Coaching Club American Oaks-Gr1
b f LALUCHE (ex Coqueluche, by Victorian Era)
  1986 May Hill Stakes-Gr3
b f LAWYER TALK (ex Jibber Jabber, by Jacinto)
  1989 Gardenia Stakes-Gr3
b c MILESIUS (ex Mindy Malone, by Tropical Breeze)
  1987 Lexington Stakes-Gr2
  1988 Manhattan Handicap-Gr1
      New Jersey Turf Classic Stakes-Gr3
  1989 Manhattan Handicap-Gr1
b c SIR HARRY LEWIS (ex Sue Babe, by Mr Prospector)
  1987 Irish Derby-Gr1

### 1985
b f ANIMATRICE (ex Alexandrie, by Val de l'Orne)
  1988 Prix de Malleret-Gr2
      Prix de la Nonette-Gr3
b c HOURS AFTER (ex Brown Berry, by Mount Marcy)
  1988 Prix du Jockey-Club-Gr1
b c MAZZACANO (ex Fall Aspen, by Pretense)
  1989 Goodwood Cup-Gr3

### 1986
b c BRUSH ASIDE (ex Top Twig, by High Perch)
  1990 John Porter Stakes-Gr3
b c HUSYAN (ex Close Comfort, by Far North)
  1990 Brigadier Gerard Stakes-Gr3
b c LEGAL CASE (ex Maryinsky, by Northern Dancer)
  1989 Select Stakes-Gr3
      Champion Stakes-Gr1
b f SLENDER STYLE (ex Cold Buns, by Far North)
  1989 Meld Stakes-Gr3

### 1987
b f MISS ALLEGED (ex Miss Tusculum, by Boldnesian)
  1990 Prix de Royaumont-Gr3

# Alydar

THERE can be little doubt that Secretariat was the best American racehorse of the 1970s, but for many people some of the best racing was provided by the double act of Affirmed and Alydar, who were far and away the best of their generation and pretty much on a par. They met on no fewer than ten occasions, nine times filling the first two places; in terms of how they passed the Judge, the score was 8-2 in favour of Affirmed, but one result was reversed in the Stewards' room. The margin between them was generally close, in five races (all won by Affirmed) half a length or less. Alydar seemed to possess the more striking burst of acceleration, but against Affirmed, the more resolute runner, it was always a problem – often an insoluble one – for his jockey to know when to use it to maximum advantage. The upshot was that Affirmed took all the available championships and a Triple Crown, earning almost $2.4 million in the process, while Alydar wound up with under a million in his account and the unenviable distinction of having been the only Triple Crown runner-up in history. Significantly, though, the rivalry between the pair in the 80s, in their second careers, has been one-sided and much to the embarrassment of Affirmed, who became just an ordinarily respectable sire; Alydar, from the outset, was decidedly one of the best.

Alydar was bred and raced by Calumet Farm, which had been the dominant stable in America through the 40s and 50s (best exemplified by the seven Kentucky Derby victories of Whirlaway, Pensive, Citation, Ponder, Hill Gail, Iron Liege and Tim Tam), but had subsequently encountered a lean spell, briefly relieved by an eighth Derby win from Forward Pass in 1968. The decline of Calumet, occasioned to some extent by the failure of those Derby heroes to achieve distinction at stud, was at last checked in the late 70s by successful recourse to outside stallions, and today – thanks chiefly to Alydar – the vast and beautiful farm on the outskirts of Lexington is firmly re-established as one of the top centres of excellence in the Thoroughbred world.

It was Alydar's half-sister, Our Mims (by Herbager), who signalled the revival with a splendid 1977 season which earned her honours as the nation's top three-year-old filly. Two more female champions, Davona Dale and Before Dawn, were to emerge over the next few years, but by then the star colt had already made his mark. Alydar came from the eleventh crop of his sire, Raise a Native, an unbeaten son of Native Dancer whose career ended after only four starts as a two-year-old. Blistering speed and precocity were Raise a Native's hallmarks as a runner, and they were characteristics he handed on faithfully to his stock – along, it must be said, with a tendency to unsoundness. Alydar was by no means a typical son of his sire. Although he was ready to run early, he improved from two to three, and while he owned exceptional pace, he was not deterred by distance.

Alydar won five of his ten races as a juvenile, finishing behind Affirmed (whose own sire was Exclusive Native, a son of Raise a Native) in four of the others. His best wins also came against Affirmed - in the Great American Stakes, when the weights favoured Alydar, and in the Grade 1 Champagne Stakes, when they met at levels and Alydar was clearly the master over a muddy Belmont track. But for Affirmed, Alydar would have enjoyed a perfect second season. His record in 1978 showed seven wins from ten efforts, the defeats – all by his familiar rival – being by a length and a half in the Kentucky Derby, a neck in the Preakness and a head in the Belmont. Affirmed also beat Alydar in the Travers but knocked him out of the way in the process, and the Stewards reversed the order of finish. The paths of the big two did not cross in 1979, when Alydar did not seem to be quite the force he had been as a three-year-old. He did win twice, but he also suffered four defeats. In midsummer he had to be taken out of training on account of a hairline fracture of the sesamoid bone on his off-hind leg.

Alydar had plenty to offer by way of stallion potential. Effective in the top league from five furlongs to a mile and a half, he had demonstrated instant acceleration (a quality associated with many – perhaps most – top sires), and in terms of both pedigree and physique he assuredly had an edge on Affirmed. Most especially, perhaps, he appealed on looks, being big (nearly 16.2 hands), muscular and masculine. He was also a relatively sound horse, considering the rigours of his career, and he

*Alydar, a stallion with performance, pedigree and physique.*

possessed an equable temperament. In brief, he was bound to be popular. His – and Calumet's – owner, Lucille Markey, elected not to syndicate him, making him available to breeders for $40,000. If that was not exactly cheap, it seemed like value compared with fees for other newcomers Affirmed ($100,000) Exceller ($75,000) and the by no means established Secretariat ($80,000). At that time you could get to Northern Dancer for $125,000.

Success came to Alydar in his second career about as quickly as it can come to a stallion. In his first crop of 35 foals he had the two best juvenile fillies of 1983, Althea and Miss Oceana, and because of their brilliant performances Alydar found himself both leading freshman sire and leading sire of two-year-olds. While Althea and Miss Oceana went on to distinguish themselves further in Grade 1 company at three, the second batch of Alydar foals (which numbered 60) set about proving that the initial results had been no flash in the pan. They included one real flying machine in Saratoga Six, who might have passed for a replica of Raise a Native in that he, too, won his first four starts in scintillating style, then broke down and had to be retired. Of the other early starters, Endear proved tough enough, becoming a Grade 1 winner at four, while the ambitiously named Alydar's Best, the sire's first European-based

celebrity, failed to reach the heights predicted for her after her Group 1 Grand Critérium triumph.

In time a discernible pattern emerged with the Alydars. They could – and commonly did – indicate their ability at two, but many tended to be better for a patient policy. As yearlings they were generally big, awkward, gangly creatures, particularly immature about the knees and fetlocks, and when given time to develop, free from stress, they both lasted longer and rose to greater heights. Turkoman, raced only once as a juvenile, proved best in his third and last season; Red Attack peaked at five after a gentle introduction; Alysheba, though he was a contender for top prizes late in his two-year-old campaign, remained under-exposed by the time of the Kentucky Derby, which gave him his first Graded victory. Over the following 18 months he added nine more, retiring as Horse of the Year and with total earnings of over $6.6 million. By then – the end of 1988 – Alydar had been second on the general sires' list for three consecutive seasons. In 1989 he filled the same position.

Few horses of real class get a son who is even better, but Alydar seemed to be making an agreeable habit of it when Easy Goer succeeded Alysheba. Here was a colt who was ready to dominate at two, and he did so in unmistakably brilliant style. At three he threatened to emulate his sire in the Triple Crown, finishing second in both the Kentucky Derby and the Preakness Stakes, but a resounding victory in the Belmont stopped the rot and four more Grade 1 wins followed before his classic conqueror, Sunday Silence, thwarted him again at the Breeders' Cup.

While Easy Goer starred in the States, Cacoethes and Alydaress were doing their best to change the European perception of their sire. Several of the early Alydars, purchased expensively at American auctions for racing on this side of the Atlantic, had failed to come up to expectations, their failures merely serving to feed a prejudice against the entire Raise a Native tribe. In truth the record was not impressive compared with the success achieved by the Northern Dancers, but the comparison was never really fair. Mr Prospector, the most consistently prominent sire son of Raise a Native, had done well in Europe; Alydar had been given far fewer chances. After the Irish Oaks win by Alydaress and the narrow defeat of Cacoethes by Nashwan in the King George VI & Queen Elizabeth Stakes, it seemed likely that

Europeans would re-appraise the Alydar performance here.

Alydar's fee peaked at $350,000 in 1986, declining steadily thereafter in line with the general market adjustments in the industry, but the consistency of his record and the achievements of such as Alysheba and Easy Goer resulted in an upward revision for 1990. He was then set to cover at $250,000, making him, jointly with Mr Prospector and Nureyev, the most highly-priced stallion in the world. His stud earnings have been colossal, as he is habitually also one of the most active; in 1987 (when his fee stood at $310,000) he covered 98 mares, more than any other horse in America. There were 81 live foals in that crop, plenty of them with plain heads and forelegs which turned out, but that did not worry yearling buyers. When a stallion gets stock who run fast in spite of supposed faults, those defects cause little offence to the eye, and the 46 Alydar yearlings who went to market in 1989 averaged more than $475,000.

## Racing record

| Year | Starts | Wins | 2nd | 3rd | 4th | $ |
|------|--------|------|-----|-----|-----|-----|
| 1977 | 10 | 5 | 4 | - | - | 285,026 |
| 1978 | 10 | 7 | 3 | - | - | 565,071 |
| 1979 | 6 | 2 | 2 | 1 | - | 107.098 |
| | 26 | 14 | 9 | 1 | - | 957,195 |

## Principal wins

| | | |
|---|---|---|
| 1977 | Sapling Stakes-Gr1 | |
| | Champagne Stakes-Gr1 | |
| 1978 | Flamingo Stakes-Gr1 | |
| | Florida Derby-Gr1 | |
| | Blue Grass Stakes-Gr1 | |
| | Arlington Classic-Gr2 | |
| | Whitney Stakes-Gr2 | |
| | Travers Stakes-Gr1 | |
| 1979 | Nassau County Handicap-Gr3 | |

## Principal progeny
### 1981
ch f ALTHEA (ex Courtly Dee, by Never Bend)
| 1983 | Hollywood Juvenile Championship Stakes-Gr2 |
|------|------|
| | Del Mar Debutante Stakes-Gr2 |
| | Del Mar Futurity Stakes-Gr2 |
| | Hollywood Starlet Stakes-Gr2 |
| 1984 | Santa Susana Stakes-Gr1 |
| | Arkansas Derby-Gr1 |

b f MISS OCEANA (ex Kittiwake, by Sea-Bird)
| 1983 | Arlington-Washington Lassie Stakes-Gr1 |
|------|------|
| | Selima Stakes-Gr1 |
| 1984 | Bonnie Miss Stakes-Gr3 |
| | Acorn Stakes-Gr1 |
| | Gazelle Handicap-Gr1 |
| | Maskette Stakes-Gr1 |

## ALYDAR                                            (chesnut, 1975)

| | | | |
|---|---|---|---|
| Raise a Native (ch 1961) | Native Dancer | Polynesian | Unbreakable Black Polly |
| | | Geisha | Discovery Miyako |
| | Raise You | Case Ace | Teddy Sweetheart |
| | | Lady Glory | American Flag Beloved |
| Sweet Tooth (b 1965) | On-and-On | Nasrullah | Nearco Mumtaz Begum |
| | | Two Lea | Bull Lea Two Bob |
| | Plum Cake | Ponder | Pensive Miss Rushin |
| | | Real Delight | Bull Lea Blue Delight |

### 1982
ch f ALYDAR'S BEST (ex Berkut, by Sea-Bird)
| 1984 | Silken Glider Stakes-Gr3 |
|------|------|
| | Grand Criterium-Gr1 |
| 1985 | Pretty Polly Stakes-Gr2 |

ch c BUCKLEY BOY (ex Plankton, by Quack)
| 1986 | Florida Turf Cup Handicap-Gr3 |
|------|------|
| | Gallant Fox Handicap-Gr3 |

b f ENDEAR (ex Chappaquiddick, by Relic)
| 1984 | Miss Grillo Stakes-Gr3 |
|------|------|
| 1986 | Rampart Handicap-Gr3 |
| | Hempstead Handicap-Gr1 |

b f FATAH FLARE (ex Beaconaire, by Vaguely Noble)
    1985    Musidora Stakes-Gr3
ch c RED ATTACK (ex Miss Betty, by Buckpasser)
    1986    Razorback Handicap-Gr2
    1987    Equipoise Mile Handicap-Gr3
b c SARATOGA SIX (ex Priceless Fame, by Irish Castle)
    1984    Hollywood Juvenile Championship Stakes-Gr2
              Balboa Stakes-Gr3
              Del Mar Futurity Stakes-Gr1
b c TURKOMAN (ex Taba, by Table Play)
    1985    Affirmed Handicap-Gr3
    1986    Widener Handicap-Gr1
              Oaklawn Handicap-Gr2
              Marlboro Cup Invitational Handicap-Gr1

### 1983

ch f CLABBER GIRL (ex Jedina, by What a Pleasure)
    1988    Top Flight Handicap-Gr1
              Rancho Bernardo Handicap-Gr3
              Chula Vista Handicap-Gr2
ch f I'M SWEETS (ex Too Many Sweets, by Full Pocket)
    1985    Gardenia Stakes-Gr2
              Demoiselle Stakes-Gr1
    1986    Honey Bee Handicap-Gr3
    1987    Ballerina Stakes-Gr2

### 1984

b c ALYSHEBA (ex Bel Sheba, by Lt Stevens)
    1987    Kentucky Derby-Gr1
              Preakness Stakes-Gr1
              Super Derby Invitational-Gr1
    1988    Charles H. Strub Stakes-Gr1
              Santa Anita Handicap-Gr1
              San Bernardino Handicap-Gr2
              Philip H. Iselin Handicap-Gr1
              Woodward Handicap-Gr1
              Meadowlands Cup Handicap-Gr1
              Breeders' Cup Classic Stakes-Gr1
b f CADILLACING (ex Relaxing, by Buckpasser)
    1988    Distaff Handicap-Gr3
              Ballerina Stakes-Gr1
ch f HIAAM (ex Kamar, by Key to the Mint)
    1986    Princess Margaret Stakes-Gr3

ch c TALINUM (ex Water Lily, by Riverman)
    1987    Flamingo Stakes-Gr1
    1988    Bold Reason Handicap-Gr3
              Stuyvesant Handicap-Gr2

### 1985

ch c CRIMINAL TYPE (ex Klepto, by No Robbery)
    1990    San Pasqual Handicap-Gr2
              San Antonio Handicap-Gr2
              Pimlico Special Handicap-Gr1
              Metropolitan Handicap-Gr1
b c LUCKY SO N' SO (ex Spring Sunshine, by Nashua)
    1987    Juvenile Stakes-Gr3
b c SARHOOB (ex Repetitious, by Northfields)
    1988    Prix Eugene Adam-Gr2

### 1986

gr f ALYDARESS (ex Balidaress, by Balidar)
    1989    Ribblesdale Stakes-Gr2
              Irish Oaks-Gr1
b c CACOETHES (ex Careless Notion, by Jester)
    1989    Lingfield Derby Trial Stakes-Gr3
              King Edward VII Stakes-Gr2
ch c EASY GOER (ex Relaxing, by Buckpasser)
    1988    Cowdin Stakes-Gr1
              Champagne Stakes-Gr1
    1989    Gotham Stakes-Gr2
              Wood Memorial Invitational Stakes-Gr1
              Belmont Stakes-Gr1
              Whitney Handicap-Gr1
              Travers Stakes-Gr1
              Woodward Handicap-Gr1
              Jockey Club Gold Cup Stakes-Gr1
ch f TIS JULIET (ex My Juliet, by Gallant Romeo)
    1990    Shuvee Handicap-Gr1

### 1987

b f STELLA MADRID (ex My Juliet, by Gallant Romeo)
    1989    Spinaway Stakes-Gr1
              Matron Stakes-Gr1
              Frizette Stakes-Gr1
    1990    Acorn Stakes-Gr1
ch f TRAIN ROBBERY (ex Track Robbery, by No Robbery)
    1990    Honeybee Stakes-Gr3

# Alzao

AS Alzao's eldest progeny reached four years old only in 1990, these are early days in his career as a stallion. Even so, the first chapter in the story of his life at stud has been an eventful one, with striking illustrations of how the modern market behaves in the case of a horse enjoying a rising tide of popularity.

Alzao was bred in Kentucky and imported to France to race in the colours of Jean-Luc Lagardère, a prominent stud owner in Calvados. An extremely well-bred horse, he was by Lyphard (a champion sire twice in France and later once in America) out of Lady Rebecca, a half-sister, by the celebrated Sir Ivor, to the outstanding US runner and successful sire Tom Rolfe. With a pedigree like that, Alzao was entitled to develop into a high-class racehorse, and as a well-made, compact sort, typical of his sire, he certainly looked the part. His trainer, François Boutin, took an instant liking to him, and liked him better still after two October starts, in minor races at Evry and Maisons-Laffitte, had produced easy victories.

Those were Alzao's only efforts as a two-year-old. At three he won a Listed race at Longchamp and generally ran with credit, once as an honourable eighth in the Champion Stakes at Newmarket, but he had promised to take rather higher rank and connections admitted to some disappointment. In the following spring, despairing of finding that all-important Pattern-winning opportunity in France, Boutin sent him on two excursions to Italy. On the first he finished only fourth in a Group 3 event at San Siro, but a return trip three weeks later, this time to Rome for the Premio Ellington, yielded the desired result. Alzao had got his Group 3 win, albeit by only a nose from an ordinary rival whose female rider had made her challenge too late, and as that seemed to represent the limit of his talents, he was not exposed to further examination on the racecourse.

Alzao had unquestionably deteriorated considerably between the ages of three and four, but he still had his pedigree, he had been unbeaten as a two-year-old, and he did have a Pattern victory to his name. With that background he might yet make a stallion, notwithstanding that he was obviously surplus to the requirements of his owner, who now had the Prix du Jockey-Club winner Bikala in service

at his Haras du Val Henry. It was left to an Irishman from County Cork to give Alzao his chance. Liam Cashman, experienced and successful at marketing young horses for stallion duty at his Rathbarry Stud, bought him privately, took him home and swiftly sold shares among his regular clients at IR£12,000 a time.

As his covering fee was set at IR3500gns, shareholders could, with ordinary luck, expect to show profit on their investment by the time Alzao's first foals reached the races; they were spared the worry over whether he would actually get successful progeny. As it turned out, the shareholders had better than ordinary luck. Alzao attracted 62 mares in his first season and got 53 foals; as many as 41 were sold as yearlings, and the average price of 9464gns was a sure indication that the market liked them. They tended to be more scopy than Alzao himself, and the general impression was that the sire was getting stock of the true Northern Dancer type; that had always been a possibility, as Northern Dancer had no more faithful agent than Alzao's sire Lyphard.

Alzao had himself waited until he was four - and for his first race over a mile and a half - before he recorded his sole prestige victory, but his progeny were different. They came out running, and winning, over five furlongs in the spring of their two-year-old season, and within a short time people began to take notice of their young unknown sire. There were prospective buyers on the scene by the summer, when Aldbourne was already a three-time winner and runner-up in the Group 3 Cherry Hinton Stakes. By the autumn, when Pass the Peace capped a Group 3 win in Ireland with a much more significant victory in the Group 1 Cheveley Park Stakes at Newmarket, there had been substantial offers from several would-be buyers, among them Sir Tristan Antico in Australia, Walmac Farm in Kentucky and, much closer to home, Coolmore Stud. The bids kept coming, and kept being rejected, the last being one of IR£2.8 million from Coolmore.

At the start of 1988 Alzao's fee had been reduced to IR3000gns in line with general market trends; by the end of that year he had sired ten individual winners of 22 races in Britain and Ireland from his first batch of two-year-olds, and Cashman announced that the charge for the horse's services in 1989 would be IR18,000gns. A sale was now inevitable, with many of the original shareholders keen to take the rare opportunity of vast profit on a modest investment. For obvious reasons Cashman wanted to sell Alzao out of Ireland, and he was particularly keen not to let him go to Coolmore. When a bid of IR£3.6 million came from America, apparently on behalf of Walmac Farm, a deal was done, to be effective after the horse had served one last season - his fifth - at Rathbarry. A week later it emerged that the Walmac involvement had been an elaborate ruse; its owner, Johnny Jones, did figure in the partnership who had bought Alzao, but there had never been any intention to stand the horse in Kentucky. The plan was to employ him as a dual-season stallion, at Coolmore in the northern hemisphere spring and at Lindsay Park, in South Australia, in the southern hemisphere spring; the pooling of resources between those two prominent studs had provided the funds – and the justification – for an outlay which would have seemed reckless for either acting on its own.

Alzao had another successful season in 1989, with Pass the Peace and Aldbourne again showing up well, but his prize-money haul of over £300,000 owed much to minor place-earners. His ratio of winners to runners was poor, and the second crop of two-year-olds made less impact than the first. The great thing about the Alzaos is that they are honest-to-goodness racehorses, triers every one. To date his best performers have excelled up to a mile, but in theory he should get stayers as well. Now that he has sired a few good runners from a large number of

*Alzao – early impact as a stallion.*

ordinary mares, it will be fascinating to see what he can achieve from supposedly better opportunities. Back from his initial Australian stint, Alzao covered his first Coolmore mares at a fee of IR20,000gns in 1990.

## Racing record

| Year | Starts | Wins | 2nd | 3rd | 4th | FR |
|------|--------|------|-----|-----|-----|-----|
| 1982 | 2 | 2 | - | - | - | 125,000 |
| 1983 | 6 | 1 | 1 | 1 | 1 | 212,000 |
| 1984 | 4 | 1 | 1 | - | 2 | 290,000 |
| | 12 | 4 | 2 | 1 | 3 | 627,000 |

### Principal wins

    1983   Prix Matchem
    1984   Premio Ellington-Gr3

### Principal progeny

**1986**
b f ALCANDO (ex Kaniz, by Darius)
    1989   Prix de Psyche-Gr3
b c MIRROR BLACK (ex Flaxen Hair, by Thatch)
    1990   Badener Meile-Gr3
b f PASS THE PEACE (ex Lover's Rose, by King Emperor)
    1988   Debutante Stakes-Gr3
            Cheveley Park Stakes-Gr1
    1989   Fred Darling Stakes-Gr3

## ALZAO     (bay, 1980)

| | | | |
|---|---|---|---|
| Lyphard (b 1969) | Northern Dancer | Nearctic | Nearco / Lady Angela |
| | | Natalma | Native Dancer / Almahmoud |
| | Goofed | Court Martial | Fair Trial / Instantaneous |
| | | Barra | Formor / La Favorite |
| Lady Rebecca (b 1971) | Sir Ivor | Sir Gaylord | Turn-to / Somethingroyal |
| | | Attica | Mr Trouble / Athenia |
| | Pocahontas | Roman | Sir Gallahad / Buckup |
| | | How | Princequillo / The Squaw |

# Ardross

FOR almost as long as there has been Thoroughbred racing, it has been recognized that the best and most admirable racehorses do not always make the best sires. Nevertheless, for 200 years some lip-service has been paid to the rather pretentious creed that the purpose of racing is to improve the breed, in that colts who pass the racecourse test with the highest marks are generally given better opportunities at stud than lesser athletes – at least for a while. In the modern era, though, there is a blatant exception to the general rule. It really does not matter how good an out-and-out stayer proves himself to be; the market is so overwhelmingly prejudiced against the horse who excels over long distances that he can never expect breeders to reward him for his merit.

Ardross is the latest example of this phenomenon – a horse of quite exceptional talents who expressed his class and courage over a long period, equalled the record for the number of Pattern wins in Europe and became a great public favourite. As a six-year-old he was voted Britain's 'Racehorse of the Year', and it was a richly deserved honour. Yet there was never a chance of his making the grade as a sire of high-class Flat horses, and it was no surprise when, after seven seasons chasing an impossible dream, he changed hands and embarked on a new career as a prospective sire of jumpers.

The trouble is that while Britain prides itself on the variety of its racing and the public patently enjoys the spectacle of staying races, demand for slow-maturing horses is non-existent in today's market-place. The emphasis is so much on speed that stamina is regarded as a negative quality. The fact that no winner of the Ascot Gold Cup has become champion sire since Alycidon (who won in 1949 and was top stallion six years later) is often quoted, rarely with the qualification that few of his successors were given appropriate chances. We no longer attempt to breed stayers, and the horses who contest the best staying races are almost invariably horses who have failed to establish their quality over more fashionable distances.

Ardross committed the cardinal sin of winning the Gold Cup not once, but twice – and of failing in it at the first attempt. Only two of his 14 victories came at a mile and a half, while seven were at two miles or beyond. It could never be said that he was devoid of speed. Time and again he displayed formidable powers of acceleration, never more strikingly than on his final appearance, when he all but caught Akiyda in a desperately close finish for the Prix de l'Arc de Triomphe. That was his second attempt to win Europe's greatest prestige event – he had been fifth in the previous year – the idea in each instance being to establish that he did not need extreme distances and that he was worthy of top-class mares at stud. We shall never know what difference it would have made if the 1982 photo verdict had gone the other way.

Ardross was bred by the late Paddy Prendergast, an outstanding Irish trainer, and his pedigree pre-ordained that he would be a stayer. He did not run as a two-year-old and was a 50/1 shot when he scored his first win, in the Group 3 Gallinule Stakes at The Curragh in the following season. During the terminal illness of his breeder, the colt was transferred to the care of Kevin Prendergast (Paddy's son), and at four he developed into a stayer of the highest class, finishing a close second to Le Moss in the Gold Cup, the Goodwood Cup and the Doncaster Cup. At the end of that season he was sold to Charles St George and moved to England to be trained by Henry Cecil.

Over the next two years Ardross was easily the dominant stayer in Europe, his victories including two Gold Cups, two Yorkshire Cups, a Goodwood Cup, a Doncaster Cup and a Prix Royal-Oak. His Doncaster win was his thirteenth in Pattern company, which matched the record of Brigadier Gerard and has subsequently been equalled only by the German horse Acatenango. After his narrow defeat in the 'Arc' he was syndicated at a valuation of £2 million and took up residence at Beech House Stud, near Newmarket; his fee was set at £13,000.

Poor Ardross was a hopeless case from the start. He inevitably had little appeal to commercial breeders, and there simply were not sufficient private breeders around to give him the necessary support. It might have helped if St George had himself been a prominent owner-breeder, prepared to lead by example; as it was, he had no notable mares and had owed his enduring success as an owner to the facts that he had bought young stock wisely and had

*Ardross wins his second Yorkshire Cup – one of thirteen Pattern race successes.*

## ARDROSS (bay, 1976)

| | | | |
|---|---|---|---|
| Run the Gantlet (b 1968) | Tom Rolfe | Ribot | Tenerani Romanella |
| | | Pocahontas | Roman How |
| | First Feather | First Landing | Turn-to Hildene |
| | | Quill | Princequillo Quick Touch |
| Le Melody (b 1971) | Levmoss | Le Levanstell | Le Lavandou Stella's Sister |
| | | Feemoss | Ballymoss Feevagh |
| | Arctic Melody | Arctic Slave | Arctic Star Roman Gallery |
| | | Bell Bird | Mustang Belpatrick |

### Racing record

| Year | Starts | Wins | 2nd | 3rd | 4th | £ |
|---|---|---|---|---|---|---|
| 1978 | 0 | | | | | |
| 1979 | 3 | 1 | - | - | - | 7,284 |
| 1980 | 7 | 2 | 3 | 1 | 1 | 49,488 |
| 1981 | 6 | 5 | - | - | - | 136,262 |
| 1982 | 8 | 6 | 1 | 1 | - | 219,424 |
| | 24 | 14 | 4 | 2 | 1 | 412,458 |

### Principal wins

| | |
|---|---|
| 1979 | Gallinule Stakes-Gr3 |
| 1980 | Jockey Club Cup-Gr3 |
| 1981 | Yorkshire Cup-Gr2 |
| | Gold Cup-Gr1 |
| | Goodwood Cup-Gr2 |
| | Geoffrey Freer Stakes-Gr2 |
| | Prix Royal-Oak-Gr1 |
| 1982 | Jockey Club Stakes-Gr3 |
| | Yorkshire Cup-Gr2 |
| | Henry II Stakes-Gr3 |
| | Gold Cup-Gr1 |
| | Geoffrey Freer Stakes-Gr2 |
| | Doncaster Cup-Gr3 |

### Principal progeny
**1986**
b f FILIA ARDROSS (ex Sari Habit, by Saritamer)
| | |
|---|---|
| 1989 | Schwarzgold Rennen-Gr2 |
| | Preis der Diana-Gr2 |
| | Grosser Hansa Preis-Gr2 |

never become deeply involved in the precarious business of breeding. A better plan for the horse would have been not to syndicate him and to have him cover at a much lower fee at the outset, but the course taken was understandable. Inevitably, his fee came down by stages – to £4500 in 1989 – and before the end of that year (when he was represented by a good filly, Filia Ardross, in Germany and a useful two-year-old colt, Karinga Bay, at home) the news came that he had been sold to stand at Cobhall Court Stud in Herefordshire as a National Hunt stallion. His fee there was to be 1500gns.

# Assert

ONE of the oldest – and most easily verifiable – adages in the business says that 'nothing can make a fool of a man like a horse'. It goes for mares, too. In 1971 a yearling filly by Sea-Bird out of Irish Lass was bought at Deauville for a record price of FR700,000 by Swiss breeder Walter Haefner, owner of Moyglare Stud in Ireland. Named Irish Bird, she proved to be a disappointing runner, managing only three starts and a single modest victory. Given the opportunity to redeem herself at stud, she promptly produced two nonentities, and Haefner decided to rid himself of her and her produce; over a 12-month period he disposed of the mare and her young colts by Kalamoun and Be My Guest, collecting around £42,000 for the lot. Over the next couple of years the Kalamoun colt, Bikala, won the Prix du Jockey-

Club, the Be My Guest colt, Assert, became the first-ever winner of both the Prix du Jockey-Club and the Irish Derby, and Irish Bird came to be regarded as the most valuable mare in Europe.

Assert, from the first crop of his sire, was a FR160,000 (about £16,000) purchase by Robert Sangster, who at that time was generally a keen bidder for the stock of young stallions in whom he had an interest. He had expected to pay much more and could not have been more right when he declared he had got a bargain. The proof of that was evident by the end of his first season in training with David O'Brien, his best effort in three starts producing an emphatic victory in the Group 2 Beresford Stakes at The Curragh.

At three he was for a time overshadowed by his

*Assert defeats Norwick (rails) and Amyndas (spots) by a wide margin in the Benson and Hedges Gold Cup at York.*

owner's more forward Golden Fleece (in Vincent O'Brien's stable), who beat him in the Nijinsky Stakes at Leopardstown and went on to a brilliant victory in Derby. Assert, meanwhile, won the Group 2 Gallinule Stakes, and with the unsound Golden Fleece permanently on the missing list after Epsom the stage was set for the one-time understudy to assume the role of Europe's dominant three-year-old. He won the Prix du Jockey-Club by three lengths and the Irish Derby by eight. He could not quite resist four-year-old Kalaglow in the King George VI & Queen Elizabeth Stakes, but he came out rampant again to register two more wide-margin Group 1 wins, in the Benson & Hedges Gold Cup at York and the Joe McGrath Memorial Stakes at Leopardstown. This was the form of a prospective Arc de Triomphe winner, and he duly started a firm 5/2 favourite on the day, but a combination of the soft ground and his long season found him out; he finished a well-beaten eleventh.

Assert did not run again after his Longchamp effort. He had already been syndicated at a valuation of $25 million to stand at Windfields Farm in Maryland, and he began his stud career there, alongside his grandsire Northern Dancer, at a fee of $125,000. A big, handsome horse with a glorious action, rated only 1lb below the best of his year (Golden Fleece) in Europe, Assert was entitled to plenty of respect at the outset, but neither at Windfields nor after a change of base to Ashford Stud in Kentucky was he able to attain a consistent level of success. His fee came tumbling down by stages as breeders reacted to his disappointing results and for the 1990 season he stood at only $10,000 – less with no guarantee of a foal.

It is not that Assert has proved unable to get winners. He even had three individual Graded winners – all fillies – from his first two crops, and among his third batch of foals was Dancehall, one of the leading three-year-old colts in Europe, winner of the Grand Prix de Paris and runner-up to Old Vic in the Prix du Jockey-Club. The trouble is that the good Asserts have been too few and far between, the preponderance of his stock seeming to lack courage and be devoid of finishing speed. They tend to stay well, but even stayers need pace to win in good company, and Assert is going to need more than a single Dancehall to retrieve a reputation that has been sinking fast.

## ASSERT (bay, 1979)

| | | | |
|---|---|---|---|
| Be My Guest (ch 1974) | Northern Dancer | Nearctic | Nearco / Lady Angela |
| | | Natalma | Native Dancer / Almahmoud |
| | What a Treat | Tudor Minstrel | Owen Tudor / Sansonnet |
| | | Rare Treat | Stymie / Rare Perfume |
| Irish Bird (b 1970) | Sea-Bird | Dan Cupid | Native Dancer / Vixenette |
| | | Sicalade | Sicambre / Marmelade |
| | Irish Lass | Sayajirao | Nearco / Rosy Legend |
| | | Scollata | Niccolo Dell' Arca / Cutaway |

### Racing record

| Year | Starts | Wins | 2nd | 3rd | 4th | £ |
|---|---|---|---|---|---|---|
| 1981 | 3 | 1 | 1 | - | - | 8,227 |
| 1982 | 8 | 5 | 2 | - | - | 345,514 |
| | 11 | 6 | 3 | - | - | 353,741 |

### Principal wins

| 1981 | Beresford Stakes-Gr2 |
|---|---|
| 1982 | Gallinule Stakes-Gr2 |
| | Prix du Jockey-Club-Gr1 |
| | Irish Derby-Gr1 |
| | Benson & Hedges Gold Cup-Gr1 |
| | Joe McGrath Memorial Stakes-Gr1 |

### Principal progeny

**1984**
gr f TIMELY ASSERTION (ex Timely Roman, by Sette Bello)
1987    Las Virgenes Stakes-Gr2
        Santa Anita Oaks-Gr1

**1985**
ch f BETTY LOBELIA (ex Fair Rosalind, by Exclusive Native)
1988    Nijana Stakes [Div.1]-Gr3
b f WILLA ON THE MOVE (ex Willamae, by Tentam)
1988    Ashland Stakes-Gr1

**1986**
b c DANCEHALL (ex Cancan Madame, by Mr Prospector)
1988    Prix de Conde-Gr3
1989    Prix Noailles-Gr2
        Prix Hocquart-Gr2
        Grand Prix de Paris-Gr1

# Ballad Rock

AS plenty of even the supposedly best-qualified prospective stallions fail to make the grade, breeders are understandably reluctant to pin much faith on horses who have not attained a certain level of competence in their racing careers. These days a horse without a victory in a Pattern or equivalent race to his credit has a serious credibility gap to bridge from the outset. Few manage to cross it, the vast majority foundering sooner or later under the weight of apathy.

However, there are exceptions. There are worthwhile races outside the Pattern, and there are horses who put up performances every bit as good as some recorded in Pattern races. Ballad Rock only once came close to a Group 3 win, when beaten a head by Solinus in the Ballyogan Stakes at The Curragh; he also failed miserably in the Cork and Orrery Stakes at Ascot (his only effort outside Ireland) and beat only two in the Irish 2000 Guineas, when asked to compete out of his class and distance. On the other hand, this big and burly sprinter did win the five-furlong Rockingham Handicap as a three-year-old under 9st 12lb, and at four he collected three wins in competitive events over six furlongs, including one Curragh contest – the Greenlands Stakes – which was subsequently elevated to Group 3 status. His reputation in his native land was high, and if he had not had an aversion to stalls (on account of his sheer bulk), which occasionally caused him to start slowly, he would assuredly have attained greater racing distinction.

In the circumstances, Ballad Rock seemed to have something going for him as a stallion in Ireland, especially as he owned a pedigree which local breeders had reason to respect. He was as good a son of Bold Lad as could be found in the area, and he came from a female line familiar with success over a long period in the McGrath family's Brownstown Stud. The very fact that in 1990 he stood his twelfth season, and at a fee of IR6000gns, is an indication that he has done creditably; in fact, he has gone some way towards emulating his sire in achieving

*Ballad Rock puts daylight between himself and his rivals in the Greenlands Stakes at The Curragh.*

success spasmodically rather than consistently.

Ballad Rock's first two seasons were compromised by a venereal disease – to the extent that he got only 25 foals in that period. His conception rate improved dramatically in the third year, but from a strictly limited book of mares, and it was not until his fourth season that he began to be represented by a normal quota of foals. No sooner had a complete cure been effected than he had a son of genuinely high calibre to advertise him. Chief Singer, one of only ten foals in his second crop, burst on the scene with a brilliant debut victory in the 1983 Coventry Stakes at Royal Ascot. A subsequent failure in the July Stakes took some of the gloss from that first impression, but the colt clearly had a physical problem and he did not reappear that year. At three he more than rediscovered his ability, and consecutive triumphs in the St James's Palace Stakes, July Cup and Sussex Stakes established him as one of the best sprinter-milers in recent years.

Chief Singer's performances did his sire a power of good in terms of stud reputation, but Ballad Rock failed to capitalize; the knowledge that he could get a runner of outstanding merit cut little ice with breeders who wanted evidence that he could do so more often. Then, just as the market was preparing to write him off as a 'one horse wonder', Ballad Rock regained favour through the exploits of two high-class two-year-olds in 1989. Rock City emulated Chief Singer in the Coventry Stakes and went on to win twice more in Pattern company before the season was over; Balla Cove earned Group 1 honours in the Middle Park Stakes and was sold to the States, where he ran creditably in the Breeders' Cup Juvenile Stakes.

The best of Ballad Rock's progeny are clearly those who take after him, but he is not really a dominant sire and cannot be depended upon to upgrade his mares. That hit-and-miss kind of performance suggests that he is unlikely to exert long-term influence, and there is little comfort to be gained from the first two crops of runners by Chief Singer, whose racing aptitudes seem to have been determined more by their dams than by their sire and who generally are light on class.

## BALLAD ROCK (chesnut, 1974)

| | | | |
|---|---|---|---|
| **Bold Lad** (b 1964) | Bold Ruler | Nasrullah | Nearco / Mumtaz Begum |
| | | Miss Disco | Discovery / Outdone |
| | Barn Pride | Democratic | Denturius / Light Fantasy |
| | | Fair Alycia | Alycidon / Fair Edwine |
| **True Rocket** (gr 1967) | Roan Rocket | Buisson Ardent | Relic / Rose o' Lynn |
| | | Farandole | Deux pour Cent / Faramoude |
| | True Course | Hill Gail | Bull Lea / Jane Gail |
| | | Arctic Rullah | Nasrullah / Arctic Blue |

### Racing record

| Year | Starts | Wins | 2nd | 3rd | 4th | £ |
|---|---|---|---|---|---|---|
| 1977 | 4 | 2 | 1 | - | - | 5,973 |
| 1978 | 6 | 3 | 2 | - | - | 22,918 |
| | 10 | 5 | 3 | - | - | 28,891 |

### Principal wins

1977  Rockingham Handicap
1978  Greenlands Stakes
　　　 Matt Gallagher Sprint Stakes

### Principal progeny
#### 1981
br c CHIEF SINGER (ex Principia, by Le Fabuleux)
　　1983  Coventry Stakes-Gr2
　　1984  St James's Palace Stakes-Gr2
　　　　　 July Cup-Gr1
　　　　　 Sussex Stakes-Gr1

#### 1987
b c BALLA COVE (ex Coven, by Sassafras)
　　1989  Middle Park Stakes-Gr1
br c ROCK CITY (ex Rimosa's Pet, by Petingo)
　　1989  Coventry Stakes-Gr3
　　　　　 July Stakes-Gr3
　　　　　 Gimcrack Stakes-Gr2
　　1990  Greenham Stakes-Gr3

# Be My Guest

MATING a champion with a champion is by no means an infallible formula for success, but it worked out pretty well when America's best three-year-old colt of 1964 met up with the best three-year-old filly of 1965. The May date between Northern Dancer and What a Treat in 1973 resulted in a bonny chesnut colt, and though he did not attain the level of distinction as a racehorse that his parents had reached, he proved to be no mean achiever in several respects. His life-size figure in bronze at the entrance to Goffs' sale ring in County Kildare stands as a permanent reminder of his impact on breeding in Ireland.

Be My Guest was foaled in America, but it was always his destiny to come to Ireland where his breeder Walter Haefner was in the throes of developing Moyglare Stud as a prominent commercial enterprise. The colt made his first public appearance at Kill in the initial auction held by the reconstituted Goffs company in its brand-new arena, and he arrived with all the ballyhoo appropriate to the occasion. As the first yearling by Northern Dancer offered in Europe since Lyphard, the product of a champion racemare, and supposedly a good individual to boot, he was widely expected to top Goffs' record price of 55,000gns, set in the previous year by a Habitat colt. He did rather better than that, leaving the ring as the highest-priced yearling of all time in Europe after a 127,000gns bid from Vincent O'Brien finally persuaded Frank More O'Ferrall (agent for Stavros Niarchos) to abandon pursuit. It did not matter that the record endured for no more than a month. On the racecourse Be My Guest was to achieve far more than the colt – a 202,000gns colt called Million – who erased his mark from the book; much more significantly, Be My Guest was to win a sires' championship, and that is a feat which none of the previous 17 colts to have held the record had achieved and which none of the succeeding ten has emulated.

Be My Guest did his racing in the colours of Virginia Manning, but actually represented a partnership in which Robert Sangster was involved. As a two-year-old he indicated potential by winning the second of his only two races, a six-furlong maiden at The Curragh, and at three the principal problem

he gave his trainer was that of procuring him worthwhile opportunities to express his talent. In 1977 the O'Brien stable was in irresistible form, its colts winning almost everything that meant anything between May and October. The official end-of-year handicap indicated that Be My Guest had been only sixth-best in his stable, after Alleged, The Minstrel, Artaius, Godswalk and Marinsky, and it is a moot point whether he would have shown to greater or lesser advantage in a year when Ballydoyle was not so embarrassed with riches. He would certainly have been campaigned differently.

After a spring victory in the Blue Riband Trial Stakes, which really did not amount to much, Be My Guest was perceived as a middle-distance horse. He tried his luck in the Nijinsky Stakes over ten furlongs and was beaten by Orchestra; he also went to Epsom as his stable's second string to The Minstrel in the Derby, and patently failed to stay after holding a good position at the turn for home. With his own shortcomings over 12 furlongs ruling out one option, and Artaius becoming dominant in the mile and ten-furlong categories, O'Brien was for a while undecided about how to advance Be My Guest's cause. He eventually chose a mile programme and after a two-month break the colt came back for an easy victory in a not-too-competitive Desmond Stakes at The Curragh. A sterner test was to come in the Goodwood Mile, and Be My Guest did not impress, finding nothing off the bridle and barely retaining his advantage in a tight finish with Don, a contemporary who conceded him 2lb. Nevertheless, he now had a Group 2 victory to his credit and was intending to bid for a second, in the Queen Elizabeth II Stakes at Ascot, when a bruised foot called a halt to both the plan and his career.

Be My Guest may have been only the sixth-best three-year-old in his stable, but in the official handicap for Britain and Ireland he ranked ninth-best overall. Furthermore, only two of those rated above him – Artaius and Godswalk – were booked for stud duty in Ireland in 1978, Robert Sangster having already despatched The Minstrel to Maryland and decided to keep Alleged in training, while the immaculately bred Marinsky had died; breeders thus had sound reasons for finding this good-looking,

*Be My Guest, a good-looking, gifted miler.*

gifted miler an attractive proposition at a fee of 5000gns. He appealed to private and commercial breeders alike and soon had around 60 mares booked to him for his first season at Coolmore.

Few horses in modern times have made more impressive starts at stud. As he had not been a very precocious horse himself, Be My Guest was not expected to figure significantly with his two-year-olds, but ten in his first crop were winners, including Anfield (twice) and Assert in Pattern company. More remarkably still, when those first foals were three he was champion sire, largely through the exploits of his classic winners Assert and On the House, the former a sale yearling, the latter representing her breeder on account of her failure to reach a quite modest reserve at auction.

On the House was one of the first of many fillies by her sire who failed to impress as physical specimens but who nevertheless displayed superior racing merit. The market soon got used to the thought that they might be better than they looked. On the whole, though, the Be My Guests found a ready market and were substantial earners for their breeders in the early years. The stallion had four seasons at 5000gns, and from those crops the yearlings always averaged upwards of 30,000gns, once better than 40,000. After the first two-year-olds

had run with such promise, his fee was doubled and Coolmore yielded to the temptation to exploit his more fashionable status, accepting more than 90 mares to him in 1982. Many commercial breeders still contrived to benefit in spite of the resulting bumper foal crop of 71, as by then Be My Guest had a sires' championship under his belt and was being written and talked up prematurely as Ireland's counterpart to Northern Dancer, rather than as a worthy son of that sire.

In fact, things were already beginning to go wrong for Be My Guest and it soon became clear that the policy of managing him to maximize his earning capacity would prejudice his prospects of a consistent career as a top-level sire. He was neither the first nor the last of the stallions based at Coolmore to have suffered from that syndrome, but he may well represent the saddest case. He did show enormous potential, and managed with discretion he might well have realized much more than he has. In recent years the successes he has achieved have been in spite of the way he has been handled, rather than because of it.

For the 1983 breeding season, the first after his championship, Be My Guest's fee was raised from IR10,000gns to IR75,000gns. His own efforts supposedly supplied most of the justification; part could be attributed to some imagined reflected glory from his distant cousin Golden Fleece, a brilliant but overgrown and unsound Derby winner just retired to Coolmore at an even more ridiculous fee of IR100,000gns. (As it turned out, Golden Fleece died of cancer early in his second stud season, having done more harm than good in his brief career, and left not a single runner of consequence.) In the course of his first season at IR75,000gns, in which he covered more than 60 mares, Be My Guest's inferior mates of the preceding year dropped 71 foals, not one of whom proved capable of winning a Pattern race in either England or Ireland. Inevitably, he did get a better class of mare initially, and among that 1984 crop of 46 foals were six Pattern winners, the best of them a Derby runner-up in Most Welcome, but commercially a tremendous amount of damage had been done. In each of his three seasons at IR75,000gns, more than half of his auction yearlings realized less than that amount; the story

was the same over the following two years when his fee stood at IR50,000gns. Subsequent reductions, first to IR40,000gns and in 1989 to IR25,000gns (which was his fee again in 1990), reflect his loss of credibility, the more regrettable for the fact that, in some measure, it has been foisted on him.

The industry has waited in vain for a second Assert to appear, and though Go and Go won the 1990 Belmont Stakes, he is not in that class. Be My Guest has never been one to stamp his stock, and was probably never going to be another Northern Dancer, however he was managed; what is more, he has made some people a lot of money, which is regarded by many as the main reason for a stallion's existence nowadays. For all that, it is fascinating to speculate what he might have achieved, in terms of a more meaningful contribution to the breed, if he had spent his stud career as the number one stallion on a smaller stud, kept at a reasonable fee and mated to a limited number of mares of consistently high quality.

## Racing record

| Year | Starts | Wins | 2nd | 3rd | 4th | £ |
|------|--------|------|-----|-----|-----|-----|
| 1976 | 2 | 1 | - | - | - | 690 |
| 1977 | 5 | 3 | 1 | - | - | 28,124 |
|      | 7 | 4 | 1 | - | - | 28,814 |

## Principal wins

1977   Blue Riband Trial Stakes-Gr3
       Desmond Stakes-Gr3
       Goodwood Mile-Gr2

## Principal progeny

**1979**
b c ANFIELD (ex Mother, by Whistler)
    1981   Railway Stakes-Gr3
           Ashford Castle Stakes-Gr3
    1982   Desmond Stakes-Gr3
b c ASSERT (ex Irish Bird, by Sea-Bird)
    1981   Beresford Stakes-Gr2
    1982   Gallinule Stakes-Gr2
           Prix du Jockey-Club-Gr1
           Irish Derby-Gr1
           Benson & Hedges Gold Cup-Gr1
           Joe McGrath Memorial Stakes-Gr1
b f ON THE HOUSE (ex Lora, by Lorenzaccio)
    1982   1000 Guineas Stakes-Gr1
           Sussex Stakes-Gr1
ch c WHAT A GUEST (ex Princess Tiara, by Crowned Prince)
    1982   Prix de la Jonchere-Gr3
           Prix Eugene Adam-Gr2

**1980**
b c FAITH GUEST (ex Faith Lift, by Nearctic)
    1982   Premio Primi Passi-Gr3
           Criterium Nazionale-Gr3

## BE MY GUEST                                    (chesnut, 1974)

| | | Nearco | Pharos |
|---|---|---|---|
| | Nearctic | | Nogara |
| Northern Dancer | | Lady Angela | Hyperion |
| (b 1961) | | | Sister Sarah |
| | | Native Dancer | Polynesian |
| | Natalma | | Geisha |
| | | Almahmoud | Mahmoud |
| | | | Arbitrator |
| | | Owen Tudor | Hyperion |
| | Tudor Minstrel | | Mary Tudor |
| What a Treat | | Sansonnet | Sansovino |
| (b 1962) | | | Lady Juror |
| | | Stymie | Equestrian |
| | Rare Treat | | Stop Watch |
| | | Rare Perfume | Eight Thirty |
| | | | Fragrance |

ch f LUTH ENCHANTEE (ex Viole d'Amour, by Luthier)
    1983   Prix d'Astarte-Gr2
           Prix Jacques le Marois-Gr1
           Prix du Moulin de Longchamp-Gr1
ch c PREGO (ex Audrey Joan, by Doutelle)
    1984   Hungerford Stakes-Gr3

**1981**
ch f FREE GUEST (ex Fremanche, by Jim French)
    1984   Sun Chariot Stakes-Gr2
    1985   Nassau Stakes-Gr2
           Sun Chariot Stakes-Gr2
           Princess Royal Stakes-Gr3

**1982**
ch f SOJOURN (ex Melody, by Lord Gayle)
    1985    Honey Bee Handicap-Gr3

**1983**
b c DOUBLE BED (ex Claire's Slipper, by Welsh Saint)
    1986    Prix de la Cote Normande-Gr3
    1988    Hialeah Turf Cup Handicap-Gr1

ch c EVE'S ERROR (ex Apple Peel, by Pall Mall)
    1986    Oettingen Rennen-Gr3
            Grosser Preis von Dusseldorf-Gr2

**1984**
b c ASTRONEF (ex Mill Princess, by Mill Reef)
    1988    Goldene Peitsche-Gr3
    1989    Premio Melton-Gr2
            Goldene Peitsche-Gr3

b c GRAND CHELEM (ex Racquette, by Ballymore)
    1986    Prix La Rochette-Gr3

ch f GUEST PERFORMER (ex Melody, by Lord Gayle)
    1987    Kiveton Park Stakes-Gr3

ch f INVITED GUEST (ex Welcome Break, by Wollow)
    1986    Waterford Candelabra Stakes-Gr3
            Fillies' Mile-Gr2
    1987    Prix de Psyche-Gr3
            Dahlia Handicap [Div.1]-Gr3
    1989    Golden Poppy Handicap-Gr3
    1990    San Gorgonio Handicap-Gr2
ch c MEDIA STARGUEST (ex Diomedia, by Sea-Bird)
    1988    Earl of Sefton Stakes-Gr3
ch c MOST WELCOME (ex Topsy, by Habitat)
    1987    Select Stakes-Gr3
    1989    Lockinge Stakes-Gr2

**1985**
ch f INTIMATE GUEST (ex As You Desire Me, by Kalamoun)
    1987    May Hill Stakes-Gr3

**1986**
b f BE EXCLUSIVE (ex Exclusive Fable, by Exclusive Native)
    1989    Prix Chloe-Gr3

**1987**
ch c GO AND GO (ex Irish Edition, by Alleged)
    1989    Laurel Futurity-Gr2
    1990    Belmont Stakes-Gr1

# Blakeney

WITH hindsight, the five years up to 1972 in British racing and breeding seem to mirror the period immediately prior to 1914 in the real world. Things were happening that were different. The pattern of events, established generations ago and maintained through decades of cosy complacency, was no longer so predictable. The perceptive few foresaw the imminence of a day when the industry would wake up to the realization that things were never going to be the same again.

What turned our little bloodstock world upside-down was, of course, the American invasion. In consecutive seasons star three-year-olds Sir Ivor, Habitat, Nijinsky, Mill Reef and Roberto, all of them products of North American studs, rampaged through our schedule of top races, humiliating the home-bred

*Blakeney, one of the last stallions from the old classic tradition.*

horses who, so recently, we had imagined to be at least the equals of any on earth. The sad fact was that, obviously and embarrassingly, we were no longer capable of producing the horses most suitable for the environment we had created for them. Things never were the same again, and not since the 1969 season have all five English classics been won by horses bred in England or Ireland from English- or Irish-based parents.

The last three home-trained Derby winners of the sixties, Charlottown, Royal Palace and Blakeney, were all bred to the time-honoured pattern which had served its admirable purpose for two centuries. Charlottown was by a winner of the Prix du Jockey-Club out of a winner of the fillies' Triple Crown; Royal Palace was the son of a St Leger winner from an established classic family; Blakeney was by a St Leger winner out of a mare who had finished second in the Oaks. Every one was a European through and through. Three times in four years the Derby result seemed to confirm that the traditional methods were best; yet the formula was never to work again.

Blakeney was – by several pounds – the worst of those three Derby winners. He managed to win only one race in each of his three seasons in training, his career ratio of one victory to four defeats being one of the worst on record among those who triumphed at Epsom. Having failed to fetch a modest 5000gns reserve as a yearling at Newmarket, probably on account of his want of size, the little colt went home to Whatcombe, where his owner-breeder, Arthur Budgett, added him to the relatively small string he trained himself. At two he won the Houghton Stakes at Newmarket in promising style, and in the following spring he became a popular fancy for the Derby as a result of his patently unlucky defeat in the Derby Trial at Lingfield. Ridden on the big day by Ernie Johnson, Blakeney enjoyed much better fortune at Epsom, finding an opening on the rails in the straight and wearing Shoemaker down inside the last furlong, but his subsequent efforts that season, in the Irish Derby (fourth), the St Leger (fifth) and the Prix de l'Arc de Triomphe (ninth), underlined his shortcomings instead of confirming his superior merit.

Nonetheless, Blakeney was able to enhance his reputation a little as a four-year-old. He won the

Ormonde Stakes at Chester, and his fifth place in the Arc de Triomphe was a commendably stout effort in his toughest-ever assignment. The trouble was that the race which tended to stick in the memory was the King George VI & Queen Elizabeth Stakes, when he was humiliated by a cantering Nijinsky. He was also beaten in the Ascot Gold Cup – and by a colt (Precipice Wood) who had been a long way short of classic calibre in the previous year.

Few Derby winners have embarked on a stud career with quite so much to live down, yet while Charlottown failed and was banished to Australia and Royal Palace (with the solitary exception of Dunfermline) proved incapable of getting a really high-class performer, Blakeney was successful at the outset and continued to make a mark in spite of the ever-growing numbers of more fashionably-bred horses, with their American connections, who generally succeeded in cutting off the supply of top-grade mares which had formerly been deemed the right of any Derby winner.

Make no mistake. Blakeney has never been a great sire, and his faults – in an environment where speed and early maturity are considered all-important – are plain to see. For the most part his two-year-olds are of little account, and his runners who excel at under a mile and a half are rare exceptions to the rule. Typically his stock are plain little horses, devoid of early pace, requiring time as well as distance. Mated with fast mares, more often than not he continues to turn out stayers. For a horse with the capability to get classic winners (Juliette Marny was out of the first mare he covered) he has not been notably consistent in the quality of his production.

Even so, Blakeney has been a qualified success, almost uniquely among the last of the Europeans bred to the old classic pattern. Still active at the National Stud in 1990, at the age of 24, and recently back in the public eye through the exploits of his daughter Roseate Tern, he may be seen as a living relic of a bygone age. The new era made him the concession of some fleeting moments of fame as a sire, but the next generation has proved unable to stem the tide of change. His sons have been uniformly bad stallions, his daughters deeply disappointing broodmares.

## Racing record

| Year | Starts | Wins | 2nd | 3rd | 4th | £ |
|---|---|---|---|---|---|---|
| 1968 | 2 | 1 | - | - | 1 | 1,573 |
| 1969 | 5 | 1 | 1 | - | 1 | 67,112 |
| 1970 | 5 | 1 | 2 | - | - | 14,970 |
| | 12 | 3 | 3 | - | 2 | 83,655 |

## Principal wins
1968 Houghton Stakes
1969 Derby Stakes
1970 Ormonde Stakes

## Principal progeny
**1972**
b f JULIETTE MARNY (ex Set Free, by Worden)
1975 Lingfield Oaks Trial Stakes-Gr3
Oaks Stakes-Gr1
Irish Oaks-Gr1

**1973**
br c NORFOLK AIR (ex Melody Maid, by Tudor Melody)
1976 Lingfield Derby Trial Stakes-Gr3

**1975**
b c JULIO MARINER (ex Set Free, by Worden)
1978 St Leger Stakes-Gr1
b c ROSCOE BLAKE (ex Rhodie, by Rasper)
1978 Grosser Hansa Preis-Gr2
gr c SEXTON BLAKE (ex Mayo Blues, by Abernant)
1977 Seaton Delaval Stakes-Gr3
Champagne Stakes-Gr2
1978 Gordon Stakes-Gr3
1979 Westbury Stakes-Gr3

**BLAKENEY** (bay, 1966)

| | | | |
|---|---|---|---|
| Hethersett (b 1959) | Hugh Lupus | Djebel | Tourbillon / Loika |
| | | Sakountala | Goya / Samos |
| | Bride Elect | Big Game | Bahram / Myrobella |
| | | Netherton Maid | Nearco / Phase |
| Windmill Girl (b 1961) | Hornbeam | Hyperion | Gainsborough / Selene |
| | | Thicket | Nasrullah / Thorn Wood |
| | Chorus Beauty | Chanteur | Chateau Bouscaut / La Diva |
| | | Neberna | Nearco / Springtime |

b f TINTAGEL (ex Ysolda, by Elopement)
1979 Prix Corrida-Gr3
Prix Fille de l'Air-Gr3

**1976**
b c TWO OF DIAMONDS (ex Santa Maria, by Tropique)
1979 Dee Stakes-Gr3

**1977**
br c COMMODORE BLAKE (ex Ribamba, by Ribocco)
1982 Prix Perth-Gr3
Premio Ribot-Gr2

b c TYRNAVOS (ex Stilvi, by Derring-Do)
    1980    Craven Stakes-Gr3
            Irish Derby-Gr1

**1978**

b f HUNSTON (ex Catherine Wheel, by Roan Rocket)
    1981    Cheshire Oaks-Gr3
    1982    Matchmaker Stakes-Gr2
            Queen Charlotte Handicap [Div.1]-Gr2

**1979**

b f BELIEVER (ex Seein Is Believin, by Native Charger)
    1982    Princess Royal Stakes-Gr3
b c ELECTRIC (ex Christiana, by Double Jump)
    1982    White Rose Stakes-Gr3
            Gordon Stakes-Gr3
            Great Voltigeur Stakes-Gr2
    1983    Jockey Club Stakes-Gr3
b f MOUNTAIN LODGE (ex Fiddlededee, by Acropolis)
    1983    Irish St Leger-Gr1
b f RADIANCE (ex Sybarite, by Royal Record)
    1983    Prix Corrida-Gr3

**1980**

b c BAND (ex Zither, by Vienna)
    1983    Cumberland Lodge Stakes-Gr3
    1984    Yorkshire Cup-Gr2

**1983**

br c SATCO (ex Satwa, by Nonoalco)
    1986    Prix Berteux-Gr3

**1984**

b f PERCY'S LASS (ex Laughing Girl, by Sassafras)
    1988    September Stakes-Gr3
b f THREE TAILS (ex Triple First, by High Top)
    1986    Premio Dormello-Gr2
    1987    Lancashire Oaks-Gr3
            Meld Stakes-Gr3

**1986**

b f ROSEATE TERN (ex Rosia Bay, by High Top)
    1989    Lancashire Oaks-Gr3
            Yorkshire Oaks-Gr1
    1990    Jockey Club Stakes-Gr2

# Blushing Groom

THE Aga Khan, having inherited a racing empire he really did not want, thought long and hard before deciding to maintain it. In his youth Prince Karim had shown no interest in, and at times displayed remarkable ignorance of, the pursuit which had been at least the principal pastime of his grandfather, the 'old Aga', and the ruling passion of his father, Prince Aly Khan's, life. Insiders reckoned that young 'K' would be bored by racing within a couple of years, and would abandon his involvement.

In fact, the man who took up racing as a burden and whose naivety on the subject was at first a source of much merriment among horsemen, was to confound everyone. The need to know sparked an interest which grew into an obsession. In time he not only operated studs and stables on a scale far greater than those of his forbears; he also surpassed their achievements, becoming the most successful breeder in the world. Furthermore, what he developed was no massive plaything, but a self-supporting international enterprise, controlled and conducted with the shrewdness of a consummate professional.

The present Aga's operation differs in numerous respects from that which his grandfather and father ran, in partnership, for many years. Most significantly, he has concentrated on breeding and racing his own stock and has never been an habitué of the auction scene, except as a vendor of horses surplus to requirements. However, it was a rare exception to that rule which provided him with one of his most successful racehorses, and it was as a result of that purchase that he was able to acquire the facility to enhance the quality of his stud and extend his lead over his competitors.

Although he resolutely spurned the yearling sales, the Aga occasionally commissioned an agent to buy him a foal or two, and in 1974 Keith Freeman was entrusted with the purchase of a couple at the Newmarket December Sales. He bought the two most highly-priced in the catalogue. One of them, Fayyaad, cost 28,000gns and turned out moderate; the other was a 16,500gns colt who received the name Blushing Groom.

An excellent reason for breeding rather than buying is that it is easy enough to produce one's own mistakes without going to the expense of acquiring someone else's. In Blushing Groom's case it was not quite like that, as the Aga had actually bred his dam and he had won two Group 3 events with his brother, Bayraan, a 12,000gns foal purchase three years earlier. The pedigree was familiar territory, and as the mating had already worked once there was reason to hope that it would do so again. Bayraan had already more than paid his way with four wins between six furlongs and a mile, and that bay colt was to add a further victory as a four-year-old before his sale to Japan as a stallion. His little brother was a horse of a different colour – and of a different class as well.

Blushing Groom was put into training at Chantilly with François Mathet and his first race was on his home course in June 1976. Inexperience beat him there, but nothing was to beat him again for nearly 12 months. After his maiden win at Evry his trainer was so convinced of his merit – and of his superiority to the rest of a vintage crop of juveniles in his stable – that he resolved to prepare Blushing Groom for the series of Group 1 races which made up the two-year-olds' 'Quadruple Crown'. Only one horse – English-trained My Swallow – had previously earned that distinction, which involved beating the best of one's contemporaries at five and a half, six, seven and eight furlongs over a period of three months and at three different courses. Mathet never doubted that Blushing Groom was up to the task, and his judgment was gloriously vindicated.

In the Prix Robert Papin the colt came from a long way back to defeat River Dane by three-quarters of a length. In the Prix Morny he raced closer to the pace, then accelerated to open a three-length gap over the last half-furlong. In the Prix de la Salamandre he seemed to lack his usual sparkle but got by comfortably without it, winning by two lengths. The real test was supposed to come in the Grand Critérium, where the championship of Europe was at stake. The English imagined they had unearthed a real celebrity in J.O. Tobin, the style of whose victories at Newmarket, Goodwood and Doncaster had caused his trainer, Noel Murless, to reconsider his retirement plans, with a view to saddling his fourth Derby winner in 1977. This colt, reputedly the best two-year-old seen in England for many years, failed in his mission to cut the so-called

French pretender down to size. Instead, Blushing Groom ensured that Murless settled for armchair and slippers and that J.O. Tobin left England for America where, in his most fabled run, he put an end to Seattle Slew's unbeaten record. Blushing Groom was brilliant in the Critérium, J.O. Tobin so completely outpointed that he lost second place close home to Amyntor. Unsurprisingly, the winner's four-length margin ensured that he headed the official French juvenile ratings with a rare 7lb advantage over the best of his contemporaries.

Blushing Groom had only four races in his second season, losing the last two, and it might be argued that he did not show appreciable improvement from two to three. He soon registered easy victories in the Prix de Fontainebleau and Poule d'Essai des Poulains, which effectively confirmed that he was still the best miler around, but the decision to run him next in the Derby set him a question which even François Mathet could not be convinced he would be able to answer. For reassurance, Mathet gave Blushing Groom two strong gallops over a mile and a half against Exceller, a proven stayer of Group 1 calibre; in one of them they carried level weights in spite of the year's difference between them, and Blushing Groom won by five lengths. In the circumstances it was no wonder that he started 9/4 favourite for the Derby, but the stud book proved a better guide than the form book on this occasion. Red God never had sired a son capable of winning a major race at 12 furlongs, and Blushing Groom was not to be the first. He tried hard and failed honourably, finishing five lengths behind The Minstrel and Hot Grove in third place. On the following day his galloping companion Exceller won the Coronation Cup.

Blushing Groom reverted to a mile for the Prix Jacques le Marois but was beaten again, finding racing room only after Flying Water had gone beyond recall. The form was not right, and Blushing Groom was going to prove the point in one last effort, but circumstances beyond his control dictated that his career was already over. Before the Derby the Aga Khan had negotiated a deal with Gainesway Farm in Kentucky whereby the colt was to be syndicated to stand there at a valuation of $6.26 million, with his owner retaining a significant number of shares. That summer an outbreak of a hitherto unknown venereal disease, contagious equine metritis, occurred on European studs, causing alarm bells to ring in other countries. The Americans were particularly concerned about the prospect of introducing this strange new affliction into their breeding stock, eventually deciding that a temporary embargo on imports provided the safest solution. The ban inevitably had to take immediate effect, and it was only because word of the impending move leaked out that Blushing Groom and several others were able to beat the deadline to the States.

The consequences of thwarting the embargo were tremendous, though for a while more significant to the Aga Khan than to anyone else. For him the horse's safe arrival in Kentucky meant that he could embark at once on a new phase in the development of his breeding interests. In Blushing Groom he had an ideal bargaining counter, an asset he could use to procure him access (by way of exchange nominations and similar deals) to America's best stallions; and if the horse should prove successful, the scope for enhancing the quality in his stud would be boundless. The outstanding success of the plan is readily illustrated by the pedigrees of the Aga's latest two Derby winners. Kahyasi was produced by a mare who resulted from Blushing Groom's first crop; Shahrastani was the product of a nomination to Nijinsky, a horse his breeder was never in a position to use until the deal which took Blushing Groom to Gainesway went through. No less significant is the fact that the deal provided the finance for the Aga's acquisition, over the next two years, of the Dupré and Boussac studs, from which countless other successes were to stem in the 1980s.

There was, though, a slight hiatus before the overall benefits of the stallion's residence in Kentucky became apparent. If Europe's two-year-old champion could not get high-class two-year-olds, what was he going to get? That question exercised many minds at the end of 1981, by which time Blushing Groom's first crop had succeeded only in maintaining an ultra-low profile in the big juvenile races on both sides of the Atlantic. The answer came, forcibly expressed, in 1982, and it established the pattern which has become familiar from the exploits of the horse's subsequent progeny. More often than not the Blushing Grooms were not precocious, and if they were good at two they were likely to be better still at three; they tended not to be specialists over any particular distance, many of them being far more amply endowed with stamina than their sire, and they were generally indifferent to ground conditions. Most crucially, he got runners capable of competing with the best in both European and American environments, ensuring keen demand for his stock from horsemen of two continents.

That first crop, so unimpressive at two, produced no fewer than six individual Pattern or Graded winners in the following year, five of them at Group 1 or Grade 1 level. The wins were divided between

*Blushing Groom, sire of Derby winner Nashwan and leading stallion in 1989.*

England, France, Italy and the States, perhaps the most notable coming when Runaway Groom, down from Canada, upset the winners of the US Triple Crown events (Gato del Sol, Aloma's Ruler and Conquistador Cielo) in the important Travers Stakes at Saratoga. Blushing Groom's fee, which had drifted upwards from a starting point of $35,000 to $60,000 for no better reason than general inflation in the market, suddenly had real cause to rise. For 1983 it was set at $150,000.

Crystal Glitters was the pick of the second crop, with his Group 1 victories in the Prix d'Ispahan at both three and four, but for quality in quantity the third was better. The range of aptitudes expressed by the seven major stakes-winners was remarkable, Mt Livermore excelling in sprints, Morning Bob at around a mile, Rainbow Quest at a mile and a half, and Spicy Story at two miles-plus.

Blushing Groom's excellent results in Britain and France in 1985 – he figured among the top four stallions on both sides of the Channel – ensured that a high proportion of future crops would find their way to Europe. The lovely – yet fiercely competitive – Al Bahathri was one of three Group 1 winners that year, along with Baillamont and the Arc de Triomphe winner Rainbow Quest.

The top-class performers kept coming. There was the admirable Groom Dancer, one of the best three-year-old colts of 1987, and Blushing John, having emulated him in that respect in 1988, switched happily to America in 1989, proving himself as proficient on dirt as on grass. Best of all, 1989 brought Nashwan, who so dominated the season that Blushing Groom was able to clinch his first sires' championship. Nashwan, a powerfully-built chestnut with an enormous stride and a wonderfully fluent action, recorded an unprecedented sweep of the 2000 Guineas, Derby, Eclipse and King George VI & Queen Elizabeth Stakes, only to lose his unbeaten certificate in a race of comparatively little significance in France. His retirement to stud after that defeat left many questions unanswered, and the arguments over his true status were conducted almost in the manner of an Arts *v* Science debate. The scientists who compiled the official handicap, translating his form into figures, reckoned he was only the third-best of his generation and denounced the horses he beat as sub-standard. The artists would have none of that. For them he was poetry in motion, a creature whose qualities could not be reduced to mathematics, perhaps the horse of the decade. His closest connections, the trainer of Brigadier Gerard and the rider of Troy, came down on the side of the artists, declaring him to have been superior to both those champions.

Blushing Groom's fee, having risen to a peak of $275,000, was reduced to reach $160,000 in 1989, when he covered successfully in spite of the removal of a testicle following the development of a tumour in the previous year. Nashwan's performances resulted in another upward revision of the charge, to $225,000 in 1990, but problems occurred from the start of that season; none of the first 11 mares he covered was tested in foal. His book was promptly cut from 45 to 22 in the hope that the lighter work-load would rectify matters.

Nashwan, meanwhile, began his stallion career at Hamdan Al-Maktoum's Nunnery Stud at a fee of £100,000, which made him the highest-priced stallion in England, but by no means ensured that he was likely to prove the most successful. It is rarely a wise move to price a young horse beyond the reach of the vast majority of breeders, and even the support of the Maktoum family, who kept most of the shares, cannot guarantee that he will be mated with the mares who will suit him best.

Few stallions get everything right, and one aspect of Blushing Groom's career which may be open to criticism is that his sons have yet to establish themselves as sires. Coquelin has been bad, Jalmood, Shy Groom, Runaway Groom and Local Suitor all disappointing. By contrast, Rainbow Quest has begun well, and others will surely succeed, but if Blushing Groom were going to be another Northern Dancer, one or two of those early failures would have made a more notable mark.

## Racing record

| Year | Starts | Wins | 2nd | 3rd | 4th | FR |
|------|--------|------|-----|-----|-----|-----|
| 1976 | 6 | 5 | - | 1 | - | 1,242,000 |
| 1977 | 4 | 2 | 1 | 1 | - | 635,892 |
| | 10 | 7 | 1 | 2 | - | 1,877,892 |

## Principal wins

|      | 1976 | Prix Robert Papin-Gr1 |
|------|------|----|

1976    Prix Robert Papin-Gr1
Prix Morny-Gr1
Prix de la Salamandre-Gr1
Grand Criterium-Gr1
1977    Prix de Fontainebleau-Gr3
Poule d'Essai des Poulains-Gr1

## Principal progeny

**1979**
ch f BLUSH WITH PRIDE (ex Best in Show, by Traffic Judge)
    1982    Santa Susana Stakes-Gr1
            Ashland Stakes-Gr2
            Kentucky Oaks-Gr1
            Golden Harvest Handicap [Div.1]-Gr3

ch c COQUELIN (ex Topolly, by Turn-to)
    1982    Prix du Lys-Gr3
            La Coupe de Maisons-Laffitte-Gr3
    1983    Premio Vittorio di Capua-Gr2

b c JALMOOD (ex Fast Ride, by Sicambre)
    1982    Lingfield Derby Trial Stakes-Gr3
    1983    Premio Presidente della Repubblica-Gr1

ch f ROSANANTI (ex Clarina, by Klairon)
    1982    Premio Regina Elena-Gr1

gr c RUNAWAY GROOM (ex Yonnie Girl, by Call the Witness)
    1982    Travers Stakes-Gr1

## BLUSHING GROOM      (chesnut, 1974)

| | | | Nearco | Pharos |
|---|---|---|---|---|
| | | Nasrullah | | Nogara |
| | Red God | | Mumtaz Begum | Blenheim |
| | (ch 1954) | | | Mumtaz Mahal |
| | | | Menow | Pharamond |
| | | Spring Run | | Alcibiades |
| | | | Boola Brook | Bull Dog |
| | | | | Brookdale |
| | | | Rialto | Rabelais |
| | | Wild Risk | | La Grelee |
| | Runaway Bride | | Wild Violet | Blandford |
| | (b 1962) | | | Wood Violet |
| | | | Tudor Minstrel | Owen Tudort |
| | | Aimee | | Sansonnet |
| | | | Emali | Umidwar |
| | | | | Eclair |

b/br f TOO CHIC (ex Remedia, by Dr Fager)
    1982    Maskette Stakes-Gr1

**1980**
b c CRYSTAL GLITTERS (ex Tales to Tell, by Donut King)
    1982    Prix Eclipse-Gr3
    1983    Prix d'Ispahan-Gr1
    1984    Prix Edmond Blanc-Gr3
            Prix d'Ispahan-Gr1
ch c NASSIPOUR (ex Alama, by Aureole)
    1985    Dixie Handicap-Gr2
            Seneca Handicap-Gr3
            Canadian International Championship Stakes-Gr1
ch f OVERDOSE (ex Oropesa, by Noholme)
    1983    Premio Carlo Porta-Gr3
ch f VERRIA (ex Via Venise, by Shoemaker)
    1983    Prix Chloe-Gr3

## 1981

b f BARONESS DIRECT (ex Avum, by Umbrella Fella)
    1986   Las Flores Handicap-Gr3
ch c INNAMORATO (ex Out Draw, by Speak John)
    1985   Native Diver Handicap-Gr3
b/br c MORNING BOB (ex Guillotine Miss, by The Axe)
    1984   Tropical Park Derby-Gr2
            Pennsylvania Derby-Gr2
    1985   Excelsior Handicap-Gr2
ch c MT LIVERMORE (ex Flama Ardiente, by Crimson Satan)
    1985   Carter Handicap-Gr2
            Boojum Handicap-Gr3
            Fall Highweight Handicap-Gr2
b c RAINBOW QUEST (ex I Will Follow, by Herbager)
    1984   Great Voltigeur Stakes-Gr2
    1985   Coronation Cup-Gr1
            Prix de l'Arc de Triomphe-Gr1
b c SPICY STORY (ex Javamine, by Nijinsky)
    1985   Doncaster Cup-Gr3
ch c WESTHEIMER (ex Countess North, by Northern Dancer)
    1985   New Orleans Handicap-Gr2
            Ark-La-Tex Handicap-Gr3

## 1982

ch f AL BAHATHRI (ex Chain Store, by Nodouble)
    1984   Lowther Stakes-Gr2
    1985   Irish 1000 Guineas-Gr1
            Coronation Stakes-Gr2
            Child Stakes-Gr3
b c BAILLAMONT (ex Lodeve, by Shoemaker)
    1985   Prix Jean Prat-Gr1
    1986   Prix Ganay-Gr1
            Prix d'Ispahan-Gr1
b c IFRAD (ex Ilyaara, by Huntercombe)
    1987   Arlington Handicap-Gr1
    1988   San Francisco Mile Handicap-Gr3
            All American Handicap-Gr3
b c LOCAL SUITOR (ex Home Love, by Vaguely Noble)
    1984   Mill Reef Stakes-Gr2

## 1983

ch c ICY GROOM (ex Hey Babe, by Roberto)
    1988   Pennsylvania Governor's Cup Stakes-Gr3
b c MALAKIM (ex Mill River, by Mill Reef)
    1987   Prix d'Hedouville-Gr3
ch c SALT DOME (ex Buda Lady, by Crimson Satan)
    1988   Count Fleet Sprint Handicap-Gr2

## 1984

b c GROOM DANCER (ex Featherhill, by Lyphard)
    1986   Prix de Conde-Gr3
    1987   Prix de Guiche-Gr3
            Prix Lupin-Gr1
            Prix Daphnis-Gr3
            Prix du Prince d'Orange-Gr3
b c LOVE THE GROOM (ex Nell's Briquette, by Lanyon)
    1987   King Edward VII Stakes-Gr2
            Gordon Stakes-Gr3
b c LUTH DANCER (ex Luth de Saron, by Luthier)
    1987   Prix du Lys-Gr3
    1988   Prix d'Hedouville-Gr3
ch f NASHMEEL (ex Donut's Bunnie, by Donut King)
    1987   Prix d'Astarte-Gr2

## 1985

ch c BLUSHING JOHN (ex La Griffe, by Prince John)
    1987   Prix Saint Roman-Gr3
    1988   Prix de Fontainebleau-Gr3
            Poule d'Essai des Poulains-Gr1
    1989   Razorback Handicap-Gr2
            Hollywood Gold Cup Handicap-Gr1
            Washington Park Handicap-Gr2
ch c DIGAMIST (ex Disconiz, by Northern Dancer)
    1987   Phoenix Stakes-Gr1
ch c KEFAAH (ex Tertiary, by Vaguely Noble)
    1988   Ayr Classic Stakes-Gr3
ch c RAHY (ex Glorious Song, by Halo)
    1989   Bel Air Handicap-Gr2

## 1986

ch c DOUBLE BLUSH (ex Double Delta, by Delta Judge)
    1990   Grey Lag Handicap-Gr3
b c HEART OF GROOM (ex Polar Bear, by Hoist the Flag)
    1989   Premio Roma Vecchia-Gr3
b f MUHBUBH (ex Manal, by Luthier)
    1988   Princess Margaret Stakes-Gr3
ch c NASHWAN (ex Height of Fashion, by Bustino)
    1989   2000 Guineas Stakes-Gr1
            Derby Stakes-Gr1
            Eclipse Stakes-Gr1
            King George VI & Queen Elizabeth Stakes-Gr1
ch f SNOW BRIDE (ex Awaasif, by Snow Knight)
    1989   Musidora Stakes-Gr3
            Princess Royal Stakes-Gr3
b c TWO TIMING (ex Social Column, by Vaguely Noble)
    1989   Prince of Wales's Stakes-Gr2

# Brigadier Gerard

FOR proof that the best racehorses do not always make the best sires, look no further down the list of England's greatest than Brigadier Gerard. His place in the athletes' pantheon has never been in dispute, and many who saw him in action during the first three years of the '70s are in no doubt that he was the finest of them all. That was not just the understandably emotional response of a hero-worshipping public which took a game and handsome horse to its heart and marvelled at his capacity to win almost every time he ran. The hardened professionals who habitually enjoyed exercising their cynicism were members of the Brigadier's fan club too, as were the dispassionate form experts who dealt only in cold facts, reducing live performances to dull mathematics. *Timeform*, for over 40 years the most respected independent organization in the business of analysing performance, has rated only one horse more highly than Brigadier Gerard – the French-bred 1965 Derby and Arc de Triomphe winner Sea-Bird. The Brigadier, it reckoned, was 1lb inferior to Sea-Bird, and in its experience his merit has been matched by only one other runner, the 1947 Guineas winner Tudor Minstrel.

This Thoroughbred paragon was bred by John Hislop, a former champion amateur rider and an outstanding writer on racing and breeding for numerous publications. He had bought the grand-dam, Brazen Molly, as a barren five-year-old for 400gns, largely because she was a third-generation descendant of the celebrated mare Pretty Polly, and among the foals he bred from her were Stokes, a colt who finished second in the 2000 Guineas, and La Paiva, a filly who displayed negligible racing talent. However, La Paiva was quick enough to make her mark as a broodmare, and her first four foals were already winners before Brigadier Gerard set foot on a racecourse. The Brigadier's sire was Queen's Hussar, a gifted miler with a need for blinkers and a liking for firm ground; an attractive individual himself, he got a son of quite exceptional good looks from La Paiva. What is more, Brigadier Gerard had the constitution to match his conformation. He stood on the best of limbs, possessed the perfect racing temperament, and was an easy horse to handle for his master

trainer, Dick Hern.

Brigadier Gerard's racing career was not quite perfect. Like Sea-Bird he suffered one defeat, but he did race 18 times rather than eight, and whereas Sea-Bird beat horses who would have been champions in other years, Brigadier Gerard beat horses who were champions in one of the best editions of the 2000 Guineas on record. As a two-year-old he won four out of four, most notably the Middle Park Stakes, in which he trounced high-class sprinters in Mummy's Pet and Swing Easy. He was rated third-best of his crop that year, and the pair ranked above him, My Swallow and Mill Reef, were his chief rivals in the Guineas, his first race as a three-year-old. For seven of the eight furlongs the issue seemed certain to be decided between the other pair. My Swallow led, while Mill Reef pursued him closely. Joe Mercer, on Brigadier Gerard, let them get on with their private battle, waited until the Dip, then called for action. Many in the stands were still marvelling at the gameness of Mill Reef as he wore down My Swallow when the Brigadier flashed by on the stands side, rapidly establishing a three-length advantage.

That was an exceptional performance, and nothing was ever going to beat Brigadier Gerard over a mile after that. Nothing ever did, and just as significantly, nothing ever beat Mill Reef again over any distance. The Brigadier (who was ridden throughout his career by Joe Mercer, the supreme stylist of his era) ran and won five more times in 1971, beating the best of his own age group and older horses at a mile and ten furlongs. He had close calls on soft ground, which he never relished, but his courage and class always saw him through. At four he extended his unbeaten run to 15, conquering a wet surface in the Eclipse and a distance that was really beyond him in the King George VI & Queen Elizabeth Stakes. Inexplicably, he failed to catch the Derby winner Roberto in the Benson & Hedges Gold Cup at York, but he returned in majestic form for Ascot's Queen Elizabeth II Stakes and closed his career triumphantly by beating Riverman in the Champion Stakes.

John and Jean Hislop were deaf to American offers for their champion, preferring to stand him at Egerton Stud in Newmarket and keep a controlling interest in a partial syndication which valued him at only £1 million. The decision to keep Brigadier Gerard in England was laudable, but the controls exercised by the Hislops probably did not aid his cause as a stallion. Market breeders were actively discouraged from using the horse, and the onus of supplying him with the mares who were supposed to help him make his name at stud was left to the diminishing band of European private breeders who at that very time were ceding their age-old dominant position to the marauding Americans. It was true that Brigadier Gerard was himself the product of a small private stud, but he would have been a one-off in any era and was conspicuously so in the early '70s. In effect, he was an exception to the prevailing rule, and it was hard to see how outmoded practices could serve his interests; his successes were always likely to be exceptions rather than the rule.

That was pretty much how Brigadier Gerard's stud career worked out. He did get good horses, in Light Cavalry and Vayrann a couple who were very good. He did rather better than quite a few other highly-regarded English-based horses of his era. What he did not do was get a son anywhere near his own class, but in that respect he was certainly no worse than either Sea-Bird or Tudor Minstrel. It was more disappointing that he failed to get a son with his own toughness, consistency and guts. For the most part his progeny had weak racing characters, often showing potential they never realized and exhibiting temperamental flaws; not one owned a physique to compare with the imposing specimen who passed for the model Thoroughbred in his racing days. Yet, curiously, the Brigadier himself cut a much less commanding figure after only a brief time at stud, almost seeming to have undergone a metabolic change for the worse. His fertility failed, quite suddenly, at the age of 15, and he died of a heart attack on 29 October 1989 after five years of happy retirement at the Qualitair Stud near Newmarket.

*Brigadier Gerard extends his then-unbeaten record in the Eclipse Stakes, beating Gold Rod and Home Guard.*

## Racing record

| Year | Starts | Wins | 2nd | 3rd | 4th | £ |
|------|--------|------|-----|-----|-----|------|
| 1970 | 4 | 4 | - | - | - | 13,470 |
| 1971 | 6 | 6 | - | - | - | 79,241 |
| 1972 | 8 | 7 | 1 | - | - | 160,314 |
| | 18 | 17 | 1 | - | - | 253,025 |

## Principal wins

| | |
|------|------|
| 1970 | Middle Park Stakes |
| 1971 | 2000 Guineas Stakes-Gr1 |
| | St James's Palace Stakes-Gr2 |
| | Sussex Stakes-Gr1 |
| | Goodwood Mile-Gr2 |
| | Queen Elizabeth II Stakes-Gr2 |
| | Champion Stakes-Gr1 |
| 1972 | Lockinge Stakes-Gr2 |
| | Westbury Stakes-Gr3 |
| | Prince of Wales's Stakes-Gr3 |
| | Eclipse Stakes-Gr1 |
| | King George VI & Queen Elizabeth Stakes-Gr1 |
| | Queen Elizabeth II Stakes-Gr2 |
| | Champion Stakes-Gr1 |

## Principal progeny

**1974**

ch c ETIENNE GERARD (ex Oh So Fair, by Graustark)
    1977    Jersey Stakes-Gr3
b c GENERAL (ex Mercuriale, by Pan)
    1976    Prix Thomas Bryon-Gr3

**1975**

b c ADMIRAL'S LAUNCH (ex Cutter, by Donatello)
    1978    Craven Stakes-Gr3
ch c LEONARDO DA VINCI (ex Lupe, by Primera)
    1978    White Rose Stakes-Gr3
ch f PRINCESS EBOLI (ex Nedda, by Alcide)
    1978    Cheshire Oaks-Gr3
            Lancashire Oaks-Gr3

**1976**

b c R.B. CHESNE (ex Vive la Reine, by Vienna)
    1978    Champagne Stakes-Gr2

**1977**

b c LIGHT CAVALRY (ex Glass Slipper, by Relko)
    1980    King Edward VII Stakes-Gr2
            St Leger Stakes-Gr1
    1981    Princess of Wales's Stakes-Gr2

# BRIGADIER GERARD (bay, 1968)

| | | | |
|------|------|------|------|
| Queen's Hussar (b 1960) | March Past | Petition | Fair Trial / Art Paper |
| | | Marcelette | William of Valence / Permavon |
| | Jojo | Vilmorin | Gold Bridge / Queen of the Meadows |
| | | Fairy Jane | Fair Trial / Light Tackle |
| La Paiva (ch 1956) | Prince Chevalier | Prince Rose | Rose Prince / Indolence |
| | | Chevalerie | Abbot's Speed / Kassala |
| | Brazen Molly | Horus | Papyrus / Lady Peregrine |
| | | Molly Adare | Phalaris / Molly Desmond |

**1978**

br c BOLD BRIGADIER (ex Bold Desire, by Breakspear)
    1983    Premio Ambrosiano-Gr3
b c SIX MILE BOTTOM (ex Bamba, by Busted)
    1982    Ormonde Stakes-Gr3
br c VAYRANN (ex Val Divine, by Val de Loir)
    1981    Prix Jean de Chaudenay-Gr2
            Prix du Prince d'Orange-Gr3
            Champion Stakes-Gr1

**1979**

b c GERAL (ex Bresilia, by Habitat)
    1982    Premio d'Estate-Gr3
br f PARADISE (ex Orsa Maggiore, by Ruysdael)
    1982    Prix Cleopatre-Gr3

**1980**

b c WHITE SPADE (ex Mattinata, by Matador)
    1983    Prix La Force-Gr3

**1982**

b c COMRADE IN ARMS (ex Girl Friend, by Birdbrook)
    1985    Prix Messidor-Gr3
    1986    Prix du Palais Royal-Gr3
b f EVER GENIAL (ex Shorthouse, by Habitat)
    1984    May Hill Stakes-Gr3
    1985    Hungerford Stakes-Gr3

# Busted

A LOT of Thoroughbreds prove less than wholly suitable for their intended roles; a minority find a niche in some other form of employment. Busted was like that, but not a typical example of the syndrome. He was supposed to be a work-horse, acquired for the purpose of leading Royal Palace in his preparation for the 1967 classics. After one gallop it was clear that he was useless in the role; his trainer, Noel Murless, would have to go out and find something else while letting Busted fulfil his true destiny by becoming the best racehorse in Europe.

Busted was a big plain colt, bred at Snailwell Stud in Newmarket by multi-millionaire Stanhope Joel. He came from the fifth crop of Crepello, one of the best post-war Derby winners, and was out of Sans le Sou, a mare of no racing distinction from a mediocre background. After weaning he was sent to Ireland to grow up, and when the time came to assess the prospects of the young Joel stock he was one of those reckoned not good enough to be sent back to England; accordingly he was handed over to Brud Fetherstonhaugh to make of him what he could. That trainer did form a high opinion of Busted's potential, running him as a two-year-old only in prestige races, but sixth and ninth places provided no reward. At three he ran seven times and did win once, helped by the 10lb concession he received from Pieces of Eight in the Gallinule Stakes at The Curragh. As Pieces of Eight proceeded to win the Eclipse and Champion Stakes, the form was good, but Busted could not confirm it. His trouble was that he was headstrong, not mentally equipped for racing, and the Irish Derby showed it when he pulled his way to the front and galloped himself into the ground.

Nevertheless it was that Irish Derby effort, which ended in a dismal twelfth place, that was to enable him to realize his potential. Noel Murless had noticed it, and when Jim Joel's two-year-old Royal Palace began to shape like a classic prospect, the trainer suggested to his owner that perhaps cousin Stanhope would aid the cause by sending Busted to Newmarket to act as lead-horse. As it seemed that Busted was not going to achieve much on his own account, Stanhope Joel readily complied. The colt arrived in December and over the winter matured both physically and mentally. Most significantly, he learned to settle in the sensitive hands of his vastly experienced regular rider, Bill Rickaby.

Busted's one and only effort as a lead-horse amounted to a definition of the term 'glorious failure'. They went a strong gallop and Royal Palace finished in front as planned, but only by half a length, with Rickaby still pulling double on the supposed nonentity. Asked how the classic favourite had shaped, the new Warren Place stable jockey George Moore replied, 'Mine went all right, but nothing like so well as that thing, whatever it is!' Murless did not dare to gallop Royal Palace with 'that thing' again, rightly assessing that their work was an indication of Busted's improvement rather than of Royal Palace's deterioration. Royal Palace duly won the 2000 Guineas and the Derby, and was named the season's best three-year-old. Busted became 'Racehorse of the Year'.

Busted's first outing for Murless was in the Coronation Stakes at Sandown, which he won easily by three lengths. He was then rested until the Eclipse, when he ran as the stable's second string to the 1000 Guineas winner Fleet, but readily relegated the filly to fourth place, with Great Nephew and Appiani intervening. A week later he confirmed his new-found star status in a brilliant victory in the King George VI & Queen Elizabeth Stakes, sweeping effortlessly from last to first between the three-furlong and one-furlong markers, then drawing impressively clear for a three-length margin. In September he scored another resounding win in the Prix Henri Foy at Longchamp, his intended prep race for the Arc de Triomphe, and he would have won that too but for a tendon injury that caused his retirement nine days before the event. Salvo and Ribocco, whom he had trounced at Ascot, figured in a three-way photo-finish with Topyo in the 'Arc'.

Busted returned to his birthplace and spent 20 years as a consistently successful sire there. Never syndicated, he stood throughout as the property of Snailwell Stud Company (at first owned by Stan Joel, later by his heirs) and began at a fee of 1500gns. In looks he was not the beau ideal of a stallion; there was too much light under him, he was somewhat coarse, and he showed design faults in the slope of his shoulder and his pasterns. For all that, he was the best son of Crepello, he owned an equable temperament, and as a genuine stayer with brilliant finishing speed he had the qualifications traditionally associated with sires of classic horses.

It is probably true to say that Busted was born ten years too late to be a truly exceptional sire, but for a supposed misfit in the modern age with its accent on speed he made a remarkably good fist of his opportunities. He got big, scopy, good-looking stock who generally preferred some give in the ground, horses who stayed well and could be depended upon to improve with experience. Those who came equipped with an accelerator as well were real racehorses, the best of them pretty much on a par with their sire. For many years the St Leger and Coronation Cup winner Bustino seemed to be the best of them, but Erins Isle developed into a formidable runner when he reached California, Shernazar became very good, and towards the end Mtoto, a colt from his fifteenth crop, perhaps achieved rather more than any other. Like his sire, Mtoto had problems in his early days, but at four and five he was a match for anything around over ten

and 12 furlongs. He won the Eclipse twice, the 'King George' once, and from two sterling efforts in the Arc de Triomphe collected fourth and second prizes. Busted never sired an 'Arc' winner, but his unheralded son Labus did, when Akiyda thwarted Ardross in 1982.

Labus, who got another top-class performer in Akiyda's brother Akarad, soon retreated into obscurity. Among Busted's other sire sons, Weavers' Hall proved a decided failure, Crash Course was employed on jumping mares, and Pevero left nothing of consequence in New Zealand. Tromos, the least typical of all his sire's stock, died young and unsuccessful in the States, where Erins Isle has started inconspicuously. Busted will figure in the top line of few early 21st century pedigrees unless Shernazar or Mtoto bucks the trend, but his daughters, who have already done well as broodmares, will surely perpetuate his fame.

The old horse, who always resembled a bear in winter with his thick 'fur coat', collapsed and died at Snailwell on 11 March 1988 while preparing to cover a mare.

## Racing record

| Year | Starts | Wins | 2nd | 3rd | 4th | £ |
|------|--------|------|-----|-----|-----|---|
| 1965 | 2 | - | - | - | - | - |
| 1966 | 7 | 1 | 2 | 1 | - | 2,549 |
| 1967 | 4 | 4 | - | - | - | 56,966 |
| | 13 | 5 | 2 | 1 | - | 59,515 |

## Principal wins

1966 Gallinule Stakes
1967 Coronation Stakes
Eclipse Stakes
King George VI & Queen Elizabeth Stakes
Prix Henri Foy

## Principal progeny

**1969**
b c BOG ROAD (ex Royal Danseuse, by Prince Chevalier)
1972 Gallinule Stakes-Gr2
1974 Ballymoss Stakes-Gr3
b f GUILLOTINA (ex Tina, by Tulyar)
1972 Prix de Royallieu-Gr3

**1970**
ch f CHEVELEY PRINCESS (ex Feather Bed, by Gratitude)
1973 Ascot 1000 Guineas Trial Stakes-Gr3
Nassau Stakes-Gr2
Sun Chariot Stakes-Gr2
b c VALUTA (ex Revivre, by Never Say Die)
1973 Prix Maurice de Nieuil-Gr2
Prix Kergorlay-Gr2

## BUSTED                                              (bay, 1963)

| | | | |
|---|---|---|---|
| Crepello (ch 1954) | Donatello | Blenheim | Blandford / Malva |
| | | Delleana | Clarissimus / Duccia di Buoninsegna |
| | Crepuscule | Mieuxce | Massine / L'Olivete |
| | | Red Sunset | Solario / Dulce |
| Sans le Sou (b 1957) | Vimy | Wild Risk | Rialto / Wild Violet |
| | | Mimi | Black Devil / Mignon |
| | Martial Loan | Court Martial | Fair Trial / Instantaneous |
| | | Loan | Portlaw / Borrow |

b c WEAVERS' HALL (ex Marians, by Macherio)
1973 Irish Derby-Gr1
**1971**
b c BUSTINO (ex Ship Yard, by Doutelle)
1974 Classic Trial Stakes-Gr3
Lingfield Derby Trial Stakes-Gr3
Great Voltigeur Stakes-Gr2
St Leger Stakes-Gr1
1975 Coronation Cup-Gr1
b c CRASH COURSE (ex Lucky Stream, by Persian Gulf)
1975 Doncaster Cup-Gr3

*Busted, whose daughters seem sure to maintain his influence.*

**1973**
b c OLD BILL (ex Country Path, by Mossborough)
    1976   Chester Vase-Gr3

**1974**
b f BUSACA (ex Saraca, by Shantung)
    1977   Lancashire Oaks-Gr3
           Yorkshire Oaks-Gr1

**1975**
b c PEVERO (ex Caprera, by Abernant)
    1977   Prix de Conde-Gr3
    1979   Prix Foy-Gr3

**1976**
ch c BUTTRESS (ex Albany, by Pall Mall)
    1979   Queen's Vase-Gr3
ch c TROMOS (ex Stilvi, by Derring-Do)
    1978   Dewhurst Stakes-Gr1

**1978**
b c ERINS ISLE (ex Chemise, by Shantung)
    1981   Ballymoss Stakes-Gr2
           Gallinule Stakes-Gr2
    1982   Californian Stakes-Gr1
           Sunset Handicap-Gr1
    1983   San Luis Rey Stakes-Gr1
           San Juan Capistrano Handicap-Gr1
           Hollywood Invitational Handicap-Gr1

**1980**
ch f OPALE (ex Conning Tower, by Connaught)
    1984   Brownstown Stakes-Gr3
           Irish St Leger-Gr1

b c ROMILDO (ex Caprera, by Abernant)
    1984   Prix Ganay-Gr1
    1985   La Coupe-Gr3
           Prix du Prince d'Orange-Gr3 [dead-heat]
ch c SHARANNPOUR (ex Shamim, by Le Haar)
    1985   Red Smith Handicap-Gr2
           Bowling Green Handicap-Gr1

**1981**
b c SHERNAZAR (ex Sharmeen, by Val de Loir)
    1985   Geoffrey Freer Stakes-Gr2
           September Stakes-Gr3

**1982**
b c KHAELAN (ex Tetrazzini, by Sovereign Path)
    1985   Prix Berteux-Gr3
           Prix de Lutece-Gr3

**1983**
b c BUCKLEY (ex Queensferry, by Pindari)
    1987   Doncaster Cup-Gr3
           Jockey Club Cup-Gr3
gr c DUCA DI BUSTED (ex Lady Rushen, by Dancer's Image)
    1986   Gran Premio Citta di Napoli-Gr3
           Premio UNIRE-Gr3
b c MTOTO (ex Amazer, by Mincio)
    1987   Brigadier Gerard Stakes-Gr3
           Prince of Wales's Stakes-Gr2
           Eclipse Stakes-Gr1
    1988   Prince of Wales's Stakes-Gr2
           Eclipse Stakes-Gr1
           King George VI & Queen Elizabeth Stakes-Gr1
           Select Stakes-Gr3

# Bustino

THERE was no more exciting race in England during the 1970s than that King George VI & Queen Elizabeth Stakes in which Grundy and Bustino were pressed to perform beyond their natural ability – and did so to the extent that each broke the course record by more than two seconds. Understandably, it was also the most destructive race of the decade so far as the principals were concerned. A thoroughly game horse, in the heat of battle, may go through the pain barrier once, but it is beyond the power of man to persuade him to do so a second time.

Grundy at least got to the races once more, but at York it was evident that he had left his competitive spirit at Ascot; three of those he had slammed before found him easy meat in their second encounter. Bustino, meanwhile, indicated at home that he was now ready for a quieter life, and a trifling injury to his off-fore was all the excuse that was needed for his withdrawal from the Prix de l'Arc de Triomphe. Nobody thought any the worse of either horse, the only regret being that, because of their summer heroics, top-level competition in the autumn was bound to prove decidedly weak.

Bustino was bred by Edgar Cooper Bland at his Rutland Stud near Newmarket, and was sold as a yearling for 21,000gns to that prodigious supporter of British bloodstock, Lady Beaverbrook. From the third crop of Busted out of a mare by Doutelle with a background steeped in class, he owned a good old-fashioned staying pedigree of the type favoured by his owner and exploited to perfection by his trainer, Dick Hern. After a solitary outing at two, when third in the Acomb Stakes, Bustino was prepared for a classic campaign at three and he began propitiously with wins at Sandown and Lingfield, on each occasion beating Snow Knight. However, it was Snow Knight who won the Derby, after leading for much of the way, while Bustino, run off his legs in the early stages, stayed on stoutly to reach fourth place. He then registered an excellent second place in the Grand Prix de Paris before closing his season with well-merited victories in the Great Voltigeur Stakes and the St Leger. In the Doncaster classic he beat the second (Imperial Prince) and third (Giacometti) in the Derby much more easily than they

had beaten him, thus ensuring that he would be named the best staying three-year-old in the country. At four he became champion older horse on the strength of just two runs – his record-breaking win in the Coronation Cup and his record-breaking loss to Grundy at Ascot.

The valuation placed on Bustino for stud was £600,000, compared with the £1 million on the horse who had beaten him by half a length. That seemed about right when Grundy came up with a classic winner – Bireme – in his first crop, but as Bustino's record improved, Grundy's quickly deteriorated; after eight seasons at the National Stud the chesnut half of the Ascot double act was exported to Japan. Bustino, at whose syndication the Queen acquired a quarter-stake, had his fifteenth season at Her Majesty's Wolferton Stud in 1990. By then he had compiled a creditable record marked by several

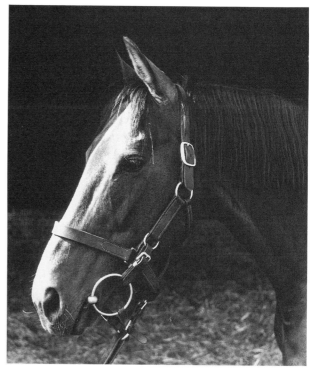

*Bustino – a growing reputation as a sire of broodmares, most notably Height of Fashion.*

## Racing record

| Year | Starts | Wins | 2nd | 3rd | 4th | £ |
|------|--------|------|-----|-----|-----|------|
| 1973 | 1 | - | - | 1 | - | 225 |
| 1974 | 6 | 4 | 1 | - | 1 | 107,067 |
| 1975 | 2 | 1 | 1 | - | - | 38,566 |
| | 9 | 5 | 2 | 1 | 1 | 145,858 |

## Principal wins

1974 Classic Trial Stakes-Gr3
Lingfield Derby Trial Stakes-Gr3
Great Voltigeur Stakes-Gr2
St Leger Stakes-Gr1
1975 Coronation Cup-Gr1

## Principal progeny

**1977**
b c EASTER SUN (ex Magical, by Aggressor)
1982 Coronation Cup-Gr1

**1978**
b f ALMA ATA (ex Armandia, by Alcide)
1981 Park Hill Stakes-Gr2
b c BUSTOMI (ex Mineown, by Roan Rocket)
1981 King Edward VII Stakes-Gr2
Gordon Stakes-Gr3
b f KITTYHAWK (ex Sky Fever, by Skymaster)
1980 Lowther Stakes-Gr3

**1979**
b f DISH DASH (ex Loose Cover, by Venture)
1982 Ribblesdale Stakes-Gr2
b f HEIGHT OF FASHION (ex Highclere, by Queen's Hussar)
1981 May Hill Stakes-Gr3
Fillies' Mile-Gr3
1982 Princess of Wales's Stakes-Gr2

**1980**
ch g BEDTIME (ex Sweet Hour, by Primera)
1984 Prix Gontaut-Biron-Gr3
September Stakes-Gr3
Cumberland Lodge Stakes-Gr3
1986 Brigadier Gerard Stakes-Gr3

## BUSTINO (bay, 1971)

| | | | |
|---|---|---|---|
| Busted (b 1963) | Crepello | Donatello | Blenheim / Delleana |
| | | Crepuscule | Mieuxce / Red Sunset |
| | Sans le Sou | Vimy | Wild Risk / Mimi |
| | | Martial Loan | Court Martial / Loan |
| Ship Yard (ch 1963) | Doutelle | Prince Chevalier | Prince Rose / Chevalerie |
| | | Above Board | Straight Deal / Feola |
| | Paving Stone | Fairway | Phalaris / Scapa Flow |
| | | Rosetta | Kantar / Rose Red |

**1981**
b f BORUSHKA (ex Valdavia, by Ribot)
1984 Park Hill Stakes-Gr2
b f STUFIDA (ex Zerbinetta, by Henry the Seventh)
1984 Premio Royal Mares-Gr3
Premio Lydia Tesio-Gr1

**1982**
b c RAKAPOSHI KING (ex Supper Time, by Shantung)
1987 John Porter Stakes-Gr3
Ormonde Stakes-Gr3
ch c SUPREME LEADER (ex Princess Zena, by Habitat)
1986 Earl of Sefton Stakes-Gr3
Westbury Stakes-Gr3

**1983**
b c PAEAN (ex Mixed Applause, by Nijinsky)
1987 Gold Cup-Gr1

**1986**
gr c TERIMON (ex Nicholas Grey, by Track Spare)
1990 Earl of Sefton Stakes-Gr3

notable high points and he had a burgeoning reputation as a broodmare sire, thanks chiefly to his most celebrated daughter Height of Fashion, the dam of Alwasmi, Unfuwain, Nashwan and Mukddaam.

Bustino has tended to get good-looking, tough horses, much neater than himself, though neither Height of Fashion nor his best male, the gelded Bedtime, could qualify as neat. On the contrary each was plain and over-big, in the region of 17 hands, yet possessed of a fluent action uncommon in horses of their size. After the season when Height of Fashion and Easter Sun recorded their most notable wins, Bustino's fee was raised to £24,000, a move which lessened his attraction to commercial breeders and did not further his cause generally. There was a long wait for his next Pattern winner, and his price came down several times, eventually reaching £6,000 in 1990.

# Caerleon

DURING the period when Robert Sangster and partners dominated the Keeneland yearling sales, it was generally possible to predict which lots they would buy. Their concentration on the best colts by Northern Dancer and Nijinsky was understandable, and while they had their share of failures, the successes tended to pay for many of them. Nijinsky's son Caerleon, an $800,000 purchase in 1981, must rank as one of their best bargains. He returned around half of that amount in prize money, and as a stallion at Coolmore he generated over £17 million in his first five seasons. With his oldest progeny only five in 1990, it is still not easy to assess whether he is or is not a good stallion, but Coolmore's bankers would not need to ponder the question for too long.

Caerleon was certainly a good racehorse on his day, though some way off being a champion on his overall form. He won both his starts as a two-year-old, in typically uncompetitive Irish events which really did little to provide a realistic assessment of his merit. The Irish handicapper's guess was that he was the second-best colt of his crop, 5lb inferior to his stable companion Danzatore. Far better guidelines were available in the following year, and though Caerleon started the season disappointingly and ended it tamely by shirking engagements, what he achieved in between was distinctly impressive. He began by finishing a dismal eighth of ten in the Ballymoss Stakes at The Curragh, form that was just too bad to be true, but he went some way towards redeeming his reputation with an honourable second place to Solford (who received 8lb) at Phoenix Park in the following month.

At that stage the form still did not appear to amount to much, but Caerleon was a progressive colt and Vincent O'Brien recognized the fact. He had no qualms about sending the colt for the Prix du Jockey-Club, and Caerleon repaid his confidence with a storming run in the straight which brought him a three-length victory. It was true that runner-up L'Emigrant would have preferred a shorter distance and that, at that level of competition, third-placed Esprit du Nord needed further, but it was nonetheless a fine performance by the winner, who ran out his race in tremendous style. Three weeks later Caerleon attempted to emulate Assert, who had won the Chantilly and Curragh Derbys in the preceding year, but was foiled in his bid for the double by Shareef Dancer; however, he did have the Epsom winner Teenoso two lengths behind him.

Caerleon had only two more races, and one of those did not count. In the King George VI & Queen Elizabeth Stakes he somehow contrived to lose both front shoes, and Pat Eddery stopped riding him at the turn for home. There was supposed to be a renewed confrontation between Caerleon and Shareef Dancer in the Benson & Hedges Gold Cup, but the Irish Derby winner defected at the eleventh hour, leaving Caerleon as the obvious favourite against a group of eight, none of whom had won – and none of whom ever would win – a Group 1 race. Remarkably, Caerleon started at the generous price of 100/30, and more remarkably he took an awfully long time to beat them, though he did so with a display of extraordinary gameness, clinging tenaciously to a lead which he had seemed certain to forfeit several times in the straight.

Projected plans for Caerleon after York included the St Leger and the Arc de Triomphe, but he turned out neither on the soft ground at Doncaster nor on the firm terrain at Longchamp. The likelihood is that his Benson & Hedges effort had got to the bottom of him; his reputation and valuation were now too high to be risked.

The ludicrous price put on Shareef Dancer's services for 1984 – $150,000 (then around £100,000) – almost made Caerleon seem cheap at IR80,000gns, but there was a significant difference. It was always going to be difficult to get to Shareef Dancer at Dalham Hall (where his book would be limited and the Maktoum family would keep many nominations for themselves) even if one was disposed to spend that amount, whereas Coolmore's invariable policy was to make any breeder's mare welcome. In his first three seasons, each at IR80,000gns, Caerleon covered around 200 mares and got at least 167 foals. In due course 89 of them went to auction as yearlings and 58 failed to recover the cost of the nomination; the third year was actually the worst for vendors, even though by then the horse stood on the brink of a sires' championship. After the first yearlings had sold indifferently in 1986, Caerleon's fee for his fourth season was slashed to IR35,000gns, but when the yearlings from that crop came up for sale in 1989, only nine out of 29 beat that nomination price. Still 'in the pipeline' were a crop conceived at IR40,000gns in 1988 and another at IR55,000gns in 1989. For 1990 he was reduced again to IR35,000gns – a horse who had ranked first and fifth on the sires' list in the last two seasons!

Caerleon provides an absurd – though by no means unique – example of a horse who, through having been wildly over-priced in the first instance and over-used, has become a commercial failure for breeders while enjoying racecourse success. As a proven sire his fee is less than half what it was when he was a newcomer to the stallion ranks, though the yearling market generally has been subject to little material change over the period. The trouble is that, human nature being what it is, breeders are attracted to new stallions and susceptible to investing whatever is demanded; at the outset their interests and those of the stallion owner appear to coincide. In fact they often do not even run parallel with one another, as Caerleon's history illustrates. Coolmore have made a fortune out of him from the involvement of commercial breeders, while most of those commercial breeders have reason to regret their involvement.

Caerleon's long-term prospects are bound to suffer from the way in which he has been managed, yet the situation may yet be retrieved. In most cases where a stallion causes breeders to lose money consistently he is swiftly sold abroad, but Caerleon has been getting results on the racecourse. It is true that his 1988 championship and his high place in the 1989 table both owed much to the victories in a valuable restricted race of Corwyn Bay and The Caretaker, and it is equally true that he has not yet been represented by a really top-class horse. His tally of 22 Pattern wins in three years seems remarkable until closer inspection reveals that 13 were recorded in Italy and only two in England. For all that, his ratio of three-year-old winners to runners is good – remarkably good for one who has runners in quantity. It is scarcely conceivable that this attractive, compact horse, whose stock come in all shapes and sizes, will fail to get something of real quality from one of the crops already conceived. If he does not, he is more than just a commercial failure; if he does, the question is: will that horse emerge before it is too late?

*Caerleon (rails) repels the challenge of Hot Touch in the Benson and Hedges Gold Cup at York.*

## Racing record

| Year | Starts | Wins | 2nd | 3rd | 4th | £ |
|------|--------|------|-----|-----|-----|---|
| 1982 | 2 | 2 | - | - | - | 11,682 |
| 1983 | 6 | 2 | 2 | - | - | 219,212 |
| | — | — | — | — | — | ——— |
| | 8 | 4 | 2 | - | - | 230,894 |

## Principal wins

1982　Anglesey Stakes-Gr3
1983　Prix du Jockey-Club-Gr1
　　　　Benson & Hedges Gold Cup-Gr1

## Principal progeny

### 1985

bl c ALQUOZ (ex I Understand, by Dr Fager)
　　1989　Premio Chiusura-Gr3
b c CAERWENT (ex Marwell, by Habitat)
　　1987　National Stakes-Gr1
　　1988　Phoenix International Stakes-Gr2
b c CAREAFOLIE (ex Balilla, by Balidar)
　　1987　Leopardstown Stakes-Gr3
　　1988　Gladness Stakes-Gr3
b f CASEY (ex Kiss, by Habitat)
　　1988　Park Hill Stakes-Gr2
b c KNIGHT LINE DANCER (ex Bottom Line, by Double Jump)
　　1989　Premio Ambrosiano-Gr3
　　　　　Premio Ellington-Gr3
　　　　　Premio Carlo Porta-Gr3
　　　　　Premio Federico Tesio-Gr3
b f TRULY SPECIAL (ex Arctique Royale, by Royal and Regal)
　　1988　Prix de Royaumont-Gr3
ch c WELSH GUIDE (ex Highland Light, by Home Guard)
　　1988　St Leger Italiano-Gr3
　　　　　Gran Premio d'Italia-Gr1
　　　　　Premio Roma-Gr1

### 1986

gr c CORWYN BAY (ex Baccalaureate, by Crowned Prince)
　　1988　Anglesey Stakes-Gr3

## CAERLEON (bay, 1980)

| | | | |
|---|---|---|---|
| Nijinsky (b 1967) | Northern Dancer | Nearctic | Nearco |
| | | | Lady Angela |
| | | Natalma | Native Dancer |
| | | | Almahmoud |
| | Flaming Page | Bull Page | Bull Lea |
| | | | Our Page |
| | | Flaring Top | Menow |
| | | | Flaming Top |
| Foreseer (b/br 1969) | Round Table | Princequillo | Prince Rose |
| | | | Cosquilla |
| | | Knight's Daughter | Sir Cosmo |
| | | | Feola |
| | Regal Gleam | Hail to Reason | Turn-to |
| | | | Nothirdchance |
| | | Miz Carol | Stymie |
| | | | No Fiddling |

b f GLORIELLA (ex Gironde, by Raise a Native)
　　1988　Queen Mary Stakes-Gr3
b f MARINA DUFF (ex Jeanie Duff, by Majestic Prince)
　　1988　Premio Dormello-Gr3 [dead-heat]
gr f ROSA DE CAERLEON (ex Carose, by Caro)
　　1989　Premio Royal Mares-Gr3
　　　　　Premio Bagutta-Gr3

### 1987

b f ATOLL (ex Shirley Reef, by Shirley Heights)
　　1990　Premio Regina Elena-Gr2
　　　　　Oaks d'Italia-Gr1
ch f MACKLA (ex Mariella, by Sir Gaylord)
　　1989　Prix d'Aumale-Gr3

# Caro

LONG before the science of genetics was founded, Thoroughbred breeders had discovered that the mating of a stayer with a sprinter could not be depended upon to produce a horse which excelled at middle distances. Thoughts of dominance and recessiveness never entered their heads, but their observation was cute enough, and they handed down to subsequent generations the adage that the formula would produce the speed of a stayer combined with the stamina of a sprinter. In fact, genes do not work quite like that either, but it is true that Caro was a rare exception to a universally accepted rule.

Caro's sire Fortino, sprint-bred on both sides of his pedigree, showed precocious brilliance over half a mile, was up to beating the best at five and six furlongs, but barely lasted seven in lesser company. Chambord, Caro's dam, was too big and backward to do herself credit at two, and as a three-year-old what she really relished was a mile and three-quarters or two miles over a galloping track; in such circumstances she was good, and she won the Newmarket Oaks and Liverpool St Leger by wide margins. Few breeders would have put Chambord to Fortino, as Gräfin Margit Batthyany did; even she was surprised at the result.

Bred in Ireland, Caro was trained in France by Albert Klimscha, whose first thought was that the grey would take after his sire. He sent him out for his debut in a minor race at Saint-Cloud over four and a half furlongs, and he won. The fact that he failed to win any of his four subsequent races as a two-year-old, all over longer distances, might have suggested that he was a sprinter, pure and simple. That was not the way Caro worked, however, and Klimscha resolved to test his stamina at three. To the surprise of many, in his first start over a mile he won the Poule d'Essai des Poulains, albeit luckily; Faraway Son, who had beaten him on merit by half a length, was disqualified for having hampered the third horse. Nevertheless, Caro had got the distance well and clearly would stay further. He next stepped up to ten and a half furlongs for the Prix Lupin, and though he finished only fourth, it did not appear to be a want of stamina that beat him. In the Prix du Jockey-Club, over a mile and a half, he was ridden like a natural stayer and claimed an excellent third place, beaten little more than a length by the winner, Sassafras.

Caro did not run over 12 furlongs again that year. Next time out he gave an extremely impressive display over nine and a half in the Prix d'Ispahan, beating top-quality older horses in tremendous style. He was defeated in his last three races in 1970, but the weights determined the results of the Prix Eugène Adam and the Prix de la Côte Normande – he was the best horse in both – and only in the Prix Henry Delamarre did he disappoint.

It was in 1971 that Caro really came into his own. There was not a four-year-old in Europe to touch him for either class or consistency; only one beat him in his six races. Horses who had defeated him, courtesy of weight allowances, in the previous autumn could not get near him on any terms now. On his three early-season Longchamp outings he was superb, registering emphatic victories in the Prix d'Harcourt, the Prix Ganay and the Prix Dollar. He did not win again, but his reputation did not suffer. Mill Reef overpowered him in the Eclipse, but he was easily second best; in the Prix Foy he lacked peak fitness after a two-month rest and narrowly failed to concede 7lb to Prominent; and in the Arc de Triomphe he ran up to his Sandown form with Mill Reef, though this time with two other three-year-olds – Pistol Packer and Cambrizzia – intervening.

Caro was retired to his owner's Haras de Bois Roussel, with Gräfin Batthyany retaining 12 shares in a syndication deal which valued him at about £360,000. If his pedigree was not one to inspire unbounded confidence in his prospects (his sire had been exported to Japan when Caro was only two), French breeders were nonetheless delighted to welcome a strong, well-made individual with consistently excellent racing performance from a mile to 12 furlongs. They were right to enthuse about him.

It did not take Caro long to establish his merit at stud. He was the champion first crop sire in France by a wide margin in 1975, with the leading juvenile filly Theia best of five individual winners. In 1976 he ranked tenth on the general list, and in the following year he was number one, aided by a pair of classic stars in Crystal Palace and unbeaten Madelia. After they had completed the Prix du Jockey-Club – Prix de

*Caro at Spendthrift Farm in Kentucky, where he spent eleven seasons at stud.*

Diane double between them, Caro became too hot a property for France to handle; the only questions were, which American stud would buy him, and for how much? The answer to the first was Spendthrift, and though the answer to the second was not revealed, it is known that the horse was re-syndicated in Kentucky at a valuation of $4.6 million. Like Blushing Groom and The Minstrel, he had to leave Europe in a hurry, only just beating the American ban on imports imposed because of the contagious equine metritis scare.

Caro continued to do well with the products he left behind in France, most notably Carwhite, Rusticaro and Tropicaro, and his parting gift to his breeder was Nebos, whom she campaigned in Germany with great success over three seasons. He became Horse of the Year there in 1980. The

American segment of Caro's stud career did not start propitiously, as he got nothing of much consequence from a smallish first crop there. It may be that some trainers in the States, knowing that he came from a line associated with speed and precocity, pressed some of his progeny too early. His young stock tended to be big, gangling and immature, with very open knees, and they needed time to develop; left alone, they could be very good late two-year-olds, but attempts to hurry them courted disaster.

The thought that perhaps Caro should have remained in France did not last long. He soon resumed his old happy habit of getting high-class horses, and what is more, he got horses capable of running with the best on American dirt. The late-developing Cozzene wanted grass, and won the Breeders' Cup Mile on it, but Dr Carter was a cracking sprinter over the main tracks and Tejano an excellent two-year-old. Caro's profile as a sire grew higher with the years, reaching new peaks in the last two years of his life. In 1988 his star turn was Winning Colors, only the third filly ever to win the Kentucky Derby, and in 1989 he had two Grade 1 winners in France in addition to the Canadian Triple Crown victor, With Approval.

Caro is by no means established yet as a sire of sires, either in Europe or America. Carwhite was bad in France and England, and Rusticaro little better during a spell in Ireland; Nebos has not realized his promise in Germany; Crystal Palace was sent to Japan in 1984 and in the following year, when his fourth crop were three-year-olds, he became champion sire in France. The rest of what he left behind, however, has not made that sale seem a catastrophe for the French breeding industry. Matters may yet improve for Caro, with such as Cozzene, Dr Carter and Tejano getting good opportunities in the

States and lesser lights Siberian Express and Sharrood available to British breeders. As befits a stallion who got many talented distaff runners, Caro is already well-established as a broodmare sire and in due course he may well rank among the best of his era in that role.

Caro spent 11 seasons at Spendthrift and was always reasonably priced in American market terms. His yearlings rarely made fortunes, but he caused few breeders any grief while rewarding some handsomely. His fee never rose above $75,000 and it was down to $35,000 in 1989, when his fertility began to fail. With around 70 individual stakes-winners already to his name, and at 22 years old, Caro had surely done enough to merit a peaceful retirement, but his owners thought otherwise; in the autumn he was subjected to hormone treatment with a view to improving the quality of his sperm. With becoming dignity, Caro dropped dead of an apparent heart attack on 6 October that year.

## Racing record

| Year | Starts | Wins | 2nd | 3rd | 4th | FR |
|------|--------|------|-----|-----|-----|-----|
| 1969 | 5 | 1 | 2 | - | 1 | 84,795 |
| 1970 | 8 | 2 | 2 | 1 | 1 | 897,360 |
| 1971 | 6 | 3 | 2 | - | 1 | 1,083,850 |
| | 19 | 6 | 6 | 1 | 3 | 2,066,005 |

## Principal wins

1970 Poule d'Essai des Poulains
Prix d'Ispahan
1971 Prix d'Harcourt-Gr2
Prix Ganay-Gr1
Prix Dollar-Gr2

## Principal progeny
### 1973
gr c CHERAW (ex Cease Fire, by Missile)
1977 Prix Exbury-Gr3
gr c PAPPAGALLO (ex Nougatine, by Hard Sauce)
1978 Prix Exbury-Gr3
b f THEIA (ex Cavadonga, by Dan Cupid)
1975 Criterium des Pouliches-Gr1
1976 Prix Vanteaux-Gr3
Prix de la Nonette-Gr3

### 1974
gr c CARWHITE (ex White Paper, by Honeyway)
1977 Prix Daru-Gr2
Prix du Prince d'Orange-Gr3
1978 Prix d'Ispahan-Gr1
gr c CRYSTAL PALACE (ex Hermieres, by Sicambre)
1977 Prix du Jockey-Club-Gr1
Prix Niel-Gr3
ch f MADELIA (ex Moonmadness, by Tom Fool)
1977 Poule d'Essai des Pouliches-Gr1
Prix Saint-Alary-Gr1
Prix de Diane-Gr1

## CARO (grey, 1967)

| Fortino (gr 1959) | Grey Sovereign | Nasrullah | Nearco |
| | | | Mumtaz Begum |
| | | Kong | Baytown |
| | | | Clang |
| | Ranavalo | Relic | War Relic |
| | | | Bridal Colors |
| | | Navarra | Orsenigo |
| | | | Nervesa |
| Chambord (ch 1955) | Chamossaire | Precipitation | Hurry On |
| | | | Double Life |
| | | Snowberry | Cameronian |
| | | | Myrobella |
| | Life Hill | Solario | Gainsborough |
| | | | Sun Worship |
| | | Lady of the Snows | Manna |
| | | | Arctic Night |

### 1975
gr f CRODA ALTA (ex Crenelle, by Crepello)
1978 Premio Chiusura-Gr2
gr f MISS CARINA (ex Miss Pia, by Olympia)
1977 Premio Dormello-Gr2
Criterium Femminile-Gr3
gr c RUSTICARO (ex Rustica, by Ribot)
1978 Prix Daphnis-Gr3
La Coupe de Maisons-Laffitte-Gr3
1979 Prix Gontaut-Biron-Gr3
Prix du Prince d'Orange-Gr3

### 1976
b f CENERENTOLA (ex Kalise, by Kashmir)
1979 Prix de Sandringham-Gr3

b f COSTLY WAVE (ex Arctic Wave, by Arctic Slave)
    1979   Premio Ribot-Gr2
b c NEBOS (ex Nostrana, by Botticelli)
    1978   Zukunfts Rennen-Gr3
    1979   Union Rennen-Gr2
           Grosser Preis von Berlin-Gr1
           Preis von Europa-Gr1
    1980   Grosser Preis von Dortmund-Gr3
           Grosser Preis von Dusseldorf-Gr2
           Grosser Preis von Berlin-Gr1
           Grosser Preis von Baden-Gr1

### 1977

ch f EXACTLY SO (ex Exactitude, by Exbury)
    1981   Gallorette Handicap-Gr3

### 1978

gr f BERNICA (ex Bernicia, by Native Prince)
    1980   Prix du Calvados-Gr3
    1981   Prix Vanteaux-Gr3
b f TROPICARO (ex Tropical Cream, by Creme Dela Creme)
    1980   Prix Marcel Boussac-Gr1
    1981   Prix de la Grotte-Gr3

### 1980

gr c CAST PARTY (ex Casting Call, by Stage Door Johnny)
    1982   Laurel Futurity-Gr1
gr c COZZENE (ex Ride the Trails, by Prince John)
    1985   Oceanport Handicap-Gr3
           Longfellow Handicap-Gr2
           Breeders' Cup Mile Stakes-Gr1
gr c HARLOW (ex Sensitive Lady, by Sensitivo)
    1984   Prix du Palais Royal-Gr3
b f KARKISIYA (ex Kalkeen, by Sheshoon)
    1983   Premio Roma Vecchia-Gr3
ch f SMUGGLY (ex Call Me Goddess, by Prince John)
    1983   Prix Penelope-Gr3
           Prix Saint-Alary-Gr1

### 1981

gr c DR CARTER (ex Gentle Touch, by Chieftain)
    1983   Remsen Stakes-Gr1
    1985   Gulfstream Park Handicap-Gr1
           Trenton Handicap-Gr3
gr c SIBERIAN EXPRESS (ex Indian Call, by Warfare)
    1983   Prix Morny-Gr1
    1984   Poule d'Essai des Poulains-Gr1
b c TRIAL BY ERROR (ex Perfect Pigeon, by Round Table)
    1984   Dee Stakes-Gr3

### 1982

b/br c PADUA (ex Miss Magnetic, by Nodouble)
    1985   Swaps Stakes-Gr1

### 1983

gr c SHARROOD (ex Angel Island, by Cougar)
    1987   Stars and Stripes Handicap-Gr2
           Eddie Read Handicap-Gr2

### 1984

ch g CANANGO (ex Hustle On, by Raise a Native)
    1988   Prix du Petit Couvert-Gr3
           Premio Umbria-Gr3
    1989   Premio Certosa-Gr3
gr f DEVIL'S BRIDE (ex Satan's Pride, by Crimson Satan)
    1987   Comely Stakes-Gr3
gr c IRON COURAGE (ex Fleet Courage, by Fleet Nasrullah)
    1988   Red Bank Handicap-Gr3
    1989   Robert F. Carey Memorial Handicap-Gr3

### 1985

gr f GABINA (ex Gold Bird, by Rheingold)
    1988   Prix d'Astarte-Gr2
    1989   Prix du Muguet-Gr3
           Prix de la Porte Maillot-Gr3
           Prix de la Foret-Gr1
ch c TEJANO (ex Infantes, by Exclusive Native)
    1987   Sapling Stakes-Gr2
           Arlington-Washington Futurity-Gr1
           Cowdin Stakes-Gr1
           Hollywood Futurity-Gr1
gr f WINNING COLORS (ex All Rainbows, by Bold Hour)
    1988   Santa Anita Oaks-Gr1
           Santa Anita Derby-Gr1
           Kentucky Derby-Gr1

### 1986

ch c GALETTO (ex Gold Bird, by Rheingold)
    1989   Prix Lupin-Gr1
gr c GOLDEN PHEASANT (ex Perfect Pigeon, by Round Table)
    1989   Prix Niel-Gr2
    1990   John Henry Handicap-Gr2
gr c TURGEON (ex Reiko, by Targowice)
    1989   Prix de l'Esperance-Gr2
    1990   Prix Vicomtesse Vigier-Gr2

# Chief's Crown

WHEN Danzig was burning up the track in morning work-outs and winning minor races in the style of the next Man o' War, his owner, Henryk de Kwiatkowski, could not begin to count his friends. Everyone wished him well with the colt who was 'obviously' going to make a great name for himself in major stakes, and everyone expressed a wish to buy a share in him when the time came to syndicate him for stud duty. When Danzig was injured, and had to be retired without ever having contested a stakes race, de Kwiatkowski did not go short on condolences, but applications for shares were conspicuous only by their absence.

One of the few who did retain faith in Danzig was Carl Rosen, owner of what many might have regarded as the best-bred mare in America. Six Crowns was the five-year-old daughter of Secretariat, winner of the 1973 Triple Crown, and Chris Evert,

winner of the 1974 New York Triple Crown for fillies, and she had been a good performer herself. From 15 starts she had managed five victories, one of them in a restricted stakes race at Meadowlands; among her eight placings was a third in the Grade 1 Ladies Handicap. Some may have felt that a mare like that deserved a better mate than the broken-down unproven horse whose owner was having difficulty in filling him at a fee of $20,000. Rosen, however, was not disposed to change his plans, and the outcome was Chief's Crown, the best runner of his generation, earner of more than $2 million and, at the age of eight, already a prominent sire. The breeder, unfortunately, did not witness the vindication of his judgment; he died when the colt was just 16 months old.

Chief's Crown needed three races to break his maiden, but did nothing much wrong after that as a

*Chief's Crown, a bright young stallion prospect.*

two-year-old. He picked up his first stakes win in the Saratoga Special, then began a collection of Grade 1 victories that would eventually amount to eight. There were four in that season, with the Breeders' Cup Juvenile as the most important. The one that went astray was the Futurity, when he appeared not to enjoy the sloppy Belmont surface; he came very wide into the straight and found top gear too late, losing by a length to Spectacular Love.

As a three-year-old Chief's Crown chose the wrong days to have off-days. He was the beaten favourite for the Kentucky Derby (third), Preakness (second), Belmont (third) and Breeders' Cup Classic (fourth), but in a busy campaign of 12 starts he still managed to win six times, most memorably in the Marlboro Cup over classic horses of the previous generation. His best victory among his own age group came in the historic Travers Stakes at Saratoga, where he beat Turkoman and Skip Trial convincingly, but was denied the chance to avenge his Churchill Downs defeat by Spend a Buck. The Derby winner habitually raced on furosemide and his connections thought better of letting him run without it in medication-free New York. Remarkably, Chief's Crown had prepared for the Travers with an outing in the Tell Stakes, a venture which yielded mixed results. He was disqualified and placed fourth after finishing first, but at least the exercise proved his competence in good company on grass. He had earlier won a race of no consequence on the Aqueduct turf.

Carl Rosen's heirs sold a half-interest in Chief's Crown to Three Chimneys Farm in Kentucky for $10 million, and he was syndicated to stand there in 1986. His fee was fixed at $150,000, almost three times the price asked for the services of Spend a Buck, who had robbed him of the three-year-old championship. There may have been some argument over which had been the better racehorse, but there was never a doubt over which had the better pedigree and brighter prospects as a stallion. An athletic bay, with a lot of presence about him, Chief's Crown attracted a top-class group of mares and duly got young stock who found demand from both American and European buyers. Some of them, it seemed, looked more like Danzig than a lot of Danzig's own progeny, and that impression also did them no harm in the market-place. About half of the first crop found their way to Europe, and it was there that the young stallion's initial notable successes were achieved. Both Be My Chief – controversially passed

over for the British juvenile championship – and Dr Somerville became Pattern winners in their first season. In line with general trends in the industry, the fee for Chief's Crown was reduced to $100,000 in 1990.

## CHIEF'S CROWN                                    (bay, 1982)

| | | | Nearco |
| | | Nearctic | Lady Angela |
| | Northern Dancer | | Native Dancer |
| | | Natalma | Almahmoud |
| Danzig | | | Crafty Admiral |
| (b 1977) | | Admiral's Voyage | Olympia Lou |
| | Pas de Nom | | Petition |
| | | Petitioner | Steady Aim |
| | | | Nasrullah |
| | | Bold Ruler | Miss Disco |
| | Secretariat | | Princequillo |
| | | Somethingroyal | Imperatrice |
| Six Crowns | | | The Doge |
| (ch 1976) | | Swoon's Son | Swoon |
| | Chris Evert | | T.V. Lark |
| | | Miss Carmie | Twice Over |

### Racing record

| Year | Starts | Wins | 2nd | 3rd | 4th | $ |
|------|--------|------|-----|-----|-----|---|
| 1984 | 9 | 6 | 2 | - | 1 | 920,890 |
| 1985 | 12 | 6 | 1 | 3 | 2 | 1,270,278 |
| | — | — | — | — | — | ———— |
| | 21 | 12 | 3 | 3 | 3 | 2,191,168 |

### Principal wins

| | |
|---|---|
| 1984 | Saratoga Special Stakes-Gr2 |
| | Hopeful Stakes-Gr1 |
| | Cowdin Stakes-Gr1 |
| | Norfolk Stakes-Gr1 |
| | Breeders' Cup Juvenile Stakes-Gr1 |
| 1985 | Flamingo Stakes-Gr1 |
| | Blue Grass Stakes-Gr1 |
| | Travers Stakes-Gr1 |
| | Marlboro Cup Invitational Handicap-Gr1 |

### Principal progeny

**1987**
b c BE MY CHIEF (ex Lady Be Mine, by Sir Ivor)
    1989   Vintage Stakes-Gr3
            Solario Stakes-Gr3
            Racing Post Trophy-Gr1
b c DR SOMERVILLE (ex Icing, by Prince Tenderfoot)
    1989   Prix de Conde-Gr3

# Dancing Brave

IN November 1989 the *Racing Post* conducted a poll of its readers with a view to identifying the 'Racehorse of the Eighties'. The outcome was a landslide victory for Dancing Brave. There were other worthy candidates, like Shergar, Nashwan, Pebbles and El Gran Senor, who appealed to the electorate on the grounds of one or two performances of obviously high merit, but there was never much doubt that the majority would favour the horse who had dominated a campaign dignified by several top-class horses and had strung together a sequence of brilliant displays. Dancing Brave attracted more media attention than any other Flat horse of the decade with the exception of the unfortunate Shergar; whatever he did was news – and treated as such by

*Dancing Brave after winning the Eclipse Stakes.*

the lay press as well as the sporting dailies.

Bred in Kentucky by Glen Oak Farm, Dancing Brave came from the fifth American-foaled crop of Lyphard, who had twice been champion sire in France and whose stock were inevitably in demand from European buyers. The colt's dam, Navajo Princess, had proved talent and toughness in a long career in the States, where she won a Grade 2 handicap on dirt and had also been successful on grass; her overall form was rather better than that of most in her family. Dancing Brave was himself anything but a handsome yearling, but the market had long since learned to forgive physical faults in the Lyphards. He satisfied James Delahooke, who bought him on behalf of Khalid Abdullah for $200,000 at the Fasig-Tipton Kentucky July Sales, and – as always happens in such circumstances – after he had achieved world fame there were several who professed to have been the under-bidder.

Dancing Brave was put into training with Guy Harwood, who gave him an easy time as a two-year-old. He ran only twice, beating nonentities easily on his Sandown debut then quickening well to defeat better – but still undistinguished – competition at Newmarket. Both races were over a mile, and after the second one leading bookmaker quoted him as 10/1 favourite for the 2000 Guineas; it was a reaction which owed nothing to the colt's proven merit and everything to racecourse rumour that he was better than Bakharoff, Harwood's recent winner of the Group 1 Futurity.

As it turned out, the rumour was correct, and after returning with a comfortable victory in the Craven Stakes, Dancing Brave duly won the Guineas, acquiring thereby some rave reviews which could not be justified by the bare form. His runner-up, Green Desert, had patently failed to stay, and as the race had been run at a very slow pace it was Dancing Brave's remarkable acceleration which was its most striking feature. The classic did not make him an outstanding miler; to some it might have suggested that he could be an outstanding sprinter. Nevertheless, he had now won four races at a mile, and his connections decided to discover whether he could reproduce that acceleration over longer distances.

*Dancing Brave quickens clear of his field to win the 2000 Guineas at Newmarket.*

Dancing Brave did not win the Derby, and many felt that he was the unluckiest loser in history when he rocketed home half a length behind Shahrastani. His jockey, Greville Starkey, was roundly castigated for, basically, having ridden him to stay the distance. The tactic, of course, was a sensible one, the debate as to what constituted overdoing it meaningless after the event. Dancing Brave's subsequent performances added fuel to the arguments, understandably in view of what he achieved, but without leading to enlightenment for the simple reason that he unquestionably improved after Epsom. He was superb in the Eclipse, trouncing Triptych in a fast-run contest, and he looked almost as good in the King George VI & Queen Elizabeth Stakes, though Shardari was beaten by only three-quarters of a length and an edgy and off-form Shahrastani failed to test him.

After an easy win in the uncompetitive Select Stakes at Goodwood, Dancing Brave faced his sternest test in the Prix de l'Arc de Triomphe. By general consent the field was richer in quality than had been assembled for any race in Europe in recent times, possibly since the 1965 'Arc' of Sea-Bird, Reliance and Diatome, but Dancing Brave was nonetheless a hot favourite at 11/10. The leaders went a cracking gallop on the firm ground and – much as Starkey had done at Epsom – Pat Eddery let them go and settled Dancing Brave towards the rear. The colt gained a little ground on the descent to the final turn, but when the serious action began to develop, a quarter of a mile from home, he was a non-participant. With a furlong to run there were six possible winners, all going hell-for-leather, and none of them was Dancing Brave. Then came the reprise of the Derby's electrifying burst. Down the wide outside came the favourite, travelling twice as fast as anything else, and certain defeat was suddenly transformed into easy victory. Bering, Triptych, Shahrastani and Shardari were flat out, having given their all; the break-neck pace and the timing of Dancing Brave's strike ruled out the chance of counter-strike.

After Longchamp even a win in the Breeders' Cup Turf might have seemed an anti-climax, but Dancing Brave went too far in making that point. At Santa Anita he was beaten into fourth place, his famed finishing kick conspicuously absent. The likelihood was that, for whatever reason, he had failed to show his true form, but it must be said that the three who beat him – Manila, Theatrical and Estrapade – belonged to a vintage group of American turf runners, among the best of the decade there.

Between the Derby and the Eclipse, Dancing Brave was the subject of something less than a true syndication. Khalid Abdullah sold a half-interest in him to Sheikh Mohammed, with a view to standing him at the latter's Dalham Hall Stud, and 16 shares were marketed at £350,000 apiece. That gave the horse a paper valuation of £14 million and for his first two seasons the few available nominations were priced at £120,000. The first year proved uneventful and eminently satisfactory, with 36 live foals resulting from his book of 40 mares, but at the end of 1987 came news that Dancing Brave was suffering from the rare Marie's Disease, which seemed to threaten at best his libido and at worst his life. For a while daily health bulletins appeared in the press, indicating the nation's concern, but the condition was gradually relieved and after a slow start to his season he again achieved excellent fertility, with only four of 39 mares recorded as barren. Of the 28 foals in that second crop, 21 were fillies.

As a physical specimen, Dancing Brave represents a poor design job in several areas and one particular fault – his parrot mouth – has already been noted in several of his progeny to date. Yet he stands as living proof that handsome is as handsome does; horsemen may have their preferences and prejudices about how Thoroughbreds should look, but nature lays down no rules and in the winner's enclosure they appear in all shapes and sizes. Among the few Dancing Brave yearlings offered at auction from his first crop in 1989, one was attractive enough to bring the year's highest bid for a filly – 600,000gns. In 1990, as his initial runners reached the racecourse, the stallion covered at £80,000.

## DANCING BRAVE (bay, 1983)

| | | | |
|---|---|---|---|
| Lyphard (b 1969) | Northern Dancer | Nearctic | Nearco |
| | | | Lady Angela |
| | | Natalma | Native Dancer |
| | | | Almahmoud |
| | Goofed | Court Martial | Fair Trial |
| | | | Instantaneous |
| | | Barra | Formor |
| | | | La Favorite |
| Navajo Princess (b 1974) | Drone | Sir Gaylord | Turn-to |
| | | | Somethingroyal |
| | | Cap and Bells | Tom Fool |
| | | | Ghazni |
| | Olmec | Pago Pago | Matrice |
| | | | Pompilia |
| | | Chocolate Beau | Beau Max |
| | | | Otra |

## Racing record

| Year | Starts | Wins | 2nd | 3rd | 4th | £ |
|---|---|---|---|---|---|---|
| 1985 | 2 | 2 | - | - | - | 6,767 |
| 1986 | 8 | 6 | 1 | - | 1 | 980,310 |
| | 10 | 8 | 1 | - | - | 987,077 |

## Principal wins

1986　Craven Stakes-Gr3
2000 Guineas Stakes-Gr1
Eclipse Stakes-Gr1
King George VI & Queen Elizabeth Stakes-Gr1
Select Stakes-Gr3
Prix de l'Arc de Triomphe-Gr1

# Danzig

THE best reason for staging big races is, as it always has been, the entertainment value offered to spectators by competition between top athletes. The breeding industry thinks differently. To those who deal in stallions and broodmares, big races are all about identifying the most suitable parent stock for the next generation; the improvement of the breed is the thing, and the way to accomplish that is to breed from horses who have proved their racing merit at the highest level. The breeding industry is, of course, quite wrong on that point, but it really would not do to put it right. Far better, for the sake of the quality of racing and some measure of order in the market, that breeders, collectively, should believe what they choose to believe.

Danzig may be the best stallion in the world today; if he is not, he certainly ranks among the top half-dozen. He did not prove himself as he was supposed to. He ran only three times, he beat only one half-decent horse, and he spent only 3 minutes 35 seconds in what could hardly be called a racing career. Exactly how good he was – or had the potential to be – as a racehorse is anybody's guess. Essentially, all that matters is that, in spite of his infirmities – and he was not unlucky, he was simply unsound – he did achieve the breakthrough to fame and distinction as a sire.

Danzig came of the same crop by Northern Dancer as Nureyev, another who had an abbreviated career but who proved rather more. Bred by the partnership of Marshall Jenney and Will Farish, he was the second foal of Pas de Nom, a good winner of nine races and the best of only eight stakes-winners by her mediocre sire, Admiral's Voyage. Sent to the Saratoga yearling sales, the stocky bay was sold to Henryk de Kwiatkowski for $310,000, almost exactly $1 million less than Nureyev had realized at Keeneland a month earlier. Danzig was turned over to one of America's outstanding trainers, Woody Stephens, who soon recognized what a talented and fragile colt he had acquired.

The only – and somewhat tenuous – line to Danzig's level of ability that we have is derived from his debut effort in a maiden race at Belmont Park on 25 June 1979. Danzig won by eight and a half lengths, completing the five and a half furlongs in quick time, and he was chased home by a colt called I Speedup. A month later I Speedup won the Tremont Stakes at Belmont, and three weeks after that the Grade 3 Sanford Stakes at Saratoga. At the end of the year, I Speedup was ranked 10lb from the top of his generation. Danzig had no Free Handicap mark. He could not be assessed on the basis of that one performance, and there were no others. Bone chips were discovered immediately after his debut win, and Stephens had no option but to give him a long rest.

Danzig did not reappear until 14 May 1980, when he ran against bad horses in a six-furlong Aqueduct allowance race; he won impressively, as well he might. On the last day of that month he turned out at Belmont, again with nothing to beat, in an allowance race over seven furlongs. To nobody's surprise he registered his third wide-margin victory, and he seemed to be progressing well towards a stakes race in the near future. Meanwhile Stephens entered him for another allowance event, this time at Monmouth Park, and New Jersey racegoers awaited the excitement of witnessing the latest Northern Dancer star in action. It was not to be. Precautionary X-rays taken on a knee after the Belmont run indicated that a slab fracture was developing. 'Run this colt again and you could destroy him,' was the vet's report, and that was that.

It was a crushing blow to de Kwiatkowski, who had had every reason to fancy that he was about to capitalize in a big way on a major investment. The colt clearly still had to be given his chance as a stallion, and Seth Hancock was still willing to give him a box at Claiborne, but the demand for shares in Danzig the broken-down 'might-have-been' was inevitably very different from the promised demand for shares in Danzig the major stakes-winner. The 'poor' owner sold what he could and kept what he had to – in brief, the majority. Three years on he found he had friends again, all of them wanting a piece of the latest sire sensation.

Danzig had 29 named foals in his first crop, conceived at a fee of $20,000, of whom 14 ran as two-year-olds in America in 1984. Eleven were winners; of the 24 races they won, nine were stakes. Of the four individual stakes-winners, three won at Grade 1 level. His best son, Chief's Crown, was the champion two-year-old colt. His best daughter, Contredance, was rated 3lb below the top filly. The stallion's total progeny earnings amounted to $2,155,218, which made him leading first crop sire and leading sire of two-year-olds. He also ranked fifteenth on the general sires' list. A lot of sires have one good year and, inevitably, for some of them it is their first. In this case there was just too much that was good for it to be a one-off. Danzig's fee, which had been raised to $40,000 on the strength of promising sales returns, rocketed to $275,000 for the 1985 season.

It was fitting that some of the best of the early Danzigs did their racing for the man who raced the sire and supported him to the hilt when others shied away. Stephan's Odyssey was a home-bred, Contredance a yearling purchase; both Danzig Connection and Lotka, from the second crop, were bred by de Kwiatkowski, who also later enjoyed successes in Europe through Polonia and Honoria.

Danzig soon established his ability to get high-class products on dirt and grass, and in the different environments of America and Europe. In recent years a high proportion of his auction yearlings have been purchased for British and French stables, with the Maktoum brothers his keenest market supporters. Shaadi (at Kildangan) and Polish Precedent (at Dalham Hall) both now stand at Maktoum studs, having proved the wisdom of the policy. That pair figured among a group of nine Pattern or Graded winners from the crop conceived in 1985, a remarkably high number partly explained by the fact that there were 58 foals in all. That was

*Danzig, a pure-breeding bay.*

the crop which resulted from his first batch of uniformly high-quality mares, so a reasonable inference must be that an already formidable record will read still more impressively before long. Danzig's fee peaked at $450,000 in 1986 when 50 foals were conceived, thus – on paper, at least – generating the astonishing sum of $22.5 million for his season's work. By the end of 1989 there were already three American Graded Stakes winners from the group, plus numerous highly regarded youngsters in European stables.

Nothing much to look at, Danzig stands on short, bad legs and measures only about 15.3 hands – though that is about as tall as many would want a Northern Dancer horse to be. He has been blind in one eye since a paddock accident in 1984, and reportedly has less than perfect vision in the other. He is a pure-breeding bay, but is apt to get stock in two different types, one – Shaadi is a good example – somewhat taller and leggier than himself; Green Desert is one of the neat variety. Most, as their racing records might tend to indicate, are better in the forelegs than their sire. From a strictly European point of view, the danger of the phenomenal success of the Danzigs appears to be their lack of stamina. Here they have virtually all been sprinters and milers, and if they breed according to the way they race, they may well accentuate the trend away from the production of stayers – a trend already deplored by many who hold to traditional values on the matters of stamina in the breed and variety in the racing programmes.

| DANZIG | | | (bay, 1977) |
|---|---|---|---|
| Northern Dancer (b 1961) | Nearctic | Nearco | Pharos<br>Nogara |
| | | Lady Angela | Hyperion<br>Sister Sarah |
| | Natalma | Native Dancer | Polynesian<br>Geisha |
| | | Almahmoud | Mahmoud<br>Arbitrator |
| Pas de Nom (b/br 1968) | Admiral's Voyage | Crafty Admiral | Fighting Fox<br>Admiral's Lady |
| | | Olympia Lou | Olympia<br>Louisiana Lou |
| | Petitioner | Petition | Fair Trial<br>Art Paper |
| | | Steady Aim | Felstead<br>Quick Arrow |

## Racing record

| Year | Starts | Wins | 2nd | 3rd | 4th | $ |
|------|--------|------|-----|-----|-----|------|
| 1979 | 1 | 1 | - | - | - | 9,000 |
| 1980 | 2 | 2 | - | - | - | 23,400 |
| | 3 | 3 | - | - | - | 32,400 |

## Principal wins

1980    Allowance race at Aqueduct
        Allowance race at Belmont Park

## Principal progeny

### 1982

b c CHIEF'S CROWN (ex Six Crowns, by Secretariat)
    1984    Saratoga Special Stakes-Gr2
            Hopeful Stakes-Gr1
            Cowdin Stakes-Gr1
            Norfolk Stakes-Gr1
            Breeders' Cup Juvenile Stakes-Gr1
    1985    Flamingo Stakes-Gr1
            Blue Grass Stakes-Gr1
            Travers Stakes-Gr1
            Marlboro Cup Invitational Handicap-Gr1
b f CONTREDANCE (ex Nimble Folly, by Cyane)
    1984    Adirondack Stakes-Gr2
            Arlington-Washington Lassie Stakes-Gr1
b c GOVERNMENT CORNER (ex Popachee, by Apalachee)
    1985    President's Cup Stakes-Gr3
b/br c STEPHAN'S ODYSSEY (ex Kennelot, by Gallant Man)
    1984    Hollywood Futurity-Gr1
    1985    Dwyer Stakes-Gr1
            Jim Dandy Stakes-Gr2
b/br c ZIGGY'S BOY (ex Joe's Lil Girl, by Sunrise Flight)
    1985    Forego Handicap-Gr2

### 1983

b c DANZIG CONNECTION (ex Gdynia, by Sir Ivor)
    1986    Peter Pan Stakes-Gr1
            Belmont Stakes-Gr1
            Pegasus Handicap-Gr2
b c GREEN DESERT (ex Foreign Courier, by Sir Ivor)
    1985    July Stakes-Gr3
            Flying Childers Stakes-Gr2
    1986    July Cup-Gr1
            Haydock Sprint Cup-Gr2
b f LOTKA (ex Kennelot, by Gallant Man)
    1986    Acorn Stakes-Gr1
            Queen Elizabeth II Challenge Cup Stakes-Gr3
    1987    La Prevoyante Invitational Handicap-Gr3
            Columbiana Handicap [Div.2]-Gr3
            Black Helen Handicap-Gr2
b c SOAR TO THE STARS (ex Flitalong, by Herbager)
    1987    Gallant Fox Handicap-Gr2

### 1984

b c I'M SO BAD (ex Betcha, by Riva Ridge)
    1987    Long Branch Stakes-Gr3

b c POLISH NAVY (ex Navsup, by Tatan)
    1986    Cowdin Stakes-Gr1
            Champagne Stakes-Gr1
    1987    Jim Dandy Stakes-Gr2
            Woodward Stakes-Gr1
b f POLONIA (ex Moss, by Round Table)
    1986    Railway Stakes-Gr3
            Lowther Stakes-Gr2
    1987    Prix de l'Abbaye de Longchamp-Gr1
b c QUALIFY (ex So Endearing, by Raise a Native)
    1986    Del Mar Futurity-Gr1

### 1985

b c ALWAYS FAIR (ex Carduel, by Buckpasser)
    1987    Coventry Stakes-Gr3
    1988    Prix Quincey-Gr3
b c POSEN (ex Michelle Mon Amour, by Best Turn)
    1988    Forerunner Stakes-Gr3
            Saranac Stakes-Gr2
            Gallant Man Stakes-Gr3
            Rutgers Handicap-Gr2

### 1986

b c BROTO (ex Bosk, by Damascus)
    1989    Hawthorne Derby-Gr3
b c DANEHILL (ex Razyana, by His Majesty)
    1989    Cork and Orrery Stakes-Gr3
            Haydock Sprint Cup-Gr1
b f HONORIA (ex Royal Honoree, by Round Table)
    1988    Railway Stakes-Gr3
b f MAGIC GLEAM (ex All Agleam, by Gleaming)
    1989    Child Stakes-Gr2
b f ONE OF A KLEIN (ex Barely Even, by Creme Dela Creme)
    1988    Oak Leaf Stakes-Gr1
b c POLISH PRECEDENT (ex Past Example, by Buckpasser)
    1989    Prix du Palais Royal-Gr3
            Prix de la Jonchere-Gr3
            Prix Messidor-Gr3
            Prix Jacques le Marois-Gr1
            Prix du Moulin de Longchamp-Gr1
b c ROI DANZIG (ex Gdynia, by Sir Ivor)
    1989    Dwyer Handicap-Gr2
b c RUSSIAN BOND (ex Somfas, by What a Pleasure)
    1988    Mill Reef Stakes-Gr2
b c SHAADI (ex Unfurled, by Hoist the Flag)
    1989    Craven Stakes-Gr3
            Irish 2000 Guineas-Gr1
            St James's Palace Stakes-Gr1

### 1987

b/br c ADJUDICATING (ex Resolver, by Reviewer)
    1989    Cowdin Stakes-Gr1
            Champagne Stakes-Gr1
    1990    Riva Ridge Stakes-Gr3
b f DANZIG'S BEAUTY (ex Sweetest Chant, by Mr Leader)
    1989    Gardenia Stakes-Gr2
b c DAYJUR (ex Gold Beauty, by Mr Prospector)
    1990    Temple Stakes-Gr2
b c SLAVIC (ex Bamesian, by Buckpasser)
    1989    Breeders' Futurity-Gr2

# Darshaan

THE Aga Khan believes that the secret of his success lies in numbers. He maintains a huge broodmare band of around 240, split between France, Ireland and America, he culls carefully, and when he parted with a batch at the 1989 Newmarket December Sales (on the grounds that some rationalization was necessary due to pressure on land resources) he seemed genuinely sorry to see some of them go. His argument for a large operation is that 'above a certain number, you are dealing in probability, not luck', and it was that philosophy which led him to make his enormously important acquisitions of the Dupré and Boussac breeding stock in the late 1970s. The Dupré purchase brought him Top Ville, already a yearling, and led to two other winners of the Prix du Jockey-Club in Mouktar and Natroun. One of the Boussac mares bred him Darshaan, the best of his four winners of that classic in a nine-year spell.

The Aga unquestionably saved both studs by incorporating them into his own. By those 'lock, stock and barrel' purchases he obtained not just 180-odd head of bloodstock but the end-products of about a century of experience in the development of top-quality Thoroughbreds. As the Aga has said, 'One had to assume that the people who ran those operations had knowledge and logic which they applied to their stock, and there would be certain things which they did which one would discover later on were very wise indeed. The probability of finding something of value among groups of mares developed on those lines had to be greater than going into the market and picking individuals out of a catalogue.' Sure enough he found plenty, and he has kept it alive by sustaining it in the private-breeder environment where it thrived.

Darshaan was the fourth living foal – and fourth

*Darshaan takes the Prix du Jockey-Club at Chantilly from Sadler's Wells (rails) and Rainbow Quest.*

winner – out of Delsy, a useful winner for Boussac who was deficient in speed and showed all her form at 12 furlongs and beyond. By mating her with Shirley Heights, a Derby winner who was himself essentially a stayer, the Aga appeared to risk a one-paced product, but what he got was a genuine mile-and-a-half horse with an impressive turn of foot, traditionally the target of every self-respecting breeder.

Trained at Chantilly by Alain de Royer-Dupré, Darshaan won the last two of his three starts as a two-year-old, a mile maiden at Saint-Cloud (by six lengths) and the Critérium over ten furlongs on the same course in November. The latter victory suggested that he would make a classic contender at three, and he duly proved that point, to the extent that he dominated the French scene in the first half of the season. He stormed home in the Greffulhe, impressed by the style of his performance in the Hocquart, then established his reputation as an international star with a smooth victory over Sadler's Wells and Rainbow Quest in the Jockey-Club. There were sound reasons for believing that he was the best staying three-year-old in Europe, and that is probably exactly what he was at his peak, but he failed to scale those heights on his two subsequent efforts. He ran no sort of race in the 'King George' on the firmest ground he ever encountered, and in the Prix Niel he looked out of sorts and raced as though he was 'over the top'. Soon afterwards his connections accepted that he was longer the force he had been, and he was taken out of training.

The Aga Khan decided to stand Darshaan at his Ballymany Stud in Ireland, and for his first season the horse's fee was set at IR50,000gns. At less than half the price of his Chantilly victim Sadler's Wells he might have been construed as a bargain, but the other one had certain advantages, not least his more fashionable pedigree and his admirable durability and consistency. While Sadler's Wells collected 59 mares, Darshaan covered 44, of whom 31 were owned by the Aga Khan. In due course, 20 of the 29 foals were returned as bred by his owner, and among them, not surprisingly, were the best of the crop, the bad-tempered Zayyani and the lengthy, somewhat unprepossessing Aliysa, whose victory in the Oaks became the subject of a Jockey-Club inquiry on account of a positive test for camphor.

While it was generally acknowledged that the Aga Khan would not have wanted Darshaan to cover more than 44 mares in his first season, there was inevitably a suspicion that his own vast contribution to the tally owed more to the need to support an unpopular horse than a deep-rooted belief in his

## DARSHAAN (bay, 1981)

| | | | |
|---|---|---|---|
| **Shirley Heights** (b 1975) | Mill Reef | Never Bend | Nasrullah<br>Lalun |
| | | Milan Mill | Princequillo<br>Virginia Water |
| | Hardiemma | Hardicanute | Hard Ridden<br>Harvest Maid |
| | | Grand Cross | Grandmaster<br>Blue Cross |
| **Delsy** (br 1972) | Abdos | Arbar | Djebel<br>Astronomie |
| | | Pretty Lady | Umidwar<br>La Moqueuse |
| | Kelty | Venture | Relic<br>Rose o' Lynn |
| | | Marilla | Marsyas<br>Albanilla |

### Racing record

| Year | Starts | Wins | 2nd | 3rd | 4th | FR |
|---|---|---|---|---|---|---|
| 1983 | 3 | 2 | - | - | - | 265,000 |
| 1984 | 5 | 3 | - | 1 | - | 1,582,000 |
| | 8 | 5 | - | 1 | - | 1,847,000 |

### Principal wins

1983   Criterium de Saint-Cloud-Gr2
1984   Prix Greffulhe-Gr2
        Prix Hocquart-Gr2
        Prix du Jockey-Club-Gr1

### Principal progeny

**1986**
b f ALIYSA (ex Alannya, by Relko)
    1989   Oaks Stakes-Gr1
b c ZAYYANI (ex Zariya, by Blushing Groom)
    1989   Greenham Stakes-Gr3

**1987**
b c SATIN WOOD (ex Satanella, by Pentathlon)
    1990   Premio Emanuele Filiberto-Gr3

future importance as a sire. That has not been borne out by subsequent events, for while the proportion of outside breeder involvement has increased – at the reduced fee of IR30,000gns since 1988 – the Aga has continued to commit 20 or more of his finest mares to the horse every year. Chances are that he will continue to obtain the best of him, and it is not unlikely that he will breed a classic colt from him before long. All his stock to date have been natural stayers, a few showing neurotic tendencies.

# Ela-Mana-Mou

RACEHORSE ownership is all about the three 'E's – enjoyment, expense and exasperation. Typically, people go into it because they believe they will enjoy it, and generally they do. They also find it expensive, and they become exasperated as they learn the hard way about the multitude of mishaps that can, and commonly do, befall a Thoroughbred in the course of its career. It is no wonder that 30 per cent of owners drop out of the game every year, to be replaced by another group of optimists. It is also no wonder that we tend to rejoice at the success stories.

Could there be anything more marvellous in racing than buying a yearling for 4500gns, running it in the best races, winning more than £110,000 with it, then selling it after two years for £500,000? Well, perhaps one thing better would be buying a horse for £500,000, winning back more than £250,000 on the racecourse, and syndicating it within a year for £3.2 million. Ela-Mana-Mou gave enjoyment – and plenty of profit – with none of the usual attendant hassle.

Bred and sold at auction in Ireland, Ela-Mana-Mou came from the first of only four crops sired there by Pitcairn, a good but not outstanding racehorse who was sold to Japan when his fertility began to fail. He was out of a mare who won in modest company and whose pedigree, like that of most mares, read better if you dug several generations into it and could persuade yourself that it mattered. In truth, the colt's breeding was just 'so-so', and at 4500gns it was a toss-up whether vendor or buyer had the better of the bargain. That issue was resolved as soon as Guy Harwood sent him to the races.

Ela-Mana-Mou was a good two-year-old, and he indicated as much on his Newbury debut, quickening smoothly to beat 15 other maidens. He went on to win four out of five races that season, and though he had to give best to Troy over seven furlongs at Goodwood, he reversed the form in a much more consequential race, the Group 2 Royal Lodge Stakes at Ascot. By the end of the year he was reckoned to be the second-best juvenile in England, and already a tremendous success story for owners Max and Andry Muinos. Not everything went right in 1979, but not too much went wrong, with Ela-Mana-Mou confirming that he was still among the best of his

generation. He ran away with the Heath Stakes at Newmarket, he ran an honest race to reach fourth in the Derby (though beaten a long way by his old adversary Troy), and he outpaced his rivals all the way in the Group 2 King Edward VII Stakes at Royal Ascot. There was no disgrace in his second to Gay Mecene in the Grand Prix de Saint-Cloud, and he did rather better in the King George VI & Queen Elizabeth Stakes, finishing third, but closer to both the winner (Troy) and to Gay Mecene than in their previous encounters. The one real disappointment of the year came in the Champion Stakes; sixth place was the best he could manage, but even that was not too bad considering that he had been off the racecourse for nearly three months. What is more, he was off-colour when he arrived home from Newmarket and had to miss a planned venture to Laurel for the Washington DC International.

With Troy departing for stud and Derby runner-up Dickens Hill for racing in America, Ela-Mana-Mou had obvious prospects of becoming a potent force in the best races of 1980, although he was still only a Group 2 winner. Of course, there was no knowing how good the new generation of three-year-olds would be, but if it was not outstanding, he might even be the best horse around. How do you value such a horse in those circumstances? When an offer of the round half-million came from a partnership comprising the Weinstock family and Tim Rogers of Airlie Stud, Max and Andry Muinos reckoned the price was right. They took the money, wished the buyers well, and turned their dreams to their new yearling, a colt they called To-Agori-Mou. In due course that one was to win the 2000 Guineas.

Guy Harwood had To-Agori-Mou to look forward to as well, but he had to say a sad farewell to Ela-Mana-Mou, who joined the Weinstock trainer Dick Hern for his third season. The second gamble on the colt duly came off, as the 1980 three-year-olds proved to be an ordinary vintage at middle distances, and Ela-Mana-Mou had their measure throughout the summer. He was not especially impressive in the spring, when winning the Earl of Sefton Stakes, but he looked better at Royal Ascot, where he collected a third Group 2 victory in the Prince of Wales's Stakes. Then came his tremendous Eclipse – 'King George'

*Ela-Mana-Mou, a game and courageous racehorse,
who, though lacking the acceleration of a champion,
won six Pattern races.*

double, a feat characterized by courage and gameness of a high order. Ela-Mana-Mou was never so much as a fair facsimile of a great racehorse, lacking the lightning acceleration associated with real champions, but he would run and keep running to the limit of his ability, and in Willie Carson he had the ideal partner to exploit that virtue. At Sandown he fought to wrest the lead from Gregorian and fought again to hold the challenge of Hello Gorgeous. At Ascot, opposed by rather more gifted athletes, he was under pressure from Carson all the way up the straight and under threat from Lester Piggott's mount Mrs Penny throughout the last two furlongs. He simply would not give in, and though the filly battled valiantly herself, she was never going to get by him.

Ela-Mana-Mou was rested until the autumn, with only the Arc de Triomphe on his agenda. He did not win it, but his courage shone again like a beacon as he tried desperately to summon pace he did not have. He went under by half a length and a short head to Detroit and Argument, the closest any English-trained horse had come to an 'Arc' victory since Rheingold had succeeded in 1973.

The deal under which Ela-Mana-Mou went to Simmonstown (one of the Airlie group of studs) put the cost of a share at £80,000, some 18 times the price of the whole horse as a yearling. There were plenty of takers, but it was always on the cards that the horse would not dispense favours so freely to his third set of owners. His pedigree was unfashionable, he seemed unlikely to get fast two-year-olds, and middle-distance horses without finishing speed were not every breeder's cup of tea. Nevertheless, he obtained the trust of many and managed to sustain sufficient strength in the market to cover for ten seasons at a fee of IR15,000gns.

What he failed to do, unfortunately, was get a plethora of high-class performers, and though he showed some improvement to reach ninth place in the 1987 sires' table, the next two years were less memorable, at least in the northern hemisphere. His stock tended to lack pace, there was a good deal of unsoundness among them, and though the odd one had class, his overall record was disappointingly inconsistent. It was a different story Down Under, where first Natski, then Almaarad surpassed his European achievements, the latter to the extent of recording three Group 1 victories, culminating in Australia's greatest weight-for-age event, the W.S. Cox Plate. In February 1990, Ela-Mana-Mou was reportedly sold – for IR£2 million – to stand in Australia, but the deal was later cancelled.

## Racing record

| Year | Starts | Wins | 2nd | 3rd | 4th | £ |
|------|--------|------|-----|-----|-----|---|
| 1978 | 5 | 4 | 1 | - | - | 27,442 |
| 1979 | 6 | 2 | 1 | 1 | 1 | 83,200 |
| 1980 | 5 | 4 | - | 1 | - | 262,822 |
| | 16 | 10 | 2 | 2 | 1 | 373,464 |

## Principal wins

| 1978 | Royal Lodge Stakes-Gr2 |
|------|------------------------|
| 1979 | King Edward VII Stakes-Gr2 |
| 1980 | Earl of Sefton Stakes-Gr3 |
| | Prince of Wales's Stakes-Gr2 |
| | Eclipse Stakes-Gr1 |
| | King George VI & Queen Elizabeth Stakes-Gr1 |

## Principal progeny

**1982**
b f FAIR OF THE FURZE (ex Autocratic, by Tyrant)
 1986 Rogers Gold Cup-Gr2
b f GAY HELLENE (ex Gaily, by Sir Gaylord)
 1985 Prix de Flore-Gr3
gr c SUMAYR (ex Sursum Corda, by Le Haar)
 1985 Grand Prix de Paris-Gr1
    Grosser Preis von Europa-Gr1

**1983**
ch c ALMAARAD (ex Silk Blend, by Busted)
 1987 Prix Kergorlay-Gr2
    Grand Prix de Deauville-Gr2
 1988 Jockey Club Stakes-Gr2
    Hardwicke Stakes-Gr2
    Aral Pokal-Gr1
 1989 Underwood Stakes-Gr1
    Caulfield Stakes-Gr1
    W.S. Cox Plate-Gr1
ch f GESEDEH (ex Le Melody, by Le Moss)
 1986 Prix de Flore-Gr3
b f ONLY A RUMOUR (ex Town Talk, by Charlottesville)
 1987 Prix de Flore-Gr3

## ELA-MANA-MOU (bay, 1976)

| | | | |
|---|---|---|---|
| Pitcairn (b 1971) | Petingo | Petition | Fair Trial / Art Paper |
| | | Alcazar | Alycidon / Quarterdeck |
| | Border Bounty | Bounteous | Rockefella / Marie Elizabeth |
| | | B. Flat | Chanteur / Ardeen |
| Rose Bertin (ch 1970) | High Hat | Hyperion | Gainsborough / Selene |
| | | Madonna | Donatello / Women's Legion |
| | Wide Awake | Major Portion | Court Martial / Better Half |
| | | Wake Island | Relic / Alor Star |

**1984**
ch f EUROBIRD (ex Irish Bird, by Sea-Bird)
 1987 Blandford Stakes-Gr2
    Irish St Leger-Gr1
ch f GRECIAN URN (ex Sea Singer, by Sea-Bird)
 1986 Criterium de Maisons-Laffitte-Gr2
b c NATSKI (ex Sweet Rhapsody, by Sea-Bird)
 1988 Queen's Cup Handicap-Gr3
    Metropolitan Handicap-Gr1

**1985**
b f ELA ROMARA (ex Romara, by Bold Lad)
 1987 Lowther Stakes-Gr2
 1988 Nassau Stakes-Gr2
b c EMMSON (ex Happy Kin, by Bold Hitter)
 1987 Futurity Stakes-Gr1
 1989 Prix Gontaut-Biron-Gr3
ch c HEAVENLY MANNA (ex Suspicious Polly, by Above Suspicion)
 1988 Royal Whip Stakes-Gr3

# El Gran Senor

THERE is – and rightly – a magic about the Derby which transcends every other horse-racing occasion. If we are honest about it, it is not always the best race of the year, but by virtue of the special status it has enjoyed over more than two centuries, it is always the race that matters most with the public and professionals alike. El Gran Senor was the best horse of his generation over a two-year period; he won seven races, and in one of them established himself as the best miler in a dozen years. Yet to Joe Public this near-paragon was the horse who lost the Derby; even those who followed his career closely and thrilled at the brilliance of his wins elsewhere remember first and foremost those moments in the Epsom straight when he somehow contrived to snatch an impossible defeat from the jaws of certain victory.

It is a pity to remember El Gran Senor for the one race he did not win, silly to speculate on how he might have won it or whether he ought to have won it. If the short-head verdict had gone the other way, it would still not have been anything like the colt's best performance. That had come a month earlier at Newmarket, and it is for what he achieved there that he should be best remembered.

El Gran Senor is listed in the American Stud Book as having been bred by E.P. Taylor, the Canadian whose Windfields Farm produced Northern Dancer, Nijinsky and a host of other great winners. The entry is misleading, as Taylor actually owned the colt's dam, Sex Appeal, in a partnership which included Robert Sangster. The latter had bought El Gran Senor's brother Try My Best from Taylor some years earlier and had entered into a deal with him over Sex Appeal in the wake of that colt's success. Sadly, in October 1980, when both El Gran Senor and Secreto were *in utero* at Windfields, Taylor suffered a series of strokes which so affected the quality of his life that, though he survived until 1989, he was never aware of what those Northern Dancer colts achieved.

The fact that Robert Sangster was part-breeder of El Gran Senor is crucial to his story, because Vincent O'Brien would not have sanctioned the purchase of the colt for Ballydoyle if he had appeared in a sale-ring. In common with most European horsemen, O'Brien hated the sight of a parrot mouth on a Thoroughbred, and though he had enjoyed phenomenal success with Northern Dancer colts bought at auction, he would have rejected El Gran Senor on that account. Obtaining him straight off the farm at no expense was different; an otherwise good-looking colt of impeccable breeding was surely worth the risk.

As a two-year-old El Gran Senor was always held in high regard at Ballydoyle, but as he learned the business of racing he was not always totally convincing on the course. His easy maiden win at Phoenix Park said nothing more than that here was another smart O'Brien-trained Northern Dancer colt. In the Railway Stakes on The Curragh he ran 'green' after hinting that he could win whenever he liked, and eventually Pat Eddery had to get serious with him. Having learned from that effort, El Gran Senor turned in a much more professional display in the National Stakes over the same course in September, but this time there were doubts about the value of the form, with the modest filly Sign-of-Life clinging on for a close second place. If he had retired for the season there and then, as his trainer initially intended, his first year's racing would have disclosed precious little about his merit. Fortunately plans were changed, El Gran Senor went to Newmarket for the Dewhurst Stakes, and a champion was revealed. Here were sterner competitors than he could ever have met at home, but he was their master, quickening to leave the French Group 1 winner Siberian Express standing at the two-furlong pole, opening a two-length advantage, then idling as Rainbow Quest delivered a resolute challenge that never quite amounted to a threat. The leading pair were six lengths clear of the rest, and the time was fast.

Naturally, the 2000 Guineas was El Gran Senor's principal target in 1984, and he prepared for Newmarket with a ready victory over stable companion Sadler's Wells in the Gladness Stakes at The Curragh. Competition in the classic promised to be somewhat fiercer, with a pair of undefeated contenders in Lear Fan and Keen, the admirable Rainbow Quest and a couple of proven Pattern performers in Chief Singer and Creag-An-Sgor. It had the makings of the best Guineas since Brigadier Gerard beat Mill Reef and My Swallow, and that is

*El Gran Senor shows brilliant class to beat Chief Singer and Lear Fan in the 2000 Guineas at Newmarket.*

surely how it turned out. There was certainly no better winner between the Brigadier and El Gran Senor. Nothing had a chance with the O'Brien colt, and nothing offered an excuse. He waited behind Lear Fan, moved out and sped by as soon as Eddery asked him, and kept going stoutly as Chief Singer tried vainly to peg him back. At the finish there were daylight margins all the way back to Creag-An-Sgor in seventh place. The winner, without a doubt, was an exceptional miler, and the performance was to gain lustre as his victims proceeded to distinguish themselves later in the season, Chief Singer in the St James's Palace and Sussex Stakes, Lear Fan in the Prix Jacques le Marois.

El Gran Senor, though, had done with mile competition, and after two more starts he had done

with racing. Vincent O'Brien's expressed opinions that he might be the best horse he had ever trained and that he would stay the Derby distance because he relaxed so well predetermined the outcome of the Epsom classic for most people. He went off an 8/11 favourite and looked about 1/20 when he cruised to the front at the quarter-mile marker, but he just could not last home against the determined challenge of Secreto, a colt himself not up to normal Derby standard. The Irish Derby might have settled a few arguments, but the Prix du Jockey-Club winner Darshaan defected when the ground remained fast and Secreto opted out while his owner engaged in negotiations to sell a half-share in him. El Gran Senor was left with an easy task, made easier by a slow early pace that suited him ideally. This time he had ample reserves in the last furlong, and a short, sharp burst comfortably accounted for Rainbow Quest.

There were promises that El Gran Senor would run again in the autumn and reappear as a four-year-old, but a foot ailment nipped those plans in the bud, and when it was learned that he was being sent to America for treatment, nobody doubted that he was going for good. Years of being overdosed with subsequently unsubstantiated Ballydoyle hype had tended to make the public cynical about the stable's motives, but in this instance there was reason enough for the early retirement. Poor El Gran Senor really did have a problem, and when he got home to Windfields there were more in the offing.

Like his brother Try My Best at the outset of his stud career, and in common with other young Northern Dancer horses, El Gran Senor proved sub-fertile. In his first season, when he covered at $200,000, he left most of his mares barren and got only 14 foals. Second time around, reduced to $100,000, he managed a tally of 22. When he at last achieved something like a normal foal crop, in his third season, things were still far from satisfactory; the 34 foals resulted from matings with 74 mares.

El Gran Senor did not remain long at Windfields, shifting from Maryland to Ashford Stud in Kentucky, and he covered there at a further reduced fee of $60,000 in 1990. It said something for him that he was able to get two useful performers in Al Hareb and Saratogan from that tiny first crop, but it said something about them when their performances tailed off dramatically after their early promise. As he has inevitably had limited racecourse representation, these are early days to be calling El Gran Senor a disappointing sire, but the signs are not good. Many of his stock have parrot mouths, and they appear to have common physical weaknesses. The stallion's low fertility is another obvious drawback, as few breeders want to risk missing a year, especially with high-quality mares.

## EL GRAN SENOR (bay, 1981)

| | | | |
|---|---|---|---|
| Northern Dancer (b 1961) | Nearctic | Nearco | Pharos / Nogara |
| | | Lady Angela | Hyperion / Sister Sarah |
| | Natalma | Native Dancer | Polynesian / Geisha |
| | | Almahmoud | Mahmoud / Arbitrator |
| Sex Appeal (ch 1970) | Buckpasser | Tom Fool | Menow / Gaga |
| | | Busanda | War Admiral / Businesslike |
| | Best in Show | Traffic Judge | Alibhai / Traffic Court |
| | | Stolen Hour | Mr Busher / Late Date |

### Racing record

| Year | Starts | Wins | 2nd | 3rd | 4th | £ |
|---|---|---|---|---|---|---|
| 1983 | 4 | 4 | - | - | - | 85,965 |
| 1984 | 4 | 3 | 1 | - | - | 284,128 |
| | 8 | 7 | 1 | - | - | 370,093 |

### Principal wins

| 1983 | Railway Stakes-Gr3 |
|---|---|
| | National Stakes-Gr2 |
| | Dewhurst Stakes-Gr1 |
| 1984 | 2000 Guineas Stakes-Gr1 |
| | Irish Derby-Gr1 |

### Principal progeny

**1986**

ch c AL HAREB (ex Icing, by Prince Tenderfoot)
    1988    Futurity Stakes-Gr1
ch c SARATOGAN (ex Patia, by Don)
    1989    Tetrarch Stakes-Gr3

**1987**

b c BELMEZ (ex Grace Note, by Top Ville)
    1990    Chester Vase-Gr3

# Forli

AN important difference between the attitudes of breeders on either side of the Atlantic is that Americans will always accept performance as proof of pedigree, whereas Europeans tend to look down their noses at horses who come from anything but a fashionable background. When one is dealing with a closed breed, where the genetic pool is already limited, it seems a short-sighted policy to restrict the available options still further and discount the possible benefits to be gained by deviating from the norm.

One of the principal reasons for the undoubted US dominance of the Thoroughbred world is that breeders there, collectively, have long taken the view that a horse who has demonstrated outstanding ability as a runner is a reasonable bet to pass on the attributes which helped him to succeed in that role, whether or not his pedigree is fashionable and/or familiar. It is an attitude that has enabled America to preserve a variety in her pedigrees which just does not exist in Europe, and it is surely one of the reasons why we continue to lag behind in terms of quality production.

The Hancock family of Claiborne Farm have been leading proponents of the theory that performance amounts to proof of pedigree virtually throughout this century. They have imported, from Britain, France, South America and Australia, top-class runners from those environments whose pedigrees meant nothing in their adopted land, yet whose racecourse deeds were recognized there as sufficient guarantee of their merit to warrant their being given chances to succeed at stud. The contributions made to American pedigrees by the importation of such as Wrack, Sir Gallahad, Blenheim, Ambiorix, Nasrullah, Herbager and Forli have been immense, while Europe has stood still, ignoring developments elsewhere, rarely venturing away from what is familiar and seems safe.

Such was the track record of his family in this department that 'Bull' Hancock had no difficulty in rounding up a group to join with him in 1967 in the purchase of Forli, a horse whose pedigree – his sire and maternal grandsire had been mere handicappers in England – hardly appeared to be top drawer and whose form, although it read impressively, might or might not amount to much. They did not go far wrong in trusting Hancock's judgment.

Forli was bred at the Haras Ojo de Agua in Argentina, a son of the well-bred and handsome Aristophanes out of a minor winner by the useful miler Advocate. Both Aristophanes and Advocate showed useful form in England, but neither was up to winning a prestige race there and in each case a sale abroad represented the only route to a stud career. As it turned out, both did well as sires in Argentina, which did not mean – as many would have interpreted it at home – that the standard of racing in Argentina was poor.

Forli was certainly an exceptional runner by Argentinian standards, whatever they were, in the opinion of many veteran observers the best of the century. He had seven races there over a period of not much more than six months in 1966, and he won them all at distances between seven and 15 furlongs. He was far and away the dominant two-year-old of the season which ended on 30 June, winning all three of his starts by an aggregate of nearly 35 lengths. By the third, the most important juvenile event in the calendar, his reputation was such that nobody wanted to bet against him; after his inevitable victory wagers were returned with no dividend.

As a three-year-old Forli began by lowering the South American record for a mile in the Argentinian equivalent of the 2000 Guineas, which he won by 12 lengths. At four-week intervals he proceeded to land the nation's most important races over ten, 12 and 15 furlongs, and in none of them was he headed. His only problem came in the last, the Gran Premio Carlos Pellegrini, South America's greatest weight-for-age event. Foul riding by a rival jockey forced him on to the rail, and Forli's partner Rodolfe Zapata (who rode him in all his races) resorted to retaliatory action which also offended the rules. The shemozzle was soon over, Forli drew away to win comfortably, and the Stewards allowed the result to stand while suspending both jockeys.

Although Forli's owners had always said that he would never be sold out of the country, the offer they received from Hancock was irresistible, a world record for a horse in training. Far from seeking to protect their investment, though, the buyers resolved to prove the colt's merits on American tracks in

1967 before sending him to stud. He was turned over to Charlie Whittingham, who gave him four months to acclimatize before preparing him for his first start in the States.

As it turned out, he had only three starts there, all over eight and a half furlongs, the first two at Hollywood Park, the last at Arlington Park. He won the Coronado Stakes, reacting well to restraint behind the pace for the first time in his life, and accelerating impressively to open a three-length margin. That was on grass. He then experienced a spot of splint trouble, but came back to beat bad horses in an event of no consequence a month later on the dirt track. His race in Chicago was on turf in the Citation Handicap, and here he met traffic problems; after collisions with both his competition and the rail, he was forced to cede ground, and though he fought back gamely he could do no better than second place behind Dominar. As Bill Shoemaker unsaddled, it was clear that the colt was lame on his near-foreleg. X-ray examination disclosed that somewhere en route he had collected a long fracture of the cannon bone.

The Forli stud deal was unusual in that it divided him into 16 shares, with each shareholder being entitled to two nominations. Effectively, each had a

$60,000 stake in a horse valued at $960,000; none had cause to regret his involvement. Forli has been criticized for alleged inconsistency as a sire, but a horse who spends as long at stud as he did is bound to have the odd bad year. He will have the fluctuations in quality production to which every horse is subject, and as he gets older his performance is increasingly at the whim of breeders, whose tendency to give the best chances to young horses inevitably tells against him. He spent all of his 21 seasons as a stallion at Claiborne, and there was at least one Pattern or Graded winner from 15 of the first 17 crops he sired. He did not quite attain the ratio of 10 per cent stakes-winners to foals which is generally accepted as the standard mark of a 'good' sire, but few with more than 600 offspring have ever done better.

Forli was a good sire. He had his faults, most notably as a distributor of unsoundness, often in the fetlock area, and many of his sons – who at one time were hyped as rivals to the Northern Dancer tribe – have acted as agents for weak pasterns. On the other hand, he got a lot of powerful, full-bodied, handsome horses, and he got plenty who had the courage to overcome the infirmities he had bestowed on them. Forego, a gelding and much the most celebrated of

*Forli passed on to many of his progeny both unsoundness and the courage to overcome it.*

all his stock, was plagued with unsoundness problems, but he carried massive weights, excelled at all distances between six furlongs and two miles, and won 14 Grade 1 races. His stallion sons, by and large, have done him little credit, but Thatch was good and probably would have been better still had he not become neglected when his promoters – Coolmore – switched allegiance to the Northern Dancer camp.

Virtually throughout his career Forli was competing for mares with the established dynasties of Northern Dancer and Raise a Native. In that scenario it was always going to be difficult for him to found a dynasty of his own, and it is no disgrace that he failed.

While he could not beat them, he often joined them with effect, most notably when his daughter Special became the dam of Nureyev, one of Northern Dancer's richest heirs. He has been an excellent broodmare sire, and his record in that respect will become more impressive yet. Forli covered his final book of mares in 1988, getting 25 out of 28 in foal; he was put down on 16 September that year at the age of 25.

## Racing record

| Year | Starts | Wins | 2nd | 3rd | 4th | $ |
|------|--------|------|-----|-----|-----|-----|
| 1966 | 7 | 7 | - | - | - | 89,490 |
| 1967 | 3 | 2 | 1 | - | - | 26,650 |
| | 10 | 9 | 1 | - | - | 116,140 |

## Principal wins

1966    Polla de Potrillos
        Gran Premio Jockey Club
        Gran Premio Nacional
        Gran Premio Carlos Pellegrini

## Principal progeny

**1969**

br c FOLKESTONE (ex Douvres, by Sicambre)
    1973   Prix Gontaut-Biron-Gr3
bl c HOME GUARD (ex Stay at Home, by Bold Ruler)
    1972   Tetrarch Stakes-Gr3
           Hungerford Stakes-Gr3
           Diadem Stakes-Gr2

**1970**

br c BOONE'S CABIN (ex Stay at Home, by Bold Ruler)
    1975   Ballyogan Stakes-Gr3
br c DAPPER (ex Punctilious, by Better Self)
    1973   Gladness Stakes-Gr3
           Tetrarch Stakes-Gr3
b g FOREGO (ex Lady Golconda, by Hasty Road)
    1973   Roamer Handicap-Gr2
           Discovery Handicap-Gr3
    1974   Donn Handicap-Gr3
           Gulfstream Park Handicap-Gr2
           Widener Handicap-Gr1
           Carter Handicap-Gr2
           Brooklyn Handicap-Gr1
           Woodward Stakes-Gr1
           Vosburgh Stakes-Gr2
           Jockey Club Gold Cup Stakes-Gr1
    1975   Seminole Handicap-Gr2
           Widener Handicap-Gr1
           Carter Handicap-Gr2
           Brooklyn Handicap-Gr1
           Suburban Handicap-Gr1
           Woodward Stakes-Gr1

## FORLI         (chesnut, 1963)

| | | | |
|---|---|---|---|
| **Aristophanes** (ch 1948) | Hyperion | Gainsborough | Bayardo / Rosedrop |
| | | Selene | Chaucer / Serenissima |
| | Commotion | Mieuxce | Massine / L'Olivete |
| | | Riot | Colorado / Lady Juror |
| **Trevisa** (ch 1951) | Advocate | Fair Trial | Fairway / Lady Juror |
| | | Guiding Star | Papyrus / Ocean Light |
| | Veneta | Foxglove | Foxhunter / Staylace |
| | | Dogaresa | Your Majesty / Casiopea |

    1976   Metropolitan Handicap-Gr1
           Nassau County Handicap-Gr3
           Brooklyn Handicap-Gr1
           Woodward Handicap-Gr1
           Marlboro Cup Handicap-Gr1
    1977   Metropolitan Handicap-Gr1
           Nassau County Handicap-Gr3
           Woodward Handicap-Gr1

b c THATCH (ex Thong, by Nantallah)
    1973   Vauxhall Trial Stakes-Gr3
           St James's Palace Stakes-Gr2
           July Cup-Gr2
           Sussex Stakes-Gr1

b/br f TUERTA (ex Continue, by Double Jay)
    1973   Long Island Handicap-Gr3
    1974   Chrysanthemum Handicap-Gr3

**1971**

b f LISADELL (ex Thong, by Nantallah)
    1974   Athasi Stakes-Gr3
           Coronation Stakes-Gr2

## 1972

b/br c FORCETEN (ex She's Beautiful, by On-and-On)
    1975    Argonaut Handicap-Gr2
             Swaps Stakes-Gr1
             Jim Dandy Stakes-Gr3
    1976    Malibu Stakes-Gr2
ch c GAY FANDANGO (ex Gay Violin, by Sir Gaylord)
    1975    Jersey Stakes-Gr3
             Waterford Crystal Mile-Gr3
ch c IMPERIAL MARCH (ex Victorian Dancer, by Northern Dancer)
    1975    Queen Anne Stakes-Gr3
b c INTREPID HERO (ex Bold Princess, by Bold Ruler)
    1975    Boardwalk Stakes [Div.2]-Gr3
             Hollywood Invitational Derby-Gr1
             Secretariat Stakes-Gr2
    1976    Bernard Baruch Handicap-Gr3
             United Nations Handicap-Gr1

## 1973

b/br f FORLANA (ex Tusi Bella, by Better Bee)
    1977    Susquehanna Handicap-Gr2

## 1974

ch c BROADWAY FORLI (ex Broadway Melody, by Tudor Melody)
    1977    Jerome Handicap-Gr2

## 1975

b c FORDHAM (ex Bold Enchantress, by Bold Ruler)
    1978    Cumberland Lodge Stakes-Gr3
    1979    Joe McGrath Memorial Stakes-Gr1
b c FORMIDABLE (ex Native Partner, by Raise a Native)
    1977    Mill Reef Stakes-Gr2
             Middle Park Stakes-Gr1

## 1976

ch c FORETAKE (ex Take Warning, by Traffic Judge)
    1980    Longfellow Handicap-Gr3
             Knickerbocker Handicap [Div.1]-Gr3

## 1977

ch f FLOS FLORUM (ex Broadway Melody, by Tudor Melody)
    1980    Ashland Stakes [Div.1]-Gr2
b f FORLENE (ex Arkadina, by Ribot)
    1979    Silken Glider Stakes-Gr3
ch c HUGUENOT (ex Captain's Mate, by Turn-to)
    1979    Beresford Stakes-Gr2
    1980    Prix Daphnis-Gr3
b c KEY TO CONTENT (ex Key Bridge, by Princequillo)
    1980    Saranac Stakes-Gr2
    1981    Fort Marcy Handicap [Div.2]-Gr3
             United Nations Handicap-Gr1

ch c POSSE (ex In Hot Pursuit, by Bold Ruler)
    1980    St James's Palace Stakes-Gr2
             Sussex Stakes-Gr1

## 1978

b c McCANN (ex Tusi Bella, by Better Bee)
    1981    Lamplighter Handicap-Gr3
    1983    Laurance Armour Handicap-Gr3

## 1979

ch f MADEMOISELLE FORLI (ex Come on Sunshine, by T.V. Lark)
    1983    Wilshire Handicap-Gr2
             Ladies Handicap-Gr1
ch f MIRAFLORA (ex Salvatico, by Sir Ivor)
    1982    Brownstown Stakes-Gr3
b c PUNCTILIO (ex Minstrelete, by Round Table)
    1982    Whitehall Stakes-Gr3

## 1981

b c HOT RODDER (ex In Hot Pursuit, by Bold Ruler)
    1985    Oettingen Rennen-Gr3

## 1982

ch c FREEDOM'S CHOICE (ex Full of Hope, by Bold Ruler)
    1988    Premio Natale di Roma-Gr3

## 1983

b f ASTEROID FIELD (ex Star Strewn, by Native Dancer)
    1985    Waterford Candelabra Stakes-Gr3
    1987    Supreme Stakes-Gr3
             Challenge Stakes-Gr2
             Matriarch Invitational Stakes-Gr1
ch c SADEEM (ex Miss Mazepah, by Nijinsky)
    1987    Sagaro Stakes-Gr3
    1988    Gold Cup-Gr1
             Goodwood Cup-Gr3
             Prix Gladiateur-Gr3
    1989    Henry II Stakes-Gr3
             Gold Cup-Gr1

## 1985

ch c ORAIBI (ex Dancing Liz, by Northern Dancer)
    1988    Malibu Stakes-Gr2
    1989    Sierra Madre Handicap-Gr3

## 1986

ch c FORLI LIGHT (ex Sky Light Princess, by Jeff D.)
    1990    Essex Handicap-Gr3

# Great Nephew

IF he had never achieved anything else in his life, Great Nephew would always have had a place in the history of British racing as the first advertisement for starting stalls. He was a two-year-old in 1965, the year when the Jockey Club started experimenting with the 'new-fangled' contraptions which had been employed on racecourses in most other countries for years or decades. On his debut he had thrown his jockey at the gate, and having been reunited with Ron Hutchinson, he whipped around when the tapes rose. Second time out Great Nephew swerved at the start and lost ground he could never hope to recover. Trainer Jack Jarvis, a dedicated opponent of stalls, reluctantly decided to see whether they might help the colt, running him next in the Chesterfield Stakes at Newmarket, the first race ever started from them in England. He came out as straight as a die, was always in the front rank and kept going well to finish third.

On the following morning the press made much of the difference the stalls had made to Great Nephew, with quotes elicited from his 77-year-old trainer before and after the race. Jarvis changed tack from: 'Regardless of the result, I dislike stalls intensely' to: 'Well, I suppose they might be all right for short races.' They were certainly all right for Great Nephew, as the only race he was to win that season was the Norfolk Stakes, the third in the experimental series of stalls-start events. Those races cured the colt of his bad habits; on his subsequent outings he gave no trouble, running honestly and well. By the end of the year he had established himself as a distinctly useful performer, who perhaps ought to win a decent handicap in his second season.

Jack Jarvis expected no better from Great Nephew, whom he quite simply did not like. He had trained both the colt's parents, retaining some affection for his sire Honeyway (although his stud

*Great Nephew at Dalham Hall Stud.*

record had been inconsistent) but abhorring the memory of his dam, Sybil's Niece. In all his long career he had seldom had to suffer such embarrassment as she had caused him as a three-year-old, when she repeatedly worked like a champion at home, he kept running her in the best races (she started joint favourite for the Oaks), and she rewarded him by racing ungenuinely every time. He was obliged to train Great Nephew, because he was owned and had been bred by a loyal patron, Jim Philipps, and he had trained for his father, Lord Milford, before him. Nevertheless he did not have to like the colt, and nothing was going to persuade him that he was good.

It went against the grain that Jarvis had to prepare Great Nephew for the 2000 Guineas in 1966. In those days horses had to be entered for the classics as yearlings and Philipps had nominated his pride and joy before sending him into the Park Lodge stable. Furthermore, the owner insisted that his colt should run in the Guineas even after Jarvis had advised him he was wasting his money; the trainer reckoned he was going to win the race with Pretendre, who had won both the Dewhurst Stakes and the Observer Gold Cup in the previous autumn. Both colts had an outing before the Guineas, Pretendre winning the Blue Riband Trial at Epsom and Great Nephew contriving to fall (when going well in the straight) in the Coventry Stakes at Kempton Park. Pretendre went off as 9/4 favourite at Newmarket, with Great Nephew among the 66/1 outsiders. Neither was the winner, but the result was an embarrassment to Jarvis, because while Pretendre faded out of the picture, Great Nephew finished like an express train under Bill Rickaby, failing by only a short head to reach Kashmir.

Four weeks later Jarvis threw Great Nephew in at the deep end, requiring him to take on the best senior milers in the country in the Lockinge Stakes at Newbury. If the assignment seemed tough, measuring his lack of experience against the proven merit of such seasoned campaigners, at least he was getting a good weight allowance from the best of them, and he was made a hot favourite. Nothing went right. He became stuck in traffic when full of running, had to be switched, then finished as fast as he had at Newmarket. Paul Cook dismounted in the winner's enclosure, congratulating himself on having just made it, then heard the announcement that Silly Season had beaten him by a head.

Those two hard races appeared to take the stuffing out of Great Nephew, who ran indifferently in the St James's Stakes at Epsom and deplorably in the Queen Anne Stakes at Royal Ascot. He did not

run again for the Park Lodge stable. The colt's switch to Etienne Pollet in France was a matter of expediency. The unenthusiastic Jarvis had made no worthwhile entries for Great Nephew after Ascot and there was nothing for him in England now. On the Paris circuit, where there were plenty of suitable late-closing events, he might yet prove that his spring form had been no fluke. He did, winning the seven-furlong Prix Michel Houyvet and running creditably – fifth both times – in the Prix Jacques le Marois and Prix Quincey.

Great Nephew was better than ever at four. He notched three good wins, including the Prix Dollar (ten furlongs) and the Prix du Moulin de Longchamp (a mile), and he was twice a valiant runner-up, first to Behistoun in the Prix Ganay, then to Busted in the Eclipse Stakes. His Sandown Park display gave particular pleasure to the group of British breeders who had just taken shares in the colt for his stud career. The deal valued him at 100,000gns and ensured that he would stand in England at Jim Philipps' Derisley Stud; an offer from America of $300,000 had been rejected.

If his record of five wins and 18 defeats was far from impressive at first glance, it clearly did not tell the whole story of a commendable career. He had made remarkable progress from his obscure early days, in terms of both ability and physique. He had shown a fine turn of foot and an abundance of courage, and he had proved he was adaptable to different tactics, excelling as a front-runner as a four-year-old. With prominent breeders to back him, his prospects seemed good. It was a long time before they were realized.

Great Nephew had 18 two-year-old runners in his first crop; only four of them won – each a race of no importance. He ranked tenth on the list of first season sires, below nonentities who had started their stud careers at a fee of £250. There was little improvement in the second year, and so it went on. The stallion was 11 years old and had completed seven seasons at stud before he was represented by a Pattern winner. The first was Grundy; the rest is history.

Exactly why Great Nephew should have made such a slow start is hard to explain, but all stallions have bad years and his came at the start rather than in the middle or at the end of his career. If he was lucky to have retained support until Grundy came along, it is equally certain that many breeders did not realize how lucky they were even after Grundy had established himself as the best Derby winner in years and the best racehorse in Europe. For the 1976 season it was still possible to get to Great Nephew for £2000, the same as the previous year, and a share was obtainable for £4000. He had got a triple Group 1 winning filly, a winner of the Irish 2000 Guineas, and a second Derby winner of exceptional class – Shergar – before his fee rose to as much as £15,000.

Great Nephew's stud career was extraordinary in many ways. He got no female Pattern winner until Mrs Penny in his ninth crop, yet four of the last five were fillies. At no time did he ever command the total confidence and commitment of breeders, yet he sired two colts who were the equals or superiors of anything Northern Dancer ever got. Neither Grundy nor Shergar resembled him even remotely, which seemed to count against him rather than for him and was surely an unfair judgment, bearing in mind that he did sire others of classic standard. He was put down on 31 May 1986 at Dalham Hall (the renamed Derisley Stud) and is buried there alongside his sire.

Unlike a lot of stallions whose influence survives them by many years, Great Nephew disposed of his assets some time before his death and even lived to see the legacy squandered. Grundy, his only credible sire son in England, failed to make the grade and was sent to Japan; Shergar presumably met a worse fate, and that after a single season; Centurius died young in New Zealand. As a broodmare sire, his impact to

| GREAT NEPHEW | | | (bay, 1963) |
|---|---|---|---|
| Honeyway (br 1941) | Fairway | Phalaris | Polymelus Bromus |
| | | Scapa Flow | Chaucer Anchora |
| | Honey Buzzard | Papyrus | Tracery Miss Matty |
| | | Lady Peregrine | White Eagle Lisma |
| Sybil's Niece (ch 1951) | Admiral's Walk | Hyperion | Gainsborough Selene |
| | | Tabaris | Roi Herode Tio-toe |
| | Sybil's Sister | Nearco | Pharos Nogara |
| | | Sister Sarah | Abbots Trace Sarita |

date has been negligible. The first colt of some distinction out of one of his daughters was Natroun, winner of the 1987 Prix du Jockey-Club, but after a year at the National Stud he left for Japan. Later came Tirol, who scored wins in both the Newmarket and Curragh 2000 Guineas in 1990.

*Great Nephew's son Grundy (nearside) wins his epic struggle with Bustino for the King George VI and Queen Elizabeth Stakes at Ascot.*

## Racing record

| Year | Starts | Wins | 2nd | 3rd | 4th | £ |
|------|--------|------|-----|-----|-----|---|
| 1965 | 7 | 1 | 1 | 2 | - | 751 |
| 1966 | 9 | 1 | 3 | 2 | - | 10,098 |
| 1967 | 7 | 3 | 2 | - | 1 | 55,012 |
| | 23 | 5 | 6 | 4 | 1 | 65,861 |

## Principal wins

1967    Prix Dollar
Prix du Moulin de Longchamp

## Principal progeny

### 1970

b c FULL OF HOPE (ex Alpine Bloom, by Chamossaire)
1976    Prix Edmond Blanc-Gr3
Prix du Chemin de Fer du Nord-Gr3
Prix d'Ispahan-Gr1

### 1972

ch c GRUNDY (ex Word from Lundy, by Worden)
1974    Champagne Stakes-Gr2
Dewhurst Stakes-Gr1
1975    Irish 2000 Guineas-Gr1
Derby Stakes-Gr1
Irish Derby-Gr1
King George VI & Queen Elizabeth Stakes-Gr1

### 1973

b c GREAT IDEA (ex Divine Thought, by Javelot)
1976    Dee Stakes-Gr3

### 1974

br c AEROSOL (ex Psalmodie, by Nasram)
1976    Prix Eclipse-Gr3

### 1975

b c CAPO SUNION (ex Clara Hamilton, by Clouet)
1977    Criterium Nazionale-Gr3
Premio Chiusura-Gr2
b c L'ARZIGOGOLO (ex Lucera, by Nagami)
1978    Premio Roma Vecchia-Gr3
ch c VAIGLY GREAT (ex Dervaig, by Derring-Do)
1979    Palace House Stakes-Gr3

### 1976

b c GOOD TIMES (ex Never Angel, by Never Say Die)
1979    Premio Parioli-Gr2
b c SAHER (ex Another Chance, by Romulus)
1981    Diomed Stakes-Gr3

### 1977

ch f MRS PENNY (ex Tananarive, by Le Fabuleux)
1979    Cherry Hinton Stakes-Gr3
Lowther Stakes-Gr3
Cheveley Park Stakes-Gr1
1980    Prix de Diane-Gr1
Prix Vermeille-Gr1
1981    Queen Charlotte Handicap-Gr3
b c NIKOLI (ex Aliceva, by Alcide)
1980    Vauxhall Trial Stakes-Gr3
Irish 2000 Guineas-Gr1

### 1978

ch c CENTURIUS (ex Word from Lundy, by Worden)
1981    Blue Riband Trial Stakes-Gr3
b c SHERGAR (ex Sharmeen, by Val de Loir)
1981    Classic Trial Stakes-Gr3
Chester Vase-Gr3
Derby Stakes-Gr1
Irish Derby-Gr1
King George VI & Queen Elizabeth Stakes-Gr1
b f TOLMI (ex Stilvi, by Derring-Do)
1981    Coronation Stakes-Gr2

### 1980

b f COUNTESS CANDY (ex Zoomie, by Pinza)
1982    Park Stakes-Gr3

### 1983

b c ALSHINFARAH (ex Scintillate, by Sparkler)
1985    Zukunfts Rennen-Gr2
1987    Escort Cup Handicap-Gr3
ch f CAROTENE (ex Carrot Top, by High Hat)
1987    Matchmaker Stakes-Gr2
New Hampshire Sweepstakes Handicap-Gr3
Yellow Ribbon Invitational Stakes-Gr1
1988    Pan American Handicap-Gr1

### 1984

b f DEBACH DELIGHT (ex Crack of Light, by Salvo)
1987    Deutscher Stutenpreis-Gr3

# Green Dancer

THE principal problem suffered by the French breeding industry since the late 1970s has been a dearth of genuinely high-class stallions. It is not that there have never been good horses there during that period; there have, but they have tended to leave the country as soon as foreign money has been bid for them, and the complacent feeling that such animals could always be replaced has given way in recent years to a sad realization that it is not so easy these days.

In Britain and Ireland horses were kept which should have been allowed to go; our markets could not justify a high stud-fee policy and it put an immense strain on breeders' resources when we introduced it. However, we have been fortunate in that Arab owners have tended to keep many of their best horses for duty in these islands, standing some of them – and only some of them – at fees appropriate to the state of the market for young stock. Late in 1989 leaders of the French breeding industry were making public appeals to the Arabs to confer similar benefits there.

Green Dancer was one of many horses who started his stud career in France in the 70s and was whisked off to America when the dollars were offered. At the time of his departure – early 1982 – his results were no better than they were entitled to be considering the chances he had had. Two crops of three-year-olds had appeared, and there had been one Pattern winner from each of them. One of them, Aryenne, had been among the best of her generation at both two and three years. The evidence said that Green Dancer was no great shakes as a sire, but the evidence was limited, and chances were that there would be better to come.

Needless to say, his record did improve, to the

*Green Dancer, whose stallion career was perhaps not enhanced by his move from France to America.*

extent that he figured in the first four on the French sires' list in each of the next three seasons. What is more, from his penultimate crop conceived on this side of the Atlantic he got a colt – Greinton – who developed into a top-class performer on Californian tracks as a four-year-old. Green Dancer was never going to get a string of great champions in France, but he undoubtedly was a useful sire there, and there was always the chance that he might get one or two horses of real distinction. His transfer to Gainesway, where he became just a run-of-the-mill, well-bred stallion, was never calculated to do a lot for him, and it just depleted the already diminished French resources still further.

It is a pity that now, in his late teens, covering at a fee ($45,000) which indicates his 'second-rate' status in Kentucky terms, Green Dancer does not have better to show for a life which began with such promise. He came from the first crop of Nijinsky and he was the first foal of his dam, an unraced daughter of the exceptionally fast Sly Pola; his pedigree was distinguished on both sides. His racing record was commendable too, as he was among the best of his crop in Europe as both a two- and three-year-old when trained by Alec Head for Jacques Wertheimer. As a juvenile his best performance came in the Observer Gold Cup (later the Futurity), which he won with some authority though from a group who, to be brutally honest, were not very good.

In the spring of his second season Green Dancer looked good. If he was less than spectacular in the Poule d'Essai des Poulains, he was smart enough to win it handily, and he probably needed further than a mile anyway. When he was given the opportunity to race over a longer distance, in the Prix Lupin, he overcame the previous season's champion, Mariacci, so comfortably that Freddie Head did not feel the need to draw his whip. He went to Epsom as 6/4 favourite for the Derby. A mile and a half on firm ground over a switchback course was not what Green Dancer wanted, and he disclosed as much by finishing some ten lengths behind Grundy, but excuses were irrelevant. He might have been closer if conditions had been more to his liking, but the plain fact of the matter was that he was nothing like so good a horse as the winner.

After the Derby Green Dancer was rested until the autumn, when he ran twice, creditably but without winning on both occasions. Anne's Pretender, with a 6lb pull in the weights, beat him by a neck in the Prix Niel, and in the Arc de Triomphe he was the third-best of his age group (behind Nobiliary and Bruni), though only eighth overall to Star Appeal. He seemed the type to develop into a

## GREEN DANCER (bay, 1972)

| | | | Nearco |
|---|---|---|---|
| | | Nearctic | Lady Angela |
| | Northern Dancer | | |
| | | Natalma | Native Dancer |
| Nijinsky | | | Almahmoud |
| (b 1967) | | | Bull Lea |
| | | Bull Page | Our Page |
| | Flaming Page | | |
| | | Flaring Top | Menow |
| | | | Flaming Top |
| | | | Brantome |
| | | Vieux Manoir | Vieille Maison |
| | Val de Loir | | |
| | | Vali | Sunny Boy |
| Green Valley | | | Her Slipper |
| (br 1967) | | | Balladier |
| | | Spy Song | Mata Hari |
| | Sly Pola | | |
| | | Ampola | Pavot |
| | | | Blue Denim |

### Racing record

| Year | Starts | Wins | 2nd | 3rd | 4th | FR |
|---|---|---|---|---|---|---|
| 1974 | 3 | 2 | 1 | - | - | 372,240 |
| 1975 | 5 | 2 | 1 | - | - | 1,190,950 |
| | 8 | 4 | 2 | - | - | 1,563,190 |

### Principal wins

| | | |
|---|---|---|
| 1974 | Observer Gold Cup-Gr1 | |
| 1975 | Poule d'Essai des Poulains-Gr1 | |
| | Prix Lupin-Gr1 | |

### Principal progeny

**1977**
br f ARYENNE (ex Americaine, by Cambremont)
    1979    Criterium des Pouliches-Gr1
    1980    Prix de la Grotte-Gr3
                Poule d'Essai des Pouliches-Gr1

**1978**
b f ANITRA'S DANCE (ex Azurella, by High Hat)
    1981    Prix de Minerve-Gr3

**1979**
br c CADOUDAL (ex Come to Sea, by Sea Hawk)
    1982    Prix Hocquart-Gr2
b f DANCING ROCKS (ex Croda Rossa, by Grey Sovereign)
    1982    Nassau Stakes-Gr2

more finished racehorse at four, but the temptation to turn him into a stallion proved too great. He was the first son of Nijinsky to go to stud in France, and that made him attractive to breeders there. He stood for six seasons at his trainer's Haras du Quesnay, getting big, scopy types who generally needed some cut in the ground.

**1980**
b c LOVELY DANCER (ex Janthina, by Petingo)
    1983   Prix du Prince d'Orange-Gr3
    1984   Prix d'Harcourt-Gr2
            Prix du Prince d'Orange-Gr3
ch f MAXIMOVA (ex Baracala, by Swaps)
    1982   Prix du Calvados-Gr3
            Prix de la Salamandre-Gr1 [dead-heat]
    1983   Prix de Meautry-Gr3
            Prix de Seine-et-Oise-Gr3

**1981**
b c GREINTON (ex Crystal Queen, by High Top)
    1985   San Bernardino Handicap-Gr2
            Californian Stakes-Gr1
            Hollywood Gold Cup Handicap-Gr1
    1986   Santa Anita Handicap-Gr1
b c SILVER GREEN (ex Sainte Colline, by Sanctus)
    1985   Prix de Barbeville-Gr3
    1986   Prix Gladiateur-Gr3

**1982**
b c WILL DANCER (ex Frenetique, by Tyrant)
    1984   Criterium di Roma-Gr3
            Gran Criterium-Gr1
    1985   Premio d'Estate-Gr3

**1983**
b c VILZAK (ex Zippy Do, by Hilarious)
    1987   Hollywood Turf Cup Invitational Handicap-Gr1

**1984**
b c DANCING TABLE (ex Lady Parida, by Round Table)
    1987   Premio Nearco-Gr3
b c GEM MASTER (ex Baby Diamonds, by Habitat)
    1987   Sheridan Stakes-Gr2

**1985**
b f FIRST WALTZ (ex Fell Sweep, by Huntercombe)
    1987   Prix Morny-Gr1
b/br g GREEN BARB (ex Barbs Compact, by Barbizon)
    1989   Laurance Armour Handicap-Gr2

**1986**
br f CONFIRMED DANCER (ex Confirm, by Proudest Roman)
    1989   Arlington Oaks-Gr3
ch f FANTASTIC LOOK (ex Fantastic Girl, by Riva Ridge)
    1989   Fantasy Stakes-Gr1
ch c TORJOUN (ex Tarsila, by High Top)
    1989   Dante Stakes-Gr2

**1987**
b c SENOR PETE (ex She Won't Tell, by Exclusive Native)
    1989   Futurity Stakes-Gr1

# Green Desert

ONE of the factors which a breeder must weigh when he considers supporting a new and less-than-fashionable stallion is whether he will get an appropriate opportunity to market the produce. It is natural for the best sales places to go to the offspring of the perceived top-grade horses, and even an outstanding individual by a supposedly lesser sire is likely to get overlooked. In 1983 the selection panel for the Keeneland July auction declined to accept a single first-crop yearling by Danzig. As it happened, the 14 who went to auction elsewhere did not do badly, averaging over $118,000, but that did not alter things too much when the panel came to select the 1984 July catalogue. This time just one Danzig product – a filly – was admitted to the world's number one prestige sale.

Not surprisingly, there were a few disgruntled owners of Danzig yearlings at that sale, convinced that what they had was better than the one – she made $285,000 – who was accepted. In fact, they did not realize how lucky they were. At the time of the July Sale, Danzig was just another horse whose first runners were beginning to appear on the track. By the time of the September Sale, to which most of his second crop had been relegated, he was the latest stallion sensation. His son Chief's Crown had spent August in Saratoga, and had won both the Grade 2 Saratoga Special and the Grade 1 Hopeful Stakes there; his daughter Contredance had picked up the Grade 2 Adirondack Stakes at Saratoga before moving to Chicago to land the Grade 1 Arlington-Washington Lassie Stakes. The eight Danzigs in the Keeneland September catalogue averaged nearly $187,000, with a top price of $650,000 for a little colt out of Foreign Courier bought on behalf of Sheikh Mohammed.

In fact the youngster was not destined to race in the Mohammed maroon, but in Maktoum Al-Maktoum's blue livery. When the eldest brother in the Dubai royal family expresses a wish to have anything owned by his younger brothers, the custom is that they defer to him; he took a liking to Green Desert, and he was no bad judge. Michael Stoute was pleased to take delivery of a neat and very well-made colt, the first produce of an unraced mare who conceived him when only three years old; though obviously unsound herself, Foreign Courier was a half-sister to Althea, America's best juvenile filly of 1983 and a Grade 1 winner over colts at nine furlongs in the spring of 1984.

The result of Green Desert's first race, a maiden at Newmarket for which he started at odds of 4/5, had a touch of irony about it, considering his transfer of ownership. He was beaten by Sheikh Mohammed's Sure Blade, another debutant, and one a little more forward in condition. No matter. On the day of his second outing, at the Newmarket July meeting, Sheikhs Hamdan and Mohammed won two races apiece but the most valuable event, the Group 3 July Stakes, fell to Green Desert. Much fitter and more aware of what racing was all about, he lost his early lead to Royal Ascot winner Atall Atall, but fought back gamely to wrest the prize in the dying strides. Next time out he failed to cope with Nomination in the Group 2 Richmond Stakes at Goodwood, but when brought back from six furlongs

*Green Desert canters to the start before winning the July Stakes at Newmarket as a two-year-old.*

*Green Desert defeats Grey Desire (right), Gwydion (second left) and Last Tycoon (left) in the July Cup.*

to five for the Group 3 Flying Childers Stakes at Doncaster he registered a ready victory over Marouble. After a fourth place to Luqman in the Group 2 Mill Reef Stakes at Newbury he was put away for the season. Although he had been precocious, the impression was that he still had not fully got his act together; he seemed destined to improve.

Green Desert did improve. He began at three in the Free Handicap, lasting the seven furlongs well enough to win by a length and to raise hopes that he would make a miler of some consequence. In fact, he ran second to Dancing Brave in the 2000 Guineas on his next appearance, but it was a slowly run contest; Dancing Brave beat him, and he beat the rest, more for speed than for stamina. He made two further efforts over a mile, the first of them sensibly half-hearted. When the ground became heavy on The Curragh for the Irish 2000 Guineas, Green Desert might as well not have bothered to compete, and Walter Swinburn wisely did not persevere with him when he patently could not cope. Rudolf Nureyev would not have looked good performing on the beach at Blackpool, and this was the equine

equivalent. A beautifully balanced colt with a fluent action, he had to have a sound surface in order to display his gifts.

He had the firm ground he wanted at Ascot, but here the mile was demonstrably beyond his limit, and he did creditably to reach second place behind his old adversary Sure Blade. Thereafter he ran only at sprint distances, and he won two of the season's top prizes. In the Group 1 July Cup, a nonsensical five-runner affair with no early pace, he beat Grey Desire by three-quarters of a length, and after an honourable third behind Last Tycoon and Double Schwartz in the King's Stand he landed the Group 2 Sprint Cup at Haydock, once more showing off his qualities of acceleration and resolution. These were his chief virtues; he could quicken well, and once he had obtained a lead he would battle tenaciously to maintain it.

Green Desert did not win again. Everything happened too quickly for him at Longchamp, and the Prix de l'Abbaye was virtually over before Swinburn had got him racing smoothly and found him a clear route. He finished only fourth, but that was a good deal better than he could manage on his farewell appearance. The idea of taking him to Santa Anita for the Breeders' Cup Sprint, contested over six furlongs on dirt, was totally misconceived and it got what it deserved. Never able to go the pace, Green Desert finished stone last, beaten rather more than 13 lengths.

Essentially Green Desert was a good sprinter, honest, tough and consistent. By no stretch of anyone's imagination was he a great horse, and at the end of the season he was rated below both Last Tycoon and Hallgate among the sprinters of his own crop; indeed, the message of his Guineas seemed to be that he was not so good a sprinter as the winner of that year's Arc de Triomphe! Nevertheless, his racing attitude and character impressed breeders, and the fact that he was by Danzig did him no harm. There was what seemed like a mad rush to patronize him at a fee of £25,000 when he retired to Hamdan Al-Maktoum's Shadwell Stud in Norfolk, but that madness was re-diagnosed as shrewdness two years later, when his first yearlings were offered. Half of those auctioned made six-figure sums, and around a dozen were bought by members of the Maktoum family.

Green Desert was moved down the road to the newly developed Nunnery Stud and continued to stand there (where he was joined in 1990 by Nashwan and Unfuwain) at the same fee. Because of his good patronage he seems certain to do well, at least in the short term, but he will need to do extra well, as there will be better and more appealing Danzigs available shortly, if, indeed, they are not already.

## GREEN DESERT (bay, 1983)

| | | | Nearco |
| | | Nearctic | Lady Angela |
| | Northern Dancer | | Native Dancer |
| | | Natalma | Almahmoud |
| Danzig (b 1977) | | | Crafty Admiral |
| | | Admiral's Voyage | Olympia Lou |
| | Pas de Nom | | Petition |
| | | Petitioner | Steady Aim |
| | | | Turn-to |
| | | Sir Gaylord | Somethingroyal |
| | Sir Ivor | | Mr Trouble |
| | | Attica | Athenia |
| Foreign Courier (b 1979) | | | Nasrullah |
| | | Never Bend | Lalun |
| | Courtly Dee | | War Admiral |
| | | Tulle | Judy-Rae |

## Racing record

| Year | Starts | Wins | 2nd | 3rd | 4th | £ |
|------|--------|------|-----|-----|-----|-----|
| 1985 | 5 | 2 | 2 | - | 1 | 53,768 |
| 1986 | 9 | 3 | 2 | 1 | 1 | 168,685 |
| | 14 | 5 | 4 | 1 | 1 | 222,453 |

## Principal wins

| | | |
|---|---|---|
| 1985 | July Stakes-Gr3 | |
| | Flying Childers Stakes-Gr2 | |
| 1986 | July Cup-Gr1 | |
| | Haydock Sprint Cup-Gr2 | |

# Green Forest

THERE is only one factor which can make a success in Europe of a stallion whose breeding does not place him in the acceptable mainstream of pedigrees: luck. In England, France and Ireland breeders look askance at such horses, mutter the term 'chance-bred' under their breath and go back to consideration of those animals whose backgrounds provide the cosy confidence derived from familiarity and experience. As individuals they may be wrong to think that way, but they are right if they recognize that it needs breeders to think the other way collectively before they can justify changing their minds.

Green Forest was a cracking good racehorse in France, a champion two-year-old, and the best miler around at three. He would never have got started at stud there, though, labouring as he would under the handicap of a pedigree that might as well have been printed in Chinese characters for all the meaning it conveyed. He had to go to America, and though the reported syndication deal which valued him at $14 million wanted a bit of believing, nobody doubted that that was where he belonged.

Green Forest's stud home is his birthplace, Jonabell Farm in Kentucky, but he was sold from there as a yearling before finding his way back. He went to the Fasig-Tipton July Sales in Lexington and was picked out there by Mahmoud Fustok, one Arab millionaire who gets by quite adequately with his own practised eye for a horse rather than the coterie of agents and advisers required by most of the rest. He knew an athlete when he saw one, and he gave $100,000 for him while all the other buyers for European stables were hunting for yearlings whose pedigrees they understood. Green Forest's sire was Shecky Greene, who had been America's champion sprinter in 1973 but whose deeds were inconspicuous in a year when the world had eyes only for Secretariat. He had never been – and was never destined to become – fashionable at stud. As for Green Forest's dam, Tell Meno Lies, she had won just two races of no special account, one over five furlongs as a two-year-old and the other at a mile in

*Green Forest, a real athlete who belied his unfashionable pedigree.*

the following year. He was her second foal; the first was Honest and True, a filly destined to run third in the Kentucky Oaks and to breed a champion distaff juvenile, Epitome.

Fustok took Green Forest to Chantilly, where he was trained by Mitri Saliba. The colt soon exhibited precocious speed at home and came out to win a half-mile dash in May. He ran too freely in the Prix du Bois, having to make do with fourth place, but in the more important Prix Robert Papin he perhaps settled too well, coming with a rattle at the finish to cut Maelstrom Lake's margin to half a length. The rest of the season was a triumph. He got first run on Maelstrom Lake and held his challenge by three-quarters of a length in the Prix Morny; after resisting restraint in the early stages of the Prix de la Salamandre, he then settled and delivered a challenge all too powerful for Zino; and in the Grand Critérium he trounced supposedly high-class rivals to become Europe's top two-year-old.

The entire Saliba stable was slow in coming to hand in 1982, a fact attributed to overdoses of a worming vaccine. Green Forest did not escape the general malaise, and when he failed to demonstrate his usual sparkle in both the Poule d'Essai des Poulains (fourth to Melyno) and the Prix Jean Prat (last of five behind the same colt) many felt that he had failed to train on. The theory was disproved in the Prix Jacques le Marois, when he came back to something like his best, going under by three-quarters of a length to The Wonder in an exceptionally strong field. The competition was fierce again in the Prix du Moulin, but here Green Forest gave his finest-ever display, producing a striking burst of speed which settled the issue in a few strides. This time he trounced The Wonder by three lengths in the best performance at a mile by any horse that year.

It had long been established that Green Forest's stud base would be Jonabell, so Fustok had a plan to show off his champion in the States. He proposed a two-leg match at a mile between Green Forest and any American horse, the first at Longchamp and the second on dirt at Belmont; the suggested stake was $2 million a side. To nobody's surprise nothing happened, and to everyone's disappointment the champion did not race again.

An attractive chestnut with a good action and a deal of presence about him, Green Forest began his stud career at a fee of $80,000 and began it well with the admirable little Forest Flower in his initial crop. She is typical of his progeny, who tend to be short-legged, well-balanced and thoroughly genuine. When things seemed to have gone quiet for him after his impressive start, he bounced back with a couple

## GREEN FOREST (chestnut, 1979)

| | | | |
|---|---|---|---|
| Shecky Greene (b 1970) | Noholme | Star Kingdom | Stardust / Impromptu |
| | | Oceana | Colombo / Orama |
| | Lester's Pride | Model Cadet | Requested / Hadepine |
| | | Meadow Flower | Bull Lea / Spur Flower |
| Tell Meno Lies (gr 1971) | The Axe | Mahmoud | Blenheim / Mah Mahal |
| | | Blackball | Shut Out / Big Event |
| | Filatonga | Count of Honor | Count Fleet / Honor Bound |
| | | Blarney Castle | Nasrullah / Bold Irish |

## Racing record

| Year | Starts | Wins | 2nd | 3rd | 4th | FR |
|---|---|---|---|---|---|---|
| 1981 | 6 | 4 | 1 | - | 1 | 1,288,000 |
| 1982 | 4 | 1 | 1 | - | 1 | 580,000 |
| | 10 | 5 | 2 | - | 1 | 1,868,000 |

## Principal wins

1981    Prix Morny-Gr1
          Prix de la Salamandre-Gr1
          Grand Criterium-Gr1
1982    Prix du Moulin de Longchamp-Gr1

## Principal progeny

**1984**
ch f FOREST FLOWER (ex Leap Lively, by Nijinsky)
     1986    Queen Mary Stakes-Gr3
               Cherry Hinton Stakes-Gr3
               Mill Reef Stakes-Gr2
     1987    Irish 1000 Guineas-Gr1
ch c INDIAN FOREST (ex Chic Nell, by Seaneen)
     1986    Prix d'Arenberg-Gr3
**1987**
ch f OZONE FRIENDLY (ex Kristana, by Kris)
     1989    Prix Robert Papin-Gr2
b c SOMETHINGDIFFERENT (ex Try Something New,
           by Hail the Pirates)
     1989    Zukunfts Rennen-Gr2

of 1989 juvenile Pattern winners in Europe, as well as a three-year-old of obvious merit in Green Line Express. Because of his Fustok connection, he seems certain to continue enjoying extensive representation in Britain and France. In 1990 he stood for a fee of only $12,500, which suggests that if the original syndication price really was as reported some people have suffered fearful losses along the way.

# Habitat

MULTI-MILLIONAIRE Charles Engelhard was involved in racing for only the last 12 of his 54 years, but in that short time he made an enormous contribution in Britain, France, South Africa and his native USA. The sport also gave him the greatest fun of his life. He had marvellous luck on the racecourse as reward for his indomitable pluck in the sale-ring, and he was deeply conscious of the favours bestowed on him. When, in 1970, his success reached a peak he knew he could never attain again, he acknowledged his good fortune and registered the privilege he felt at the thought that he would forever be identified by the three words: 'He owned Nijinsky.' Nearly two decades after Engelhard's death that identification does still suffice, but if there should come a time when it does not, perhaps the addition of 'and Habitat' will help.

Habitat, foaled a year before Nijinsky, was never the glamour colt in training that the younger Engelhard horse became, though he was outstanding in his field, the champion miler of Europe. He was also never quite the intercontinental star stallion that Nijinsky became, but in his own domain he reigned unchallenged for a decade and a half, Europe's prepotent sire par excellence, the most reliable source of speed and class available to breeders on this side of the Atlantic since World War II. He was a phenomenon, confined in the extent of his rule only by the limits of stamina he conferred on his stock. They could not handle 12 furlongs, the distance of the richest prizes, so he could never be champion sire. Nevertheless, he was four times runner-up on the list and had five other years in the top five. He was a better sire than most of those who did become champion in his era, and he was supreme as a sire of Pattern race performers, to date the only horse to have sired 50 individual winners and winners of 100 races in the scheme.

Bred at the Hurstland Farm in Kentucky of Charles and Alfred Nuckols, Habitat came from the third full crop of Sir Gaylord, a son of Turn-to who had been a high-class two-year-old and was supposedly on the verge of winning the 1962 Kentucky Derby when he broke down and had to be taken out of training. At the time of Habitat's appearance in the Keeneland July Sales, Sir Gaylord was just beginning to attract notice as a sire; his daughter Gay Matelda had already finished first in stakes races at Aqueduct and Delaware Park, and rumour had it that Vincent O'Brien was training a good colt called Sir Ivor, though he had disappointed a little on his recent debut. The market liked the Sir Gaylords, and it liked none better than Habitat. Charlie Engelhard had to bid $105,000 to get him, and there were only seven more highly priced yearlings all summer. A good-bodied bay, he was the seventh foal of his dam Little Hut, who had won five races herself and had bred four winners from as many runners.

Habitat was despatched to England where he joined Fulke Johnson Houghton's Blewbury string along with a Ribot colt called Ribofilio, also an Engelhard Keeneland purchase, that one for $100,000. At the end of their first season in training, Ribofilio was named England's champion two-year-old, winner of both the Champagne and the Dewhurst. Nothing had been heard of Habitat, who had been backward, had suffered one or two little physical problems and was given time to sort himself out.

The colt made his belated debut in a competitive Sandown event at ten furlongs and made it abundantly clear that he did not know what racing was all about. Next time at Windsor his inexperience showed again, but he was learning and he finished second. Johnson Houghton decided to bring him back to a mile, and that was to be the distance of all his remaining races. He broke his maiden by five lengths at Haydock and only eight days later found himself firmly in the big league, a winner over the Guineas-placed pair Jimmy Reppin and Tower Walk in the Lockinge Stakes at Newbury.

The upstart Habitat had been favoured by the Lockinge weights, so he was not expected to lower the colours of Newmarket and Curragh 2000 Guineas winner Right Tack in the St James's Palace Stakes at Royal Ascot. Sure enough he did not, but it was a close-run thing and it provided further evidence of the progress Habitat was making. He reappeared at Deauville and won the Prix Quincey convincingly from the excellent French filly Mige; six days later at Goodwood he dealt with the best mile filly in

*Habitat, Europe's leading influence for speed and class for a decade and a half.*

England, Lucyrowe, just as decisively, giving her 8lb into the bargain. His late burst of speed, under a confident Piggott ride, was profoundly impressive.

Habitat went to Ascot for the Queen Elizabeth II Stakes but left for home again without contesting it because the ground was considered too firm for him. Conditions were also fast for the Prix du Moulin de Longchamp, but as that had always been his long-term objective and was his last engagement, there could be no turning back a second time. Had he done so, his destiny might have been very different, for on the eve of the race Tim Rogers of Airlie Stud made an offer of $1 million for the colt, conditional on his winning. Engelhard was just beginning to take an interest in breeding, but he did not want the bother of a stallion. Terms were agreed, and it was left to Habitat and Lester Piggott to secure the deal. They did so memorably, storming clear a furlong from home for a two-length margin over a tightly packed group which had Boysie Boy at its head and Right Tack at its tail.

General inflation and market movements within the industry have wrought such changes over the last two decades that it might now be hard to imagine the sensation caused by the proposal to syndicate the champion miler of Europe in shares at £10,000 apiece. Many felt that the price was far too steep and that Rogers would never manage it, but in fact it was accomplished in a relatively short time. Habitat went

to Grangewilliam (one of the Airlie complex of studs), set to cover in 1970 at a fee of 2750gns. Only the dual classic winner Royal Palace (£3000) and Arc de Triomphe victor Levmoss (3000gns) commanded higher advertised prices, though the few breeders able to get to Sir Ivor in his second and last Irish season were required to pay £4000, by far the highest fee ever for a stallion in these islands.

None of the original shareholders in Habitat ever regretted having taken that £10,000 plunge. The shares were gilt-edged, almost never traded except in case of death, and when one at last went to auction it realized £94,000; that was when the stallion was already 20 years old and in failing physical condition. Nominations changed hands for IR80,000gns in 1986, his final covering season.

Habitat was a tremendous success from the start. His first yearlings averaged 11,936gns and at the end of his first season with runners he was not only leading first-crop sire but leading sire of two-year-olds as well; he was to head the latter table four times in all. After the initial racecourse results had matched his auction success, there was no stopping Habitat. He became the most sought-after sire for both commercial and private breeders, and the high-class winners kept coming.

His stock did not always look sound, and often they were not sound. He undoubtedly distributed foreleg problems, but even more reliably he passed on speed and precocity combined with class in a good-bodied package. Many were able to win good races before their inherent physical faults caught up with them; those who stayed sound could be very good indeed. For the most part they were sprinters and milers, a rare one like Rose Bowl and Flying Water managing to last ten furlongs at the top level, a unique one in Strigida capable of winning a Pattern event at a mile and a half. On the whole his fillies were better than his colts. Seven of them were Group 1 winners, among them a 'Racehorse of the Year' in Habibti.

Not surprisingly his daughters quickly became top-quality matrons, and by the time of his death he was already the leading broodmare sire of Pattern winners in Europe.

The one area where he did not excel was as a sire of sires, which need not necessarily be held against him but nevertheless is a factor which concerns breeders. A horse's genetic contribution to his children's offspring averages out at 25 per cent, which indicates that he must always be a 'minority shareholder' in the product, entitled to a minor part of the credit or censure for it. However, breeders need to have something to believe in, and the sire who gets good stallion sons makes life a lot easier for them. Habitat did not get good stallion sons – apart from a few who enjoyed passing success in Australia and New Zealand – and he never seemed likely to do so after the first few, for one reason or another, had failed him. Habat sired cripples, wrong in their knees; Hot Spark got weaklings who failed to train on; Steel Heart's fertility was poor. The early record was so discouraging that the Habitat horses who followed were given correspondingly lesser chances; Double Form died young, perhaps with the opportunity to retrieve the situation in his grasp. It is still not too late for a revival, with such as Distant Relative and the stallion's all-time leading stakes-earner, Steinlen, still to embark on their stud careers, but for the moment the Habitat legacy seems to have been left to the daughters, who – on all known form – can be trusted to distribute it widely and beneficially among the breed.

Habitat was put down at Grangewilliam on 23 June 1987, within a month of the Derby victory by his grandson Reference Point. He had developed laminitis towards the end of the previous year and had been to Kentucky for specialist treatment which at first seemed to have relieved the symptoms. Hopes that he would be able to resume covering in 1988 – he missed the entire 1987 season – proved short-lived when his condition deteriorated again within two months of his return from the States.

## HABITAT (bay, 1966)

| | | | |
|---|---|---|---|
| **Sir Gaylord** (b 1959) | Turn-to | Royal Charger | Nearco / Sun Princess |
| | | Source Sucree | Admiral Drake / Lavendula |
| | Somethingroyal | Princequillo | Prince Rose / Cosquilla |
| | | Imperatrice | Caruso / Cinquepace |
| **Little Hut** (b 1952) | Occupy | Bull Dog | Teddy / Plucky Liege |
| | | Miss Bunting | Bunting / Mirthful |
| | Savage Beauty | Challenger | Swynford / Sword Play |
| | | Khara | Kai-Sang / Decree |

## Racing record

| Year | Starts | Wins | 2nd | 3rd | 4th | £ |
|---|---|---|---|---|---|---|
| 1968 | 0 | | | | | |
| 1969 | 8 | 5 | 2 | - | - | 40,840 |
| | 8 | 5 | 2 | - | - | 40,840 |

## Principal wins

1969    Lockinge Stakes
Prix Quincey
Goodwood Mile
Prix du Moulin de Longchamp

## Principal progeny

**1971**

b f BITTY GIRL (ex Garvey Girl, by Princely Gift)
    1973    Queen Mary Stakes-Gr2
           Molecomb Stakes-Gr3
           Lowther Stakes-Gr3
gr c HABAT (ex Atrevida, by Sunny Boy)
    1973    Norfolk Stakes-Gr3
           Mill Reef Stakes-Gr2
           Middle Park Stakes-Gr1
    1974    Ascot 2000 Guineas Trial Stakes-Gr3
br f ROSE BED (ex Roseliere, by Misti)
    1974    Prix Chloe-Gr3

**1972**

b f HAMADA (ex Helvetie, by Klairon)
    1975    Prix de Sandringham-Gr3
           Prix de la Porte Maillot-Gr3
ch c HOT SPARK (ex Garvey Girl, by Princely Gift)
    1974    Flying Childers Stakes-Gr1
    1975    Palace House Stakes-Gr3
b f ROSE BOWL (ex Roseliere, by Misti)
    1975    Nell Gwyn Stakes-Gr3
           Queen Elizabeth II Stakes-Gr2
           Champion Stakes-Gr1
    1976    Queen Elizabeth II Stakes-Gr2

b f ROUSSALKA (ex Oh So Fair, by Graustark)
    1974    Cherry Hinton Stakes-Gr3
    1975    Coronation Stakes-Gr2
              Nassau Stakes-Gr2
    1976    Nassau Stakes-Gr2
b c STEEL HEART (ex A.1, by Abernant)
    1974    Gimcrack Stakes-Gr2
              Middle Park Stakes-Gr1
    1975    Duke of York Stakes-Gr3
              Goldene Peitsche-Gr3

### 1973

b f DIFFUSION (ex Dress Uniform, by Court Martial)
    1975    Prix d'Arenberg-Gr3
ch f FLYING WATER (ex Formentera, by Ribot)
    1976    Nell Gwyn Stakes-Gr3
              1000 Guineas Stakes-Gr1
    1977    Prix Maurice de Gheest-Gr3
              Prix Jacques le Marois-Gr1
              Champion Stakes-Gr1
b c HITTITE GLORY (ex Hazy Idea, by Hethersett)
    1975    Flying Childers Stakes-Gr1
              Middle Park Stakes-Gr1
b c MADANG (ex Jellatina, by Fortino)
    1977    Premio Melton-Gr3
              Prix du Gros-Chene-Gr3
b f PETIPA (ex Twaddle, by Tim Tam)
    1975    Moyglare Stud Stakes-Gr3

### 1974

b c HABITONY (ex Courteous Lady, by Gallant Man)
    1976    Sunny Slope Stakes-Gr3
              Norfolk Stakes-Gr2
    1977    Santa Anita Derby-Gr1
b c TANFIRION (ex Tingitana, by Canisbay)
    1978    Premio Umbria-Gr3
    1979    Premio Melton-Gr2

### 1975

b c DOUBLE FORM (ex Fanghorn, by Crocket)
    1979    Temple Stakes-Gr3
              King's Stand Stakes-Gr1
              Haydock Sprint Cup-Gr2
              Prix de l'Abbaye de Longchamp-Gr1
b c HEIR PRESUMPTIVE (ex Timur's Daughter, by Tamerlane)
    1978    Dee Stakes-Gr3
b c HOMING (ex Heavenly Thought, by St Paddy)
    1978    Prix du Rond Point-Gr3
              Queen Elizabeth II Stakes-Gr2

### 1976

b f SIGY (ex Satu, by Primera)
    1978    Prix d'Arenberg-Gr3
              Prix de l'Abbaye de Longchamp-Gr1
    1979    Prix du Gros-Chene-Gr3
ch f TOPSY (ex Furioso, by Ballymoss)
    1979    Fred Darling Stakes-Gr3
              Prix d'Astarte-Gr3
              Sun Chariot Stakes-Gr2

### 1977

b c DALSAAN (ex Dumka, by Kashmir)
    1981    Hungerford Stakes-Gr3

ch c HARD FOUGHT (ex Ambrosia, by Alcide)
    1980    Jersey Stakes-Gr3
    1981    Earl of Sefton Stakes-Gr3
              Westbury Stakes-Gr3
              Prince of Wales's Stakes-Gr2
b c LORD SEYMOUR (ex Lady Seymour, by Tudor Melody)
    1979    Mill Reef Stakes-Gr2
b c SAYYAF (ex Pavello, by Crepello)
    1982    Prix de Seine-et-Oise-Gr3
gr f SMOKEY LADY (ex A.1, by Abernant)
    1979    Phoenix Stakes-Gr1
b c SUVERO (ex Heavenly Form, by Reform)
    1979    Prix Eclipse-Gr3

### 1978

br f HOME ON THE RANGE (ex Great Guns, by Busted)
    1981    Sun Chariot Stakes-Gr2
b c LOU PIGUET (ex Tuneria, by Tanerko)
    1981    Prix de la Jonchere-Gr3
b f MARWELL (ex Lady Seymour, by Tudor Melody)
    1980    Molecomb Stakes-Gr3
              Flying Childers Stakes-Gr2
              Cheveley Park Stakes-Gr1
    1981    Fred Darling Stakes-Gr3
              King's Stand Stakes-Gr1
              July Cup-Gr1
              Prix de l'Abbaye de Longchamp-Gr1
b f PETROLEUSE (ex Plencia, by Le Haar)
    1981    Princess Elizabeth Stakes-Gr3
b c ROYAL HOBBIT (ex Royal Danseuse, by Prince Chevalier)
    1984    Prix du Gros-Chene-Gr3
ch f SONOMA (ex Satu, by Primera)
    1981    Prix du Gros-Chene-Gr3
b f STRIGIDA (ex Catalpa, by Reform)
    1981    Ribblesdale Stakes-Gr2

### 1979

ch f CHALON (ex Areola, by Kythnos)
    1982    Nell Gwyn Stakes-Gr3
              Coronation Stakes-Gr2
              Child Stakes-Gr3

### 1980

b c ANCESTRAL (ex Ampulla, by Crowned Prince)
    1982    Railway Stakes-Gr3
    1983    Vauxhall Trial Stakes-Gr3 [dead-heat]
    1984    San Diego Handicap-Gr3
br f HABIBTI (ex Klairessa, by Klairon)
    1982    Lowther Stakes-Gr2
              Moyglare Stud Stakes-Gr2
    1983    July Cup-Gr1
              York Sprint Championship Stakes-Gr2
              Haydock Sprint Cup-Gr2
              Prix de l'Abbaye de Longchamp-Gr1
    1984    King's Stand Stakes-Gr1
ch f MASSORAH (ex Marala, by Sir Khalito)
    1983    Premio Omenoni-Gr3
b c MUSCATITE (ex Takette, by Takawalk)
    1983    Craven Stakes-Gr3
b c TATIBAH (ex Three Tees, by Tim Tam)
    1982    Cornwallis Stakes-Gr3

### 1981

b f BROCADE (ex Canton Silk, by Runnymede)
    1984    Challenge Stakes-Gr3
    1985    Prix de la Foret-Gr1
b f ONE WAY STREET (ex Guillotina, by Busted)
    1984    Princess Royal Stakes-Gr3

### 1982

b c BASSENTHWAITE (ex Splashing, by Petingo)
    1984    Middle Park Stakes-Gr1
b f DAFAYNA (ex Dumka, by Kashmir)
    1985    Cork and Orrery Stakes-Gr3

### 1983

b c STEINLEN (ex Southern Seas, by Jim French)
    1988    Premiere Handicap-Gr3
            Inglewood Handicap-Gr2
            Saratoga Breeders' Cup Handicap-Gr3
    1989    Inglewood Handicap-Gr2
            Daryl's Joy Stakes [Div.1]-Gr3
            Bernard Baruch Handicap-Gr1
            Arlington Million Stakes-Gr1
            Keeneland Breeders' Cup Handicap-Gr3
            Breeders' Cup Mile Stakes-Gr1
    1990    El Rincon Handicap-Gr2
            Hollywood Turf Handicap-Gr1
ch f TARIB (ex Red Coral, by Red God)
    1986    Ostermann Pokal-Gr3
            Premio Umbria-Gr2

### 1984

b c EXPORT PRICE (ex Martinova, by Martinmas)
    1986    Prix du Bois-Gr3
    1988    Prix de Ris-Orangis-Gr3
ch f INTERVAL (ex Intermission, by Stage Door Johnny)
    1987    Prix Maurice de Gheest-Gr2

### 1985

b f BLUE NOTE (ex Balsamique, by Tourangeau)
    1988    Prix de la Porte Maillot-Gr3
            Prix Maurice de Gheest-Gr2

### 1986

b c HEART OF ARABIA (ex Ramiana, by Blushing Groom)
    1988    Richmond Stakes-Gr2
b f LIFE AT THE TOP (ex Bold Flawless, by Bold Bidder)
    1988    Waterford Candelabra Stakes-Gr3
b c DISTANT RELATIVE (ex Royal Sister, by Claude)
    1989    Phoenix International Stakes-Gr2
            Hungerford Stakes-Gr3
            Goodwood Mile-Gr2
            Challenge Stakes-Gr2

### 1987

b c WELNEY (ex On Show, by Welsh Pageant)
    1989    Mill Reef Stakes-Gr2

# Halo

SOME people are fated to fail in the Thoroughbred industry. One such person was film producer Irving Allen, who entered the business with high hopes in 1957, purchasing the 200-acre Derisley Wood Stud near Newmarket. This had at one time been the home of leading sprint sire Grey Sovereign, and Allen had grand ideas of reviving its fortunes as a notable stallion establishment. Slowly but surely, by dint of much ill-luck and ill-judgment, the farm developed a reputation as the 'graveyard of stallions'. Whatever went there, with whatever credentials, was bound to fail, if not catastrophically, then at least miserably.

Well into his second decade of failure, Allen had installed the former champion two-year-old My Swallow on the premises in 1972, and in the following year he set about finding a new occupant for the box lately vacated by the dreadful Court Fool. On a trip to the States he hit upon Halo, a very well-bred horse who had won five races last season as a three-year-old and had just run second to Riva Ridge in an allowance race at Saratoga. He bid $600,000 and got him. To all intents and purposes the deal was done, and an announcement to that effect was made to the press. It was, after all, news of some consequence that an English stud had acquired a stakes-winning son of Hail to Reason with the same grand-dam as Northern Dancer.

All was well until, in the course of a conversation with Allen in the Saratoga barn area, the four-year-old's trainer, Mack Miller, chanced to mention the fact that Halo was a crib-biter. That was it. The Americans might not worry too much about the habit, but in Europe crib-biting was universally abhorred. The horse grasps its manger, or box-door, or some other object, arches its neck and generally swallows air. It is often accompanied by wind-sucking, another nervous habit resulting in digestive disorders.

*Halo, who has twice sired the winner of the Kentucky Derby.*

Allen was sorry, but the deal was off. He simply could not take home a horse like that.

After a little legal wrangling, the matter was settled. Miller's owner, Jane Engelhard, agreed to take the horse back, and if no other sale could be arranged she would race him for a fourth season. Allen went away and bought another four-year-old, a colt called Dubassoff who had earned over $300,000 and was by Sea-Bird out of a mare from the family of Mill Reef.

There was no other immediate buyer for Halo, so he resumed training with Miller and in due course produced the performance of his life in the Grade 1 United Nations Handicap. His win in that Atlantic City feature, which followed a Grade 2 victory in the Tidal Handicap at Aqueduct, indicated that he was among the best half-dozen grass horses in the country. A new buyer was not long in coming forward, and he was sold for $1 million to stand as a stallion at Windfields Farm.

Six years later Halo was represented on American tracks by the two best senior fillies around, Glorious Song and Misty Gallore, and figured among the top 20 sires for the first time. A possibly unrelated development on the other side of the Atlantic was the sale of Derisley Wood Stud, where Dubassoff (like My Swallow) had failed. Irving Allen had finally accepted that he was not going to succeed in the Thoroughbred industry.

There is, of course, no guarantee that Halo would have thrived at Derisley Wood, nor even anywhere in Europe. Every stallion depends to some degree on the quality of the pool of broodmares available to him and he would not have been better served in England than he was by the mares he covered at Windfields, or later at Stone Farm in Kentucky, his base since 1984. However, he did get a Kentucky Derby winner – Sunny's Halo – out of a mare whose origins would be flattered by the epithet 'plebeian'.

Originally a $100,000 Keeneland July yearling, Halo was sold at five for $1 million and immediately syndicated for $1.2 million. When a majority interest in him was sold in 1984, he was valued at $36 million, a figure based on the acquisition of 25 shares (out of 40) for $900,000 apiece. There was madness in the market at the time, and the sellers had decidedly the better of this bargain. The price presupposed that Halo's son Devil's Bag was about to proclaim himself the second coming of Man o' War by running away with the Triple Crown – a formality already acknowledged by a $36 million deal over Devil's Bag himself. In fact, Devil's Bag did not deign to turn out for the Triple Crown, taking early retirement rather than risk a second blow to a

## HALO (bay, 1969)

| | | | Nearco |
| | | Royal Charger | Sun Princess |
| | Turn-to | | Admiral Drake |
| | | Source Sucree | Lavendula |
| Hail to Reason (br 1958) | | | Blue Larkspur |
| | | Blue Swords | Flaming Swords |
| | Nothirdchance | | Sir Gallahad |
| | | Galla Colors | Rouge et Noir |
| | | | Phalaris |
| | | Pharamond | Selene |
| | Cosmic Bomb | | Blue Larkspur |
| | | Banish Fear | Herodiade |
| Cosmah (b 1953) | | | Blenheim |
| | | Mahmoud | Mah Mahal |
| | Almahmoud | | Peace Chance |
| | | Arbitrator | Mother Goose |

### Racing record

| Year | Starts | Wins | 2nd | 3rd | 4th | $ |
|------|--------|------|-----|-----|-----|-----|
| 1971 | 2 | 1 | - | - | - | 4,710 |
| 1972 | 17 | 5 | 3 | 4 | - | 109,283 |
| 1973 | 5 | - | 3 | 1 | - | 13,316 |
| 1974 | 7 | 3 | 2 | - | 1 | 132,244 |
| | 31 | 9 | 8 | 5 | 1 | 259,553 |

### Principal wins

| 1972 | Lawrence Realization Stakes |
| 1974 | Tidal Handicap-Gr2 |
| | United Nations Handicap-Gr1 |

reputation sagging from his first defeat in Florida. The buyers' folly was soon apparent, and it was compounded two years later when they sold, for only $17,000, a yearling colt they had bred by Halo. That was Sunday Silence, 'Horse of the Year' in 1989 and earner of more than $4.6 million.

Halo led the North American sires' list for the second time in 1989, but he is not, and has never so much as resembled, a great sire. He just scrapes into the 'good' category with his ratio of 10 per cent stakes winners to foals, and is best characterized as an extremely well-bred horse, able to get the odd exceptional runner on account of his superior genetic endowment. As yet he has not had a great deal of exposure in Europe, but his daughter Coup de Folie, a Group 3 winner herself, is the dam of champion 1989 two-year-old Machiavellian. Raised to $100,000 in the year of his staggering revaluation, Halo's fee was back to $45,000 by 1990.

## Principal progeny

### 1976

b f GLORIOUS SONG (ex Ballade, by Herbager)
    1980   La Canada Stakes-Gr1
            Santa Margarita Invitational Handicap-Gr1
            Top Flight Handicap-Gr1
            Michigan Mile & One-Eighth Handicap-Gr2
            Dominion Day Handicap-Gr3
    1981   Santa Maria Handicap-Gr2
            Dominion Day Handicap-Gr3
            Spinster Stakes-Gr1
gr f MISTY GALLORE (ex Flight Dancer, by Misty Flight)
    1980   Barbara Fritchie Handicap-Gr3
            Distaff Handicap-Gr3
            Bed o' Roses Handicap-Gr3
            Hempstead Handicap-Gr2
            Long Look Handicap-Gr3
ch f SOLAR (ex Sex Appeal, by Buckpasser)
    1978   Railway Stakes-Gr3
            Park Stakes-Gr3

### 1978

b f RAINBOW CONNECTION (ex Hangin Round, by Stage Door Johnny)
    1980   Demoiselle Stakes-Gr2
b g ST BRENDAN (ex Trial Landing, by Solo Landing)
    1982   Riggs Handicap-Gr3

### 1980

ch c SUNNY'S HALO (ex Mostly Sunny, by Sunny)
    1983   Arkansas Derby-Gr1
            Kentucky Derby-Gr1
            Super Derby-Gr1

### 1981

b c DEVIL'S BAG (ex Ballade, by Herbager)
    1983   Cowdin Stakes-Gr2
            Champagne Stakes-Gr1
            Laurel Futurity-Gr1
ch g HALO FOLKS (ex Crimson Tune, by Crimson Satan)
    1986   Sierra Madre Handicap-Gr3
b/br f SOLAR HALO (ex Provenance, by Fleet Nasrullah)
    1984   Firenze Handicap-Gr2

### 1982

b f COUP DE FOLIE (ex Raise the Standard, by Hoist the Flag)
    1984   Prix d'Aumale-Gr3

b/br c DON'T SAY HALO (ex Never Babble, by Advocator)
    1985   Cinema Handicap-Gr2

### 1983

b/br c COOL HALO (ex Slight Deception, by Northern Dancer)
    1987   King Edward Gold Cup Handicap [Div.1]-Gr3

### 1984

b c PRESENT VALUE (ex Fairly Regal, by Viceregal)
    1989   National Jockey Club Handicap-Gr3
            Michigan Mile & One-Eighth Handicap-Gr2
            Equipoise Mile Handicap-Gr3
            Canterbury Cup Handicap-Gr3
            Harold C. Ramser Sr Handicap-Gr3
            Goodwood Handicap-Gr3

### 1985

ch f GOODBYE HALO (ex Pound Foolish, by Sir Ivor)
    1987   Demoiselle Stakes-Gr1
            Hollywood Starlet Stakes-Gr1
    1988   Santa Ynez Stakes-Gr3
            Las Virgenes Stakes-Gr1
            Kentucky Oaks-Gr1
            Mother Goose Stakes-Gr1
            Coaching Club American Oaks-Gr1
    1989   El Encino Stakes-Gr3
            La Canada Stakes-Gr1
            Chula Vista Handicap-Gr2
b/br c LIVELY ONE (ex Swinging Lizzie, by The Axe)
    1988   Swaps Stakes-Gr1
    1989   San Diego Handicap-Gr3
            Cabrillo Handicap-Gr3

### 1986

b c SUNDAY SILENCE (ex Wishing Well, by Understanding)
    1989   San Felipe Handicap-Gr2
            Santa Anita Derby-Gr1
            Kentucky Derby-Gr1
            Preakness Stakes-Gr1
            Super Derby-Gr1
            Breeders' Cup Classic Stakes-Gr1
    1990   Californian Stakes-Gr1

### 1987

b/br f SILVERED (ex Silvered Silk, by Fire Dancer)
    1990   Fantasy Stakes-Gr2

# High Line

THE rule saying that a horse who makes his name in staying races cannot succeed as a stallion is now so well established that it is hard to imagine its ever being broken again. The last to break it was High Line, who did so largely on account of the single-minded dedication of his owner-breeder, a man of the old school who worked on the principle that the impossible was just something that took a little longer.

William Barnett was the nephew of the man of the same name whose colours were carried to victory by Trigo in the 1929 Derby and St Leger. In due course he inherited those colours and set about owning and breeding on his own account, first in Ireland and later in England; and like his uncle he chose to board his small band of mares rather than acquire a stud of his own. In 1966 he bred a colt by the Airlie Stud stallion High Hat out of Time Call, a mare he had bought as a foal for 800gns at Newmarket, and sent him to be trained by Derrick Candy at Kingstone Warren in Berkshire. Every owner needs a dream, and Barnett's was that in High Line he had a colt to emulate Trigo.

It was not realized, and for some owners High Line might have seemed a frustrating character. It was a fact that every time a target was set for him, he missed it for one reason or another, but there were ample compensations and to complete a four-season career without ever finishing out of the frame was no mean achievement. Things began well with a maiden victory over seven furlongs and a fourth place in the Horris Hill Stakes in his first season – fair encouragement for a prospective stayer.

Candy prepared High Line for the Derby in 1969 and after a smooth two-length victory in the Warren Stakes at Epsom and a 12-length romp in the Levin Down Stakes at Goodwood, both over a mile and a half, a bid certainly seemed justified. The plan had to be scrapped when he rapped a joint at exercise, and a subsequent bout of coughing held him up when he began his preparation for the St Leger. He got to the post at Doncaster, but that was as far as he did get; he defied the handlers to install him, and after he had caused a long delay, the rest went without him. They were not a vintage collection in that St Leger field, and in view of what he showed he could do later it is

not inconceivable that he would have won. In the following month, racing over two miles for the first time, he impressed profoundly in beating Crozier by five lengths in the Jockey Club Cup – though again after causing trouble at the start.

High Line proved himself a top-class stayer as a four-year-old, twice beating the previous season's St Leger winner, Intermezzo, first in the Aston Park Stakes and later in the Geoffrey Freer Stakes, both over 13 furlongs at Newbury. His other victory that year brought him a second Jockey Club Cup, and again he won it in some style. He had a fine turn of foot for one who stayed so well, and he would put plodders in their place every time. The one thing missing from an excellent campaign was the Gold Cup, which Candy would not let him contest on account of the prevailing hard ground, but that merely provided another reason for bringing him back as a five-year-old.

As it turned out, Plan D went the same way as Plans A, B and C. High Line did not contest the Gold Cup in 1971 because a calculated risk in running him on fast ground in the Yorkshire Cup failed to come off. The horse had run a tremendous race on his reappearance, coping admirably with good to firm conditions in the John Porter Stakes and going under by only a short head to Meadowville. That was the best performance of his life at a mile and a half. However, the going at York was just too firm. He tried, as he always did, but the rewards for his effort were a modest third place and a set of severely jarred legs that craved a long rest. Off the course for three months, High Line came back in such brilliant form, trouncing Hornet and Politico in the Geoffrey Freer Stakes, that Candy began to think in terms of the Arc de Triomphe for his farewell race. Second thoughts – that Mill Reef and co. might just be too fast for him – eventually prevailed and High Line turned out instead for a third Jockey Club Cup. The wisdom of the decision was proved by an overwhelming 12-length victory, assured from the moment Joe Mercer gave him a little rein two and a half furlongs from home.

Before the war a horse with High Line's record would have been prized as a stallion, but William Barnett – unencumbered by offers to buy him or syndicate him – kept him and sent him to James

Delahooke's Adstock Manor Stud, advertising him at a fee of £600. The horse's income in 1972 was negligible; of the 15 mares he covered, seven were the property of his owner. Significantly, though, from two of the Barnett mares he got Pattern winners – Ancholia in Italy and Centrocon at home. Things looked up a little in his second season, when he had 24 mares in all, but in 1974 disaster struck. An embarrassed Delahooke was able to attract only eight outside mares, some of those at a fee discounted to £150. Fortunately, out of the nine foals in the crop, Nicholas Bill (a brother to Centrocon) and Crimson Beau proved to be Pattern winners, but there were further anxious seasons before their merit advertised the sire.

Still, William Barnett was never going to concede defeat, and as winners started to appear from those small early crops other breeders began to take notice. Business began to pick up and the owner's staunch support could be seen to be proving a point, if not yet reaping a reward. One of the colts he bred from the fifth crop he sold as a foal for 2200gns, then purchased back as a yearling for 8400gns and put into training with Henry Candy, who had taken over the Kingstone Warren stable. Named Master

Willie, that chesnut all but emulated Trigo at Epsom, finishing a close second to Henbit in the Derby. Two months later Master Willie figured in the proudest day of William Barnett's racing life, when products of High Line won four consecutive races at York, including the Group 1 double of Benson & Hedges Gold Cup and Yorkshire Oaks. Three of them were of his own breeding.

Barnett's faith had been vindicated, and he lived just long enough to see High Line's name in a proud second place on the sire's table, close behind Pitcairn. When he died in December 1980 the horse's future was secure, with a waiting list for nominations at £10,000. For a horse who really belonged in another era, High Line has done extraordinarily well, a sire of durable stayers chiefly, yet also capable of getting the occasional really classy individual blessed with a useful turn of speed. His first English Pattern winner, Centrocon, became his most celebrated daughter at stud, producing the Oaks and Coronation Cup heroine Time Charter, bred by William Barnett and raced by his heirs. Curiously, High Line was a rig until the age of 22, when the second testicle descended. In 1990 High Line was in semi-retirement, but booked to ten mares at £5000.

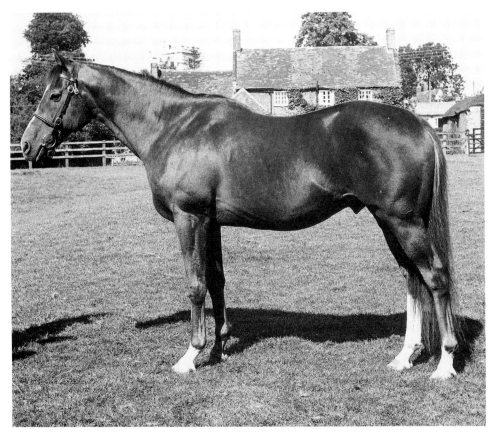

*High Line, whose record as a sire vindicated the faith of his owner-breeder William Barnett.*

## Racing record

| Year | Starts | Wins | 2nd | 3rd | 4th | £ |
|------|--------|------|-----|-----|-----|------|
| 1968 | 3 | 1 | 1 | - | 1 | 734 |
| 1969 | 4 | 3 | - | 1 | - | 5,996 |
| 1970 | 6 | 3 | 2 | 1 | - | 9,648 |
| 1971 | 4 | 2 | 1 | 1 | - | 8,421 |
| | 17 | 9 | 4 | 3 | 1 | 24,799 |

## Principal wins

| 1969 | Jockey Club Cup |
|------|-----------------|
| 1970 | Geoffrey Freer Stakes |
| | Jockey Club Cup |
| 1971 | Geoffrey Freer Stakes-Gr2 |
| | Jockey Club Cup-Gr3 |

## Principal progeny

**1973**
b f ANCHOLIA (ex Dark Finale, by Javelot)
    1975    Premio Dormello-Gr2
ch f CENTROCON (ex Centro, by Vienna)
    1976    Lancashire Oaks-Gr3

**1975**
ch c CRIMSON BEAU (ex Crimson Belle, by Red God)
    1978    Prix de la Cote Normande-Gr3
    1979    Prince of Wales's Stakes-Gr2
ch c NICHOLAS BILL (ex Centro, by Vienna)
    1979    Jockey Club Cup-Gr3
    1980    Princess of Wales's Stakes-Gr2
                Geoffrey Freer Stakes-Gr2

**1976**
b f QUAY LINE (ex Dark Finale, by Javelot)
    1979    Park Hill Stakes-Gr2
b g HEIGHLIN (ex Filiform, by Reform)
    1982    Goodwood Cup-Gr3

**1977**
ch c MASTER WILLIE (ex Fair Winter, by Set Fair)
    1980    Benson & Hedges Gold Cup-Gr1
    1981    Jockey Club Stakes-Gr3
                Coronation Cup-Gr1
                Eclipse Stakes-Gr1
b f SHOOT A LINE (ex Death Ray, by Tamerlane)
    1980    Cheshire Oaks-Gr3
                Ribblesdale Stakes-Gr2
                Irish Oaks-Gr1
                Yorkshire Oaks-Gr1
                Park Hill Stakes-Gr2

**1978**
b c CENTROLINE (ex Centro, by Vienna)
    1981    Jockey Club Cup-Gr3

# HIGH LINE (chesnut, 1966)

| | | | |
|---|---|---|---|
| High Hat (ch 1957) | Hyperion | Gainsborough | Bayardo / Rosedrop |
| | | Selene | Chaucer / Serenissima |
| | Madonna | Donatello | Blenheim / Delleana |
| | | Women's Legion | Coronach / Victress |
| Time Call (b 1955) | Chanteur | Chateau Bouscaut | Kircubbin / Ramondie |
| | | La Diva | Blue Skies / La Traviata |
| | Aleria | Djebel | Tourbillon / Loika |
| | | Canidia | Pharis / Callisto |

**1979**
b f LINE SLINGER (ex Snow Tribe, by Great Nephew)
    1983    Yorkshire Cup-Gr2

**1980**
ch c ADONIJAH (ex Shadow Queen, by Darius)
    1984    Brigadier Gerard Stakes-Gr3
                Diomed Stakes-Gr3
b c BEL SIGNORE (ex Signora, by Botticelli)
    1984    Gran Premio Citta di Napoli-Gr3

**1982**
b c METAL PRECIEUX (ex Magic Spell, by Dancer's Image)
    1985    Prix de Guiche-Gr3
                Prix Lupin-Gr1
ch c TALE QUALE (ex Centro, by Vienna)
    1985    Jockey Club Cup-Gr3
    1987    Prix Vicomtesse Vigier-Gr2
b f DUBIAN (ex Melodina, by Tudor Melody)
    1986    Royal Whip Stakes-Gr3
                Premio Lydia Tesio-Gr1

**1984**
b c DRY DOCK (ex Boathouse, by Habitat)
    1987    Chester Vase-Gr3
ch f RUFFLE (ex Button Up, by Busted)
    1988    Prix Gontaut-Biron-Gr3
ch f TRAMPSHIP (ex Nomadic Pleasure, by Habitat)
    1987    Park Hill Stakes-Gr2

# High Top

GETTING to the top as an amateur rider proved easier for Bob McCreery than acquiring a reputation as a leading commercial breeder. He spent long years gaining knowledge and experience, developing his small stud in Warwickshire, trying to mate his mares intelligently, and upgrading when he could afford it. He did rather well in a quiet way, but progress seemed painfully slow until he received the encouraging news that two of his 1970 yearling crop had been accepted for Tattersalls' Houghton Sales, Europe's premier auction market. This was the break he had been waiting for, and he left for Newmarket full of optimism. When his turn arrived he watched expectantly, then with deepening dismay, as his Le Levanstell filly and his Derring-Do colt were both led out unsold, having failed to reach their reserves.

It looked as though McCreery had fluffed his opportunity. Tattersalls always took a dim view of vendors who placed what seemed to be unrealistic reserves on their stock, and he might find himself without places in the 1971 Houghton catalogue. However, all was not yet lost. It was not as though there had been no interest in his yearlings; there had been bidders, and they might yet be persuaded to buy. Before the day was out he had concluded private deals over both yearlings, the filly for 12,000gns, the colt for 9000gns. The cheaper one, bought by Newmarket trainer Bernard van Cutsem for his patron Sir Jules Thorn, was to make McCreery's name as a breeder.

High Top came from the third crop of Derring-Do, who had been one of the best milers of his day and was a son of a 2000 Guineas winner in Darius. His dam Camenae had been much less conspicuous as a runner, managing just a single win, and that in a poorly contested maiden race over 14 furlongs at Redcar as a four-year-old. McCreery had bought her in December 1966, forgiving her lack of form and figuring that 1500gns was a reasonable sum for a half-sister to Petite Marmite, a winner of five races over a mile that season. The pedigree soon read better. Another half-sister became the dam of Tudor Music, a top-class sprinter in 1968 and 1969.

High Top did nothing wrong in his first season. On his debut, only half-fit, he ran away from poor rivals over five furlongs at Sandown Park. He did not win the Washington Singer Stakes at Newbury three weeks later, but he lost it by only half a length to Yaroslav, who was receiving 3lb and was later to win the Group 2 Royal Lodge Stakes. At Ripon he led throughout the six furlongs of the Champion Trophy, outclassing useful performers, then was pointed at the Group 1 Observer Gold Cup, where there would be more serious competition. The best of his Doncaster rivals was Steel Pulse, who had been beaten only a neck in the top French juvenile race, the Grand Criterium, but when he came that close to High Top, the burly brown colt kept battling away and extended the margin to three-quarters of a length at the finish. In a banner year for the van Cutsem stable, four of its inmates featured in the top 12 on the Free Handicap, High Top being rated joint second in the country, 2lb below another Stanley House colt, Crowned Prince.

As a three-year-old High Top did all his racing at a mile, and had a vintage crop of milers for company. His trainer campaigned him aggressively, sending him in search of the best opposition, and after his first start at Thirsk – which he won easily – he ran only in Group 1 races. The high point of his season was reached in the 2000 Guineas. There he showed tremendous courage, leading a strong field all the way up the Rowley Mile into a gale and driving rain; when the battle seemed to have been won, Roberto emerged from the pack to deliver a menacing challenge, but High Top drew on reserves which even jockey Willie Carson doubted he owned and fought on valiantly to hold his rival at bay.

That hard race told on High Top when he tried to win a second Guineas a fortnight later; he finished only seventh and came back from The Curragh distinctly sorry for himself. After two months' rest he resumed at Goodwood and at the end of a splendid set-to with Sallust was beaten only a head in the Sussex Stakes. He failed narrowly and honourably again in the Prix Jacques le Marois, going under by a nose in a desperate finish with Lyphard. Nothing

---

*OPPOSITE: Two sons of Northern Dancer fight out a thrilling Derby finish with Secreto (yellow sleeves) just catching El Gran Senor.*

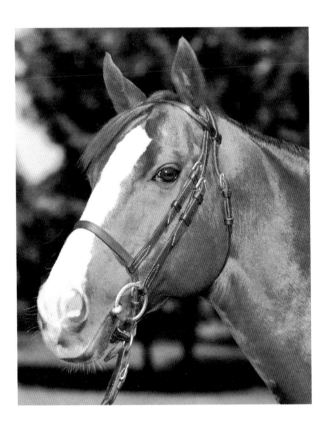

FATHERS AND SONS . . . Mill Reef (above left) and his son Shirley Heights (below left) both won the Derby, while the speedy Sharpen Up (above right) produced a son better than himself in Kris (below right) . . .

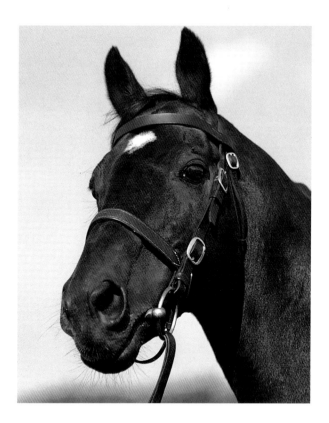

*. . . Great Nephew (above left) and Blushing Groom (above right) were both top class milers who produced Derby - winning sons in, respectively, Shergar (below left) and Nashwan (below right).*

DERBY DAY. . . and success amid the hurly burly for the owner-breeders. The Aga Khan's Shahrastani (main picture) holds off the fast-finishing Dancing Brave in 1986, while the Mollers' Teenoso (inset, left) triumphs in 1983. Slip Anchor (inset, above) is led in by Lord Howard de Walden after his 1985 victory.

*MILERS . . . Green Forest (above) shows top class form as a two-year-old to beat Maelstrom Lake and River Lady in the Prix Morny at Deauville, while (below), against the rolling backdrop at Goodwood, Rousillon lands the Sussex Stakes readily from Bairn and King of Clubs . . .*

*. . . Shadeed (above) wins the 2000 Guineas at Newmarket in a driving finish with Bairn to give Maktoum Al Maktoum victory over his brother Sheikh Mohammed.  But (below) the positions are reversed as the latter's Sure Blade outpoints Green Desert and Sharood in the St. James's Palace Stakes at Royal Ascot.*

Dancing Brave (above) proves too strong for Shardari in the King George VI and Queen Elizabeth Stakes at Ascot. And although Rainbow Quest (left) is edged out by Sagace in the Prix de l'Arc de Triomphe at Longchamp, he was later awarded the race on the disqualification of his opponent to secure another prize for Khalid Abdullah.

*The Northern Dancer influence . . .*
*Sadler's Wells (above) wins the Eclipse*
*Stakes at Sandown from Time Charter*
*and Morcon, while El Gran Senor (left)*
*defeats Rainbow Quest in the Dewhurst*
*Stakes at Newmarket . . .*

*. . . Lomond (above) scores an emphatic victory in the 2000 Guineas at Newmarket. But Nureyev (below, nearside) defeats Known Fact in the Guineas only to lose the race on a disqualification.*

PADDOCK SCENES . . . Shareef Dancer (far left) finds a gap on the rails, while Kris (above) shows his paces, Known Fact (near left) keeps cool under the trees, and Nijinsky (below) shows a liking for the 'blue grass' of Kentucky.

Busted (right) sports the thick 'fur coat' which, like his sire Crepello, he developed every winter.

STAYERS . . . Ardross (above) wins the Ascot Gold Cup for the second year in succession with contemptuous ease, while Shardari (below) powers home in the Matchmaker International at York.

SPRINTERS . . . Ajdal (above) is driven out to win the July Cup at Newmarket, Last Tycoon (below left) takes York's William Hill Sprint Championship, and Ahonoora (below right) wins a Newbury handicap.

From the dawning to the sunset of their racing careers, Brigadier Gerard (above) and Mill Reef (left) shared greatness — two closely matched champions from the same generation.

In fact, they met only once when 'The Brigadier' scored a decisive victory in the 2000 Guineas at Newmarket.

And it was to neighbouring studs at Newmarket that both retired as stallions — Mill Reef to the National Stud and Brigadier Gerard to Egerton Stud.

daunted, High Top sought revenge on both Sallust and Lyphard in the Prix du Moulin de Longchamp, but he was not quite up to the task on the firm ground. He fought back in his usual game style, but they had his measure that day and he even had to cede third place to Daring Display in the last stride.

High Top was syndicated to stand at Lord Derby's Woodland Stud in 1973, proving popular at £8000 a share. A thoroughly genuine racehorse and a high-class miler from a line of high-class milers, he was entitled to plenty of respect. What he was not was a facsimile of his sire, the compact, close-coupled, lop-eared Derring-Do, whose looks were an instant attraction to all. High Top's physique was more a matter of taste. He was either 'imposing' or 'a slob', terms which to fanciers or detractors of the type denote the same qualities – powerful, round-barrelled with plenty of bone.

Whether or not it had anything to do with the striking physical differences between Derring-Do and High Top, the fact remains that the line of milers stopped there. In the early days he was usually mated with the intention of producing milers, and trainers were naturally inclined to treat his stock as though they would be milers. In time the evidence indicated that the High Top miler was an exception to the rule,

and generally inferior to the High Top stayer. His high-class two-year-olds were rare, only Circus Ring proving a real speed merchant at that age, and he was essentially a sire of three-year-olds, the best of whom needed ten furlongs and preferred 12. It seems likely that many potentially good performers were ill-used, and their talents squandered, before the requirements of the High Tops were generally recognized. Of the eight Group 1 races they won, seven were at a mile and a half or beyond, the sole exception being Top Ville's Prix Lupin. In the circumstances it was probably just as well for Gainesway Farm that its offer for High Top in 1981 ($120,000 a share) was rejected; he was not a stallion to suit America.

High Top has made no appreciable impact as a sire of sires. Top Ville has had spasmodic successes, but Cut Above none worth recording; the former is now back in France after a spell in Newmarket, and the latter was banished to Brazil after a disastrous start in Ireland. The High Top mares, on the other hand, have been doing exceptionally well and they promise to preserve his name in pedigrees for a while. The stallion is now buried at Woodland, having been put down following a thrombosis on 9 March 1988.

## Racing record

| Year | Starts | Wins | 2nd | 3rd | 4th | £ |
|------|--------|------|-----|-----|-----|-----|
| 1971 | 4 | 3 | 1 | - | - | 20,840 |
| 1972 | 6 | 2 | 2 | - | 1 | 42,090 |
| | 10 | 5 | 3 | - | 1 | 62,930 |

### Principal wins

| 1971 | Observer Gold Cup-Gr1 |
| 1972 | 2000 Guineas Stakes-Gr1 |

### Principal progeny

**1974**
br f ALOFT (ex Over the Water, by Doutelle)
    1977   Princess Royal Stakes-Gr3
b f TRIPLE FIRST (ex Field Mouse, by Grey Sovereign)
    1977   Musidora Stakes-Gr3
           Nassau Stakes-Gr2
           Sun Chariot Stakes-Gr2

**1976**
b c TOP VILLE (ex Sega Ville, by Charlottesville)
    1978   Prix Saint Roman-Gr3
           Prix de Conde-Gr3
    1979   Prix de Guiche-Gr3
           Prix Lupin-Gr1
           Prix du Jockey-Club-Gr1

**1977**
b c MINER'S LAMP (ex Coal Face, by Kalydon)
    1980   Oettingen Rennen-Gr3

## HIGH TOP (brown, 1969)

| | | | Nearco |
|---|---|---|---|
| | | Dante | Rosy Legend |
| | Darius | | |
| | | Yasna | Dastur |
| Derring-Do | | | Ariadne |
| (br 1961) | | | Owen Tudor |
| | | Abernant | Rustom Mahal |
| | Sipsey Bridge | | |
| | | Claudette | Chanteur |
| | | | Nearly |
| | | | Rialto |
| | | Wild Risk | Wild Violet |
| | Vimy | | |
| | | Mimi | Black Devil |
| Camenae | | | Mignon |
| (b 1961) | | | Fair Trial |
| | | Court Martial | Instantaneous |
| | Madrilene | | |
| | | Marmite | Mr Jinks |
| | | | Gentlemen's Relish |

**1978**
b c CUT ABOVE (ex Cutle, by Saint Crespin)
    1981   White Rose Stakes-Gr3
           St Leger Stakes-Gr1
b c LOOKING FOR (ex Love You, by Linden Tree)
    1981   Premio Roma-Gr1
    1982   Coppa d'Oro di Milano-Gr3

*High Top, a high-class miler who proved an influence for stamina as a sire.*

**1979**
b f CIRCUS RING (ex Bell Song, by Tudor Melody)
    1981   Lowther Stakes-Gr2
b f SMAGETA (ex Christine, by Crocket)
    1981   Criterium Femminile-Gr3

**1980**
b c LOFTY (ex Enchanted, by Song)
    1983   Diomed Stakes-Gr3
b c MY TOP (ex Forgotten Dreams, by Shoemaker)
    1983   Premio Emanuele Filiberto-Gr2
             Derby Italiano-Gr1
             Premio Federico Tesio-Gr2

**1981**
b f CIRCUS PLUME (ex Golden Fez, by Aureole)
    1984   Oaks Stakes-Gr1
             Yorkshire Oaks-Gr1
b c KAYTU (ex Arawak, by Seminole)
    1984   Chester Vase-Gr3

**1983**
b f COLORSPIN (ex Reprocolor, by Jimmy Reppin)
    1986   Irish Oaks-Gr1

**1985**
b c TOP CLASS (ex Cassina, by Habitat)
    1988   Geoffrey Freer Stakes-Gr2

# Ile de Bourbon

IN a Thoroughbred population comprising, for the most part, stallions selected on the basis of their talent and mares on account of their sex, the object of the majority of matings is inevitably to produce something better than the mare. The mare owner wants to improve his stock, and he hopes to do so by mating her with a horse of superior class. Unfortunately, Mother Nature does not work exactly along those lines. She says that sire and dam will make equal genetic contributions to the offspring, and she makes no guarantees about which will dominate in terms of the most important characters. There are disconcerting examples of mares who come home with little creatures the images of themselves after matings with the best and most expensive sires in the world.

Ile de Bourbon provided a good illustration of this point, though in his case there were numerous compensating factors. His dam Roseliere had been an excellent racemare, good enough to win the Prix de Diane and Prix Vermeille in a vintage season for French-trained fillies. Fourth in the Arc de Triomphe was also no disgrace when Vaguely Noble and Sir Ivor were first and second. It hardly seemed to matter that she resembled a hat-rack. All the same, it did seem to make sense to mate her with a strapping, handsome stallion, and as her owner Jane Engelhard had inherited shares in Nijinsky along with the mare herself on her husband's death, there was no problem about implementing the plan. The result was that Mrs Engelhard became the owner of two hat-racks instead of one. Yet – and this is the uncommon element in a common phenomenon – this mother's son did turn out to represent an improvement, a colt whose class was measured at about midway between that of sire and dam.

By the time Fulke Johnson Houghton took Ile de Bourbon to the races for the first time there was already considerable public interest in the colt. Sons of Nijinsky were always entitled to respect, but so was a son of Roseliere, who had made a splendid start as a broodmare with a good filly (Rose Bed) and a very good filly (Rose Bowl), both by Habitat. As a two-year-old, Ile de Bourbon was clearly no Nijinsky. He ran fourth in a quite competitive sponsored event at Ascot, then ninth – beaten under seven lengths by the winner – in the Futurity at Doncaster. He was promising, but it was anybody's guess how good he might become.

Ile de Bourbon began at three with a sterling effort at Newmarket, where he failed by only a short head to take advantage of a 10lb concession from the fitter and more experienced Shirley Heights. At Goodwood he was second again, this time to all-the-way winner English Harbour in the Predominate Stakes. His first win came at Royal Ascot, where he could not go the early pace but eventually stayed on far too stoutly for Stradavinsky in the King Edward VII Stakes. Ile de Bourbon was obviously an improving colt, but it seemed to be asking a lot of him to run him next in the King George VI & Queen Elizabeth Stakes. Many assumed that this ambitious venture had less to do with his prospects of success than the fact that he was now part-owned by that race's sponsor, Sir Philip Oppenheimer, who had bought him from Jane Engelhard along with partners David McCall, Helen Johnson Houghton and the latter's son, the colt's trainer.

The Ascot event was a revelation. In a strongly run contest Ile de Bourbon was shrewdly ridden by John Reid, who settled him to lead the chasing pack while the sacrificial pacemaker Sea Boat charged off in front of his stable companion, dual classic heroine Dunfermline. By the time Sea Boat went into retreat, and Carson set about making the most of Dunfermline's stamina, Ile de Bourbon was bearing down strongly, while the riders of other fancied contenders seemed to have been caught off-guard. The filly could not maintain her effort on ground too fast for her, and Ile de Bourbon stormed by, quickly establishing an unassailable advantage. The subsequently disqualified Acamas, winner of the Prix du Jockey-Club, came late to be second, with Derby runner-up Hawaiian Sound finishing third. Ile de Bourbon was evidently much better than anyone had ever imagined.

The 'King George' was to remain the high point of Ile de Bourbon's career. He made rather heavy weather of winning the Geoffrey Freer Stakes at Newbury and closed his campaign with an inexplicably dull effort in the St Leger, whose winner, Julio Mariner, had finished a long way behind him in the King Edward VII Stakes. At four he took the Clive Graham Stakes at Goodwood (his first and only win at less than 12 furlongs) in a virtual canter as a preparation for the Coronation Cup, which he also won in impressive style. There were only four runners at Epsom, and when nothing else would make the running, Reid took the initiative and set his own pace. He judged it perfectly, and when he asked the colt to quicken in the straight, the others had no response; Ile de Bourbon strode on majestically to win by seven lengths from Frere Basile.

A virus infection put paid to an intended repeat bid in the 'King George' and he was never quite the same again. The three-year-old Cracaval, who was not really in his class, out-finished him in the September Stakes at Kempton, and in the Arc de Triomphe he never promised to reach contention. He bowed out then and retired to Banstead Manor Stud, syndicated in a deal which valued him at £4 million.

At this time the British breeding industry was going through a bout of euphoria, if not delirium. Ile de Bourbon was staying in England, as was the exceptional three-year-old of 1979, Troy, he having been syndicated for a European record £7.2 million.

We had believed for years that all the best horses had to go to America, yet we had managed to keep these two horses of outstanding ability. We began to take on airs. The trouble was that all the flag-waving obscured the reality of the situation. If the Americans, with their far richer industry and wider markets, reckoned that such horses were too expensive for them, what made us imagine that the prices were right for us?

In our enthusiasm we gave not a thought to the consequences, and the sad fact is that these deals paved the way for the general stallion revaluation process which in turn ensured that every breeder has found it more difficult to make his business pay ever since. This abrupt departure from the real world is best illustrated by the fact that whereas a share in the 1978 Derby winner, Shirley Heights, could be bought for £40,000 on his retirement, the same amount would buy only a nomination to Troy, the next year's winner. (Ile de Bourbon's fee, incidentally, was £20,000.) Two years later we had Kings Lake retiring at a fee of IR50,000gns and Shergar at IR70,000gns. A year after that there was Golden Fleece at IR100,000gns. The propaganda all along said that we were saving our best horses from

*Ile de Bourbon rounds Tattenham Corner on his way to a seven-length victory in the Coronation Cup at Epsom.*

America. We were saving them for breeders who could not afford them, and for a market which could not sustain them. We were also ensuring that horses who were not in the top bracket were revalued upwards too, with the result that fees at every level of the market could no longer be reconciled with the demand for the produce. The damaging side-effects of the 1979 euphoria have lingered into the 90s.

As it turned out, Troy died young after getting a preponderance of slow horses, and Ile de Bourbon,

like so many others, was sent to Japan as a presumed failure, leaving behind a two-year-old – Kahyasi – destined to become a Derby winner. Kahyasi made quite a difference to his sire's record, and in the following year Ile de Chypre, Petite Ile and Ile de Nisky all did their bits to keep his profile high. Yet overall, it has to be said, he gave us rather too many of the soft, slow and gawky sort, and most breeders would still say that the Japanese are welcome to him.

## Racing record

| Year | Starts | Wins | 2nd | 3rd | 4th | £ |
|---|---|---|---|---|---|---|
| 1977 | 2 | - | - | - | 1 | 423 |
| 1978 | 6 | 3 | 2 | - | - | 138,897 |
| 1979 | 4 | 2 | 1 | - | - | 35,852 |
| | 12 | 5 | 3 | - | 1 | 175,172 |

## Principal wins

| | | |
|---|---|---|
| 1978 | King Edward VII Stakes-Gr2 | |
| | King George VI & Queen Elizabeth Stakes-Gr1 | |
| | Geoffrey Freer Stakes-Gr2 | |
| 1979 | Coronation Cup-Gr1 | |

## Principal progeny

**1981**
b c LAGUNAS (ex Liranga, by Literat)
    1983   Preis des Winterfavoriten-Gr3
    1984   Deutsches Derby-Gr1

**1982**
br g BOURBON BOY (ex Sofala, by Home Guard)
    1987   Rain Lover Plate Handicap-Gr3
           West End Export Handicap-Gr3
b c L'IRRESPONSABLE (ex Lady Hester, by Native Prince)
    1985   Prix Daphnis-Gr3
br f PADANG (ex Palmas, by Neckar)
    1985   Preis der Diana-Gr2

**1983**
b f BONSHAMILE (ex Narration, by Sham)
    1987   Prix Corrida-Gr3
b f REJUVENATE (ex Miss Petard, by Petingo)
    1986   Musidora Stakes-Gr3
           Park Hill Stakes-Gr2

## ILE DE BOURBON (brown, 1975)

| | | | |
|---|---|---|---|
| **Nijinsky** (b 1967) | Northern Dancer | Nearctic | Nearco |
| | | | Lady Angela |
| | | Natalma | Native Dancer |
| | | | Almahmoud |
| | Flaming Page | Bull Page | Bull Lea |
| | | | Our Page |
| | | Flaring Top | Menow |
| | | | Flaming Top |
| **Roselière** (br 1965) | Misti | Medium | Meridien |
| | | | Melodie |
| | | Mist | Tornado |
| | | | La Touche |
| | Peace Rose | Fastnet Rock | Ocean Swell |
| | | | Stone of Fortune |
| | | La Paix | Seven Seas |
| | | | Anne de Bretagne |

**1985**
b c ILE DE CHYPRE (ex Salamina, by Welsh Pageant)
    1989   Rogers Gold Cup-Gr2
           York International Stakes-Gr1
b c KAHYASI (ex Kadissya, by Blushing Groom)
    1988   Lingfield Derby Trial Stakes-Gr3
           Derby Stakes-Gr1
           Irish Derby-Gr1

**1986**
b f PETITE ILE (ex Aces Full, by Round Table)
    1989   Irish St Leger-Gr1

# Kalaglow

AFTER his disappointing and unlucky campaign as a three-year-old, Kalaglow needed to be different in his last season in training. He was – in more ways than one. On the morning after the colt's impressive reappearance in the Earl of Sefton Stakes at Newmarket his trainer, Guy Harwood, was contacted by Weatherbys' Stud Book Department, who told him that a discrepancy had been uncovered in Kalaglow's pedigree. That, the Pulborough trainer was entitled to think, was all he needed.

He had developed this 11,500gns bargain colt through an unbeaten juvenile campaign (including a win in the Horris Hill Stakes) to the verge of classic stardom, then seen his dream turn into a nightmare. Undefeated in six races until the Dante Stakes, the grey could beat only one of his five York rivals. Given the opportunity to redeem himself in the Derby, Kalaglow became involved in a barging match after three furlongs, lost interest and came back with a leg injury which kept him out of action for the rest of the season. Unsurprisingly, one of the partners in the colt, owner of a one-sixth share, wanted out of his investment and Harwood, having vainly attempted to persuade him that Kalaglow would be better than ever in time, had the courage of his convictions to buy the share on his own account. Now, with the colt's come-back successfully under way and with assaults on Group 1 targets in the offing, Harwood dreaded learning that his charge was not, after all, a son of the hugely successful but short-lived sire Kalamoun.

As it turned out, the news was not as bad as he had feared. Kalaglow was, indeed, a son of Kalamoun, so if he were to go on and establish high merit in the summer he would still have substantial appeal as a stallion prospect. What had emerged was that he was not out of the Crepello mare Aglow (who had given him the second element of his name); instead he was the product of a Pall Mall mare, Rossitor. Remarkably, there had been an inadvertent switch of identities when the pair, both bred by Someries Stud, were sent into training, and it had gone unnoticed for 11 years. The mistake came to light when Rossitor, masquerading as Aglow, turned up at the Irish National Stud to be mated with Tap on Wood, and manager Michael Osborne spotted that

she did not match her passport description. She had raced for two seasons (winning two minor long-distance events) and visited stallions at various studs in both England and Ireland without previously having provoked anyone to remark that she had three 'socks' instead of one!

The amendment to Kalaglow's pedigree did not cause too much consternation. If the fact of his dam's being by Pall Mall (winner of the 2000 Guineas, but not a great influence at stud) instead of the much more consequential Crepello (winner of the Guineas and the Derby, an exceptional runner and champion sire) seemed to detract, there was consolation in the thought that Rossitor had almost certainly become a winner only because she was assumed to be by a staying horse and was trained accordingly. In addition, although the pair had different sires, dams and maternal grandsires, they had a common grand-dam in Sonsa, so Kalaglow's female line read neither better nor worse for the change.

After his rehabilitating victory in the Earl of Sefton Stakes, Kalaglow finished out of the money – but not far behind the winner – in the Prix Ganay. He then broke the course record in the Brigadier Gerard Stakes and returned to Sandown Park for a much more important victory in the Eclipse – by four lengths in impressive style. The next logical step was the King George VI & Queen Elizabeth Stakes, and though many doubted his ability to last the distance, he saw it out famously, wearing down Assert to win by a neck while relegating Glint of Gold to the worst (third) placing of his career. Kalaglow did not race again until the Champion Stakes in the autumn, and though he looked a picture of health there, he ran as though he had had enough. He had certainly done enough to retire to stud with honour.

Unfortunately, and in common with many other horses at that time, Kalaglow was syndicated for a sum which bore little relation to the state of the market. He went to Brook Stud, near Newmarket, his shares priced at £125,000 apiece and his fee set at £25,000. Neither figure was realistic. Although he had improved in looks during his last season in training, he was still leggy, lacking in substance and, like others of his grandsire Zeddaan's tribe, not at all the type who could be expected to get eye-catching sales yearlings. Commercial breeders rightly reckoned that he represented poor value for money, while the few home-based private breeders were not so convinced of his merit that they would all rally round in support.

It was not long before the folly of Kalaglow's excessive £5 million valuation became apparent. The first yearlings found limited demand, and when the first two Pattern winners – Shining Water and Knockando – came along, they were the property of reluctant owners who had failed to find buyers for them at auction.

The horse's fee was reduced to £15,000 in 1985, to £12,500 in 1989, and in 1990 it was down to £7500 with the offer of a substantial percentage refund in the event of a filly-foal. It is hard to envisage a recovery now, though his stock win their share of minor races.

What might have saved Kalaglow's career was a Derby victory for Red Glow in 1988. That seemed to be a distinct possibility after the Dante Stakes, but the colt proved to be ungenuine and was eventually packed off to stud in New Zealand.

Sadly, a number of the early Kalaglows proved difficult to train, the worst seeming to be mentally unstable. The stallion himself is not the easiest of characters to handle; led into a splendidly appointed and expensive new box at Brook Stud, he promptly set about wrecking it.

*Kalaglow beats Assert and Glint of Gold in the King George VI and Queen Elizabeth Stakes.*

## Racing record

| Year | Starts | Wins | 2nd | 3rd | 4th | £ |
|------|--------|------|-----|-----|-----|------|
| 1980 | 5 | 5 | - | - | - | 26,757 |
| 1981 | 3 | 1 | - | - | - | 5,199 |
| 1982 | 6 | 4 | - | - | - | 242,304 |
| | 14 | 10 | - | - | - | 274,260 |

## Principal wins

1980   Horris Hill Stakes-Gr3
1982   Earl of Sefton Stakes-Gr3
       Brigadier Gerard Stakes-Gr3
       Eclipse Stakes-Gr1
       King George VI & Queen Elizabeth Stakes-Gr1

## Principal progeny

**1984**
b c KNOCKANDO (ex Paddy's Princess, by St Paddy)
     1987   September Stakes-Gr3
b f SHINING WATER (ex Idle Waters, by Mill Reef)
     1986   Solario Stakes-Gr3

**1985**
b c RED GLOW (ex Cherry Hinton, by Nijinsky)
     1988   Dante Stakes-Gr2

## KALAGLOW   (grey, 1978)

| | | | Nasrullah |
|---|---|---|---|
| | | Grey Sovereign | Kong |
| | Zeddaan | | |
| Kalamoun | | Vareta | Vilmorin |
| (gr 1970) | | | Veronique |
| | | Prince Bio | Prince Rose |
| | Khairunissa | | Biologie |
| | | Palariva | Palestine |
| | | | Rivaz |
| | | Palestine | Fair Trial |
| | Pall Mall | | Una |
| Rossitor | | Malapert | Portlaw |
| (ch 1970) | | | Malatesta |
| | | Worden | Wild Risk |
| | Sonia | | Sans Tares |
| | | Sonsa | Hyperion |
| | | | Duplicity |

**1986**
ch c WELD (ex Meliora, by Crowned Prince)
     1989   Doncaster Cup-Gr3
             Jockey Club Cup-Gr3

# Known Fact

LET loose in the world's most expensive market with a commission to buy for a fabulously wealthy man, some bloodstock agents are apt to run riot. Former trainer Humphrey Cottrill, acting at Keeneland in 1978 on behalf of young Saudi multi-millionaire Khalid Abdullah, was commendably restrained. He picked out just one yearling, one whose pedigree did not make him especially attractive for European racing, and made do with that. At $225,000 the colt was not cheap, but he also was not among the 50 highest-priced lots in the sale, which was headed by a little Northern Dancer colt called Nureyev.

Abdullah was just beginning to develop a serious interest in racing, and it was the success of this dark bay youngster, whom he called Known Fact, that provided the stimulus for the expansion which led to Rainbow Quest, Dancing Brave and the massive Juddmonte commitment to bloodstock at the start of the 1990s. The shy, courteous Arab prince was to become a regular at American auctions, advised – after Cottrill's retirement – by such as James Delahooke and George Blackwell, and he frequently came away with top-class material, to be developed by either Jeremy Tree or Guy Harwood. He established studs in England, Ireland and Kentucky, while cultivating a broodmare band of the highest quality. All this – and, doubtless, much yet to come – has stemmed from that initial, inconspicuous venture at Keeneland a dozen years ago.

Known Fact was bred in Florida, and a product of the only Florida-based stallion who had sufficient market credibility to get his progeny accepted for the Keeneland selected sales. In Reality, a good racehorse in his own day (though overshadowed by illustrious contemporaries in Damascus and Dr Fager), was a consistently successful sire in the States, not often represented in Europe, where he had had only one Pattern winner until Known Fact came along. Known Fact's dam, Tamerett, had previously produced an excellent American runner in Tentam, by In Reality's sire Intentionally, which made it all the more surprising that this, her fifth foal, should be bought to race in England.

Jeremy Tree soon took a liking to the good-looking youngster, who impressed as a fluent mover on the gallops and hinted at well above average ability. The colt did have a problem, though, in that he was disinclined to settle, and for much of his first season there were fears that he would squander his natural talent. Known Fact's tearaway behaviour almost certainly cost him the Mill Reef Stakes (in which he finished third to Lord Seymour and Taufan), but the experience taught both him and jockey Willie Carson a lot. Next time out, in the Middle Park Stakes, Known Fact proved much more tractable and for the first time looked a professional racehorse; Carson dismounted after a smooth victory and declared that the colt would win the 2000 Guineas.

Known Fact did win the Guineas, but in the most controversial circumstances. Beautifully ridden, he came with a smooth challenge up the stand rails and battled on gamely as Philippe Paquet brought Nureyev with a determined run, having come by a more circuitous and hazardous route. In the last strides the Keeneland sale-topper forged a neck clear, while Posse, finishing like a train, bore down on them both. Known Fact came back as a gallant runner-up, but some 42 minutes later he was declared the winner; reckless riding by Paquet more than two furlongs from home had almost brought Posse down, and in view of what that colt had achieved in the closing stages, the Stewards felt that the result was probably affected. Nureyev was placed last, and Known Fact was awarded a classic in which many believed he might have been only third-best.

It was to be some time before Known Fact was able to correct that impression. He picked up a bronchial infection after the Guineas and was out of action until late summer. When he reappeared at Deauville, still not fully wound up, he ran creditably to reach fifth place in the Prix Jacques le Marois. Then came three wins which reaffirmed his class and, ultimately, earned him a much more exalted reputation. In the Goodwood Mile the gap he required appeared late, but he used it the moment it was offered and just got up in time, and at Doncaster, in the Kiveton Park Stakes, his acceleration was again decisive. It was at Ascot, however, that he delivered his finest performance; the way he wore down Kris after a tumultuous tussle over the last furlong showed beyond doubt that he was a tip-top miler.

*Known Fact's finest hour as he comes to beat Kris (rails) in the Queen Elizabeth II Stakes at Ascot.*

Sadly, the rest was anti-climax. The plan to give him his first test over ten furlongs in the Champion Stakes came to nothing when he worked badly a few days before the race and was withdrawn. The idea that he would enliven 1981 competition also failed to materialize, as he finished tailed off in his only race, defied the vets to find what was wrong with him, and so disappointed his trainer in subsequent work that it seemed pointless to persevere.

Rumour has it that when Khalid Abdullah was asked whether he would syndicate Known Fact for stud duty, he replied, 'Why would I want to do that?' To the stock answer that the practice spread the risks of owning a valuable property which might depreciate he merely shrugged his shoulders. Abdullah did not need protection for his investment, and it scarcely seemed that Known Fact would want for the right kind of support from breeders. They were bound to welcome a top-class horse with a pedigree which offered something a little different –

no Northern Dancer, nor even a trace of Nearco.

Known Fact went to Juddmonte Farm in Berkshire, his fee fixed at £20,000. He did not lack good support, but he did lack the early success so vital for a stallion. Expected to sire tough, honest milers in his own image, he got stock who were neither tough, nor honest, nor yet milers. Many were unsound, often deficient in the knee area, and trainers soon began to fight shy of them. After three seasons at Juddmonte, the stallion was switched to Whitsbury Manor, where his fee was reduced to £15,000, then, for the 1987 season, to £7500. During that summer it was decided that Known Fact would be better employed in America, where his male antecedents had all thrived, and the announcement of his departure for the Kentucky branch of the Juddmonte enterprise was received with no real regret.

Almost immediately, it was evident that Known Fact's long-awaited star had arrived at last. His son

Warning, an Abdullah home-bred out of Oaks runner-up Slightly Dangerous, was the best two-year-old in Britain; what is more, others in that third crop rallied round in support to give Known Fact a total of 14 individual winners of 20 runners, and fifth place on the juvenile sires' list. Warning continued his good work, brilliantly as the outstanding English miler of 1988 and less consistently, though still in the top bracket, in 1989. In both seasons Known Fact figured among the top ten in the general sires' table,

with a profusion of winners, several of respectable class. For all that, Warning remained his only scorer in Pattern company until 1990, a desperately disappointing yield from an abundance of excellent opportunities.

Known Fact covered in Kentucky at a fee of $15,000 in 1990, as his last English-conceived crop took to the races. Meanwhile, Warning began his stud career at £15,000, covering at his owner's Newmarket stud, Banstead Manor.

## Racing record

| Year | Starts | Wins | 2nd | 3rd | 4th | £ |
|------|--------|------|-----|-----|-----|------|
| 1979 | 4 | 2 | 1 | 1 | - | 36,585 |
| 1980 | 6 | 4 | - | - | 1 | 97,310 |
| 1981 | 1 | - | - | - | 1 | 769 |
| | 11 | 6 | 1 | 1 | 2 | 134,664 |

## Principal wins

| | | |
|------|------|------|
| 1979 | Middle Park Stakes-Gr1 |
| 1980 | 2000 Guineas Stakes-Gr1 |
| | Goodwood Mile-Gr2 |
| | Queen Elizabeth II Stakes-Gr2 |

## Principal progeny

**1985**
b c WARNING (ex Slightly Dangerous, by Roberto)
| 1987 | Richmond Stakes-Gr2 |
| | Champagne Stakes-Gr2 |
| 1988 | Sussex Stakes-Gr1 |
| | Queen Elizabeth II Stakes-Gr1 |
| 1989 | Queen Anne Stakes-Gr2 |

**1986**
br c MARKOFDISTINCTION (ex Ghislaine, by Icecapade)
| 1990 | Trusthouse Forte Mile-Gr2 |

## KNOWN FACT (bay, 1977)

| | | | |
|---|---|---|---|
| In Reality (b 1964) | Intentionally | Intent | War Relic / Liz F. |
| | | My Recipe | Discovery / Perlette |
| | My Dear Girl | Rough'n Tumble | Free for All / Roused |
| | | Iltis | War Relic / We Hail |
| Tamerett (b/br 1962) | Tim Tam | Tom Fool | Menow / Gaga |
| | | Two Lea | Bull Lea / Two Bob |
| | Mixed Marriage | Tudor Minstrel | Owen Tudor / Sansonnet |
| | | Persian Maid | Tehran / Aroma |

b c TEAMSTER (ex Rosetta Stone, by Guillaume Tell)
| 1990 | Sagaro Stakes-Gr3 |
| | Henry II Stakes-Gr3 |

# Kris

IT seemed ironic, to say the least, that the stallion whose chief attraction was his 'working man's fee' should sire a champion miler out of a mare owned by one of the wealthiest men in the country. 'Money goes to money,' said one disgruntled breeder, in his cups. 'I sent my best mare to Sharpen Up and got something that was useless, and Lord Howard de Walden sent his worst and got Kris. What's the point in having cheap stallions if the richest people are going to use them and get the best of them? It seems my £500 isn't as good as Lord Howard's £500.'

The poor fellow did seem to have a point. After all, Howard de Walden did spend only £500 to breed Kris, did he not? Well, on reflection, £500-plus. He did first have the expense of buying Thornton Stud and the mares on it, which included Soft Angels. Then there was the cost of mating her a few times, having her produce trained, most particularly keeping her daughter Doubly Sure in training long enough – two seasons – to learn that she was no good. When 1975 came along, there were around 15 other mares to mate, most of them going to fashionable, expensive stallions, and at the bottom of the list there was Doubly Sure, whom he had kept only because (a) her dam seemed to have stopped breeding permanently, (b) one half-sister – a good runner – had died, and (c) another half-sister had broken her pelvis and might never be able to conceive. He must have been a wealthy man to have had £500 to spare after all that. The decision to spend it on a nomination to Sharpen Up (a young horse, yet to have a runner) was based on the idea that he was a fast horse and a very good-looking one who just might enable the gawky, angular, lop-eared and woefully slow Doubly Sure to produce something better than herself. Actually, and perhaps with the help of her breeding, he got something better than himself.

Kris did not race in the very best company as a two-year-old, when he was not so highly regarded as others in a strong Henry Cecil team, but he was undefeated in four starts and he showed abundant promise. He began with an easy win at Leicester over five furlongs and followed up with a victory at Folkestone over six, gained at the cost of some jarring on the firm ground. The enforced rest did him

good, and when he returned, for the Marston Moor Stakes at York, he beat better rivals in even more impressive style. That eight-length triumph justified a test in Pattern company, and that was duly passed in a game win over Hardgreen in the Group 3 Horris Hill Stakes at Newbury. The official handicapper rated him 9lb behind the best of his generation.

A year later Kris was the undisputed champion of Britain's milers after a campaign of seven wins (six in Pattern events) and a solitary loss. Unfortunately, the defeat came in the 2000 Guineas, but his half-length reverse against Tap on Wood was not an accurate measure of their respective merits. He beat Young Generation by three lengths in the Greenham Stakes at Newbury, trounced no-hopers in the Heron Stakes at Kempton, then emphatically confirmed his superiority over Young Generation in the St James's Palace Stakes at Royal Ascot. Clearly master of his own age group, Kris turned to dealing with his seniors. He was brilliant in the Sussex Stakes, slamming Swiss Maid by five lengths, more workmanlike in the Goodwood Mile over the same course a month later. In the Queen Elizabeth II Stakes he was totally dominant, winning in a style that evoked memories of Brigadier Gerard's great victories in the same Ascot race at the start of the decade. At Newmarket, where he signed off for the season in the Challenge Stakes, his rivals did not amount to much, so he raced the clock and beat that too.

Kris set two more course records in his third season, but it was a campaign which did not go according to plan. He was pushed to those fast times at both Haydock (over seven furlongs) and in Newbury's Lockinge Stakes (a mile), on the second occasion scoring by under a length after encountering traffic problems. Then came a serious setback in the form of a pulled muscle in his quarters, and the summer went by without him. It was September before he returned, as easy winner of a weakly-contested event at Goodwood, and in his final race he aimed to complete a double in the Queen Elizabeth II Stakes. When Joe Mercer drove him into a two-length lead on the turn for home all seemed well, but he could never quite extend his advantage to a point where Willie Carson, on the pursuing Known Fact, would abandon hope. The younger colt, winner

*Kris puts up a brilliant performance to win the Sussex Stakes at Goodwood by five lengths.*

of that season's 2000 Guineas, gradually wore Kris down and in the dying strides got up to win by a neck.

If that was not the perfect send-off, it was at least defeat with honour – and only the second defeat in 16 starts. Kris was surely the best English-trained miler since Brigadier Gerard, and if there could be a stallion prospect worth £100,000 a share, this was surely he. He went back home to Thornton, and five years later he was Yorkshire's first champion sire in more than 100 years.

Kris, whose initial fee was £24,000, had more than his form to recommend him to breeders. He had developed into quite a taking individual, if not perfect about the legs, certainly impressive behind the saddle and with superb balance, a feature which gave reason to hope that he might suit mares of any physical type. When the first foals appeared, it was evident that many, like their sire, were light of bone and unsightly about the hocks. There were also some dubious-looking forelegs. The big plus was that none of them was heavy-topped; chances were they would be sound enough, if they were good enough.

We did not have to wait long to establish that they were good enough. Kris was not champion first season sire, but he was a close runner-up to Niniski and he did have a couple of two-year-olds, in Reach and Oh So Sharp, who were officially rated within 7lb of the best of their generation in Europe. Reach

proved a disappointment at three, but he was one of the few in that category, and Kris's achievement in becoming champion sire with no runners older than three was all the more impressive for the fact that fillies outnumbered colts by a ratio of two to one in his first crop. Oh So Sharp was the star, the first filly Triple Crown heroine in 30 years, particularly brilliant in the Oaks, when she ran right away from Triptych. Like a lot of his daughters she had a lean and hungry look in training, but subsequently developed into a lovely broodmare.

The first top-class colts appeared in the second crop, both Flash of Steel and Sure Blade excelling as milers before retiring to studs in Ireland. Although they were two who shared their sire's predilection for that distance, they were not typical; some of Kris's best progeny are quite happy to go a mile and a half, while many of the least distinguished positively need it. After his season at the head of the table, Kris had four years at a fee of £100,000 before dropping back to £80,000 in 1990. If he can be criticized on his performance to date, it might be said that better was expected of the 1986 crop, many of whom were out of outstanding mares. Just as remarkably, however, he got 11 individual two-year-old winners from the crop of 1987, his most precocious group to date, from matings which seemed to presage better second-season performance.

Kris is currently the best sire in England, in spite

## Racing record

| Year | Starts | Wins | 2nd | 3rd | 4th | £ |
|------|--------|------|-----|-----|-----|------|
| 1978 | 4 | 4 | - | - | - | 21,202 |
| 1979 | 8 | 7 | 1 | - | - | 131,023 |
| 1980 | 4 | 3 | 1 | - | - | 43,446 |
| | 16 | 14 | 2 | - | - | 195,671 |

## Principal wins

| | | |
|-----|-----|-----|
| 1978 | Horris Hill Stakes-Gr3 | |
| 1979 | Greenham Stakes-Gr3 | |
| | St James's Palace Stakes-Gr2 | |
| | Sussex Stakes-Gr1 | |
| | Goodwood Mile-Gr2 | |
| | Queen Elizabeth II Stakes-Gr2 | |
| | Challenge Stakes-Gr3 | |
| 1980 | Lockinge Stakes-Gr2 | |

## Principal progeny

**1982**

ch f FITNAH (ex Greenland Park, by Red God)
- 1985 Prix Vanteaux-Gr3
- Prix de Saint-Alary-Gr1
- Prix de la Nonette-Gr3
- 1986 Prix du Prince d'Orange-Gr3

b f KOZANA (ex Koblenza, by Hugh Lupus)
- 1985 Prix de Sandringham-Gr3
- Prix de Malleret-Gr2

ch f OH SO SHARP (ex Oh So Fair, by Graustark)
- 1984 Fillies' Mile-Gr3
- 1985 Nell Gwyn Stakes-Gr3
- 1000 Guineas Stakes-Gr1
- Oaks Stakes-Gr1
- St Leger Stakes-Gr1

b c REACH (ex Gift Wrapped, by Wolver Hollow)
- 1984 Royal Lodge Stakes-Gr2

**1983**

b f DUSTY DOLLAR (ex Sauceboat, by Connaught)
- 1986 Sun Chariot Stakes-Gr2

b c FLASH OF STEEL (ex Spark of Fire, by Run the Gantlet)
- 1985 Beresford Stakes-Gr2
- 1986 Tetrarch Stakes-Gr3
- Irish 2000 Guineas-Gr1

b g PUTTING (ex Popaway, by Run the Gantlet)
- 1990 San Marcos Handicap-Gr3

b c SURE BLADE (ex Double Lock, by Home Guard)
- 1985 Coventry Stakes-Gr3
- Champagne Stakes-Gr2
- 1986 St James's Palace Stakes-Gr2
- Queen Elizabeth II Stakes-Gr2

## KRIS (chesnut, 1976)

| | | | |
|---|---|---|---|
| Sharpen Up (ch 1969) | Atan | Native Dancer | Polynesian Geisha |
| | | Mixed Marriage | Tudor Minstrel Persian Maid |
| | Rocchetta | Rockefella | Hyperion Rockfel |
| | | Chambiges | Majano Chanterelle |
| Doubly Sure (b 1971) | Reliance | Tantieme | Deux pour Cent Terka |
| | | Relance | Relic Polaire |
| | Soft Angels | Crepello | Donatello Crepuscule |
| | | Sweet Angel | Honeyway No Angel |

**1984**

b c MR PINTIPS (ex Bempton, by Blakeney)
- 1988 Ormonde Stakes-Gr3

ch f SWEPT AWAY (ex Costly Wave, by Caro)
- 1987 Prix Chloe-Gr3

ch c THE SCOUT (ex Tropicaro, by Caro)
- 1987 Prix La Force-Gr3

ch f UNITE (ex Pro Patria, by Petingo)
- 1987 Oaks Stakes-Gr1
- Irish Oaks-Gr1

**1985**

b c COMMON GROUNDS (ex Sweetly, by Lyphard)
- 1987 Prix de la Salamandre-Gr1

b c KRIS KRINGLE (ex Border Dawn, by Pitcairn)
- 1988 Irish Derby Trial Stakes-Gr2
- Blandford Stakes-Gr2

b f SUDDEN LOVE (ex Sudden Glory, by Luthier)
- 1988 E.P. Taylor Stakes-Gr1

**1986**

b c SHINING STEEL (ex Lady Moon, by Mill Reef)
- 1989 Diomed Stakes-Gr3
- 1990 Shoemaker Handicap-Gr2

**1987**

b f MOON CACTUS (ex Lady Moon, by Mill Reef)
- 1989 Prestige Stakes-Gr3

b f RAFHA (ex Eljazzi, by Artaius)
- 1989 May Hill Stakes-Gr3
- 1990 Prix de Diane-Gr1

---

of his modest 25th place on the 1989 list. He has inevitably become primarily an owner-breeder's horse and has been extensively patronized by Sheikh Mohammed – understandably in view of Oh So Sharp, Sure Blade and Unite. His record can hardly fail to improve over the next few years with the kind of support he is getting, a measure of which stems from the respect earned by his younger brother Diesis, who has already achieved success on both sides of the Atlantic from his base in Kentucky. Like Kris, he got an Oaks winner – Diminuendo – at the earliest opportunity.

# Last Tycoon

WHEN Last Tycoon went to stud in 1987 he was advertised as 'the most versatile horse in the world'. He was, of course, nothing of the sort, and just so long as Red Rum was alive there would always be one Thoroughbred all too obviously better suited to that description. Last Tycoon did not win at five furlongs and at four and a half miles over 30 obstacles; his versatility, if such it could be called, encompassed a range of only three furlongs.

Still, there was nothing very new about a stallion owner making extravagant claims about his horse, even couched in such 'Barnum and Bailey' style terms. That has been going on since the eighteenth century. The bloodstock industry is well accustomed to hype, and that is why the Advertising Standards Authority has never yet been asked to deal with a complaint over the publicity material for a stallion. Anyway, in the case of Last Tycoon, most people probably accepted the claim made about him.

What Last Tycoon did was certainly unusual. As a three-year-old he won the King's Stand Stakes (by a short-head from the five-year-old Double Schwartz) and the York Sprint Championship (by three-quarters of a length from the same horse), both Group 1 races

*Last Tycoon (nearside) outguns Double Schwartz to win the King's Stand Stakes at Royal Ascot.*

over five furlongs, then went to America to win the Grade 1 Breeders' Cup Mile (by a head from the five-year-old Palace Music) at Santa Anita. In the general run of things, horses do not do that; as much to the point, they are not required to do that. In Europe horses tend to specialize, and if they prove themselves to be tip-top performers over one distance, they are rarely called upon to try something different. The most obvious exceptions to the rule are the few three-year-olds who progress through the classic series; they generally hail from a middle-distance pedigree background.

A different situation obtains in America, where nobody has ever attempted to breed specialist sprinters, middle-distance horses or stayers. The racing programme provides most opportunities in the six- to nine-furlong range, most horses keep within those parameters, and plenty are equally proficient at either end. The longer-distance races are not contested by specially constructed stayers; they are for those horses off the normal production line who happen to prove adaptable to the purpose. In his last three races of 1974, Forego won the Woodward Stakes at 12 furlongs, the Vosburgh Handicap at seven furlongs, and the Jockey Club Gold Cup at two miles. He was the best horse in the nation at all three distances – and all those in between – and a much more versatile horse than Last Tycoon.

One crucial effect of the 'American invasion' of European racing was that Europe rapidly lost its traditional ability to breed stock for specific distances. Breeders here had already given up trying to produce real stayers, which was no longer an economically viable proposition. Now there always seemed to be American-breds capable of beating our best middle-distance horses, so perseverance with the old pattern in that area was futile. As for the sprinters, well, the reliable old lines which had served so well for decades had apparently been losing their potency anyway. The upshot was that Europe threw in its lot with American breeding completely; after a century of fixing types and learning how to reproduce aptitudes, we suddenly discovered that we had no system at all. We were using horses who had found a niche at a certain distance, by accident rather than design, and we learned that they could not be depended upon to get stock with the same attributes and aptitudes. It was much like the revolution in soccer, when the old pattern of five forwards and five defenders who all knew their place and function was abandoned in favour of the theory of ten 'complete players' who ran all over the park and turned a basically simple game into something needlessly complicated. By rushing to emulate the Americans, we made breeding more difficult for ourselves.

It has now become virtually impossible to predict the staying power of any horse with American elements in its pedigree. Last Tycoon might have been anything. His sire Try My Best was untried beyond a mile (at which distance he finished tailed off last in the 2000 Guineas), but was a brother to El Gran Senor, one of those 'complete players' who – like Dancing Brave – was basically a speed horse, yet was mightily effective in other roles. Mill Princess, who produced Last Tycoon as her second (but first surviving) foal, won at ten furlongs, and on her breeding seemed slight odds-on to prove a factor for stamina rather than speed.

In recent years there have been many instances of top-class horses reverting from a mile to six furlongs, the most notable being Thatch, Chief Singer and Soviet Star; Ajdal came back to five furlongs. None was bred to be a specialist miler, but all had speed and could use it to equal effect over shorter distances because there were now no specialist sprinters to beat them. Last Tycoon came into the same category as those horses, the only difference being that he had been restricted to sprints throughout his career (bar one losing effort at seven furlongs on heavy ground) and had been pigeon-holed as a sprinter before his trip to Santa Anita. His astute trainer, Robert Collet, seems to have been the only person who recognized that fact, and others ought to have realized that he would not have taken the colt all the way from Chantilly to California just to prove to himself that he did not stay a mile.

Last Tycoon was not versatile. He showed himself to be a typical Thoroughbred of the 'post-American' era in Europe, very much an American type of horse. He was also clearly very talented, but the range of his gifts was more notable for its limitations than for its extent. His contemporary Dancing Brave would undoubtedly have outpaced him over any distance from half a mile to a mile and a half.

Collet did a tremendous job with Last Tycoon, a bad-legged, lightly made colt with neurotic

## LAST TYCOON (bay, 1983)

| | | | |
|---|---|---|---|
| Try My Best (b 1975) | Northern Dancer | Nearctic | Nearco / Lady Angela |
| | | Natalma | Native Dancer / Almahmoud |
| | Sex Appeal | Buckpasser | Tom Fool / Busanda |
| | | Best in Show | Traffic Judge / Stolen Hour |
| Mill Princess (b 1977) | Mill Reef | Never Bend | Nasrullah / Lalun |
| | | Milan Mill | Princequillo / Virginia Water |
| | Irish Lass | Sayajirao | Nearco / Rosy Legend |
| | | Scollata | Niccolo Dell' Arca / Cutaway |

### Racing record

| Year | Starts | Wins | 2nd | 3rd | 4th | FR |
|---|---|---|---|---|---|---|
| 1985 | 6 | 3 | - | - | - | 342,350 |
| 1986 | 7 | 5 | - | - | 1 | 4,886,640 |
| | 13 | 8 | - | - | 1 | 5,228,990 |

### Principal wins

| | | |
|---|---|---|
| 1985 | Prix d'Arenberg-Gr3 |
| 1986 | Prix de Saint-Georges-Gr3 |
| | Prix du Gros Chene-Gr3 |
| | King's Stand Stakes-Gr1 |
| | York Sprint Championship Stakes-Gr1 |

tendencies. On his return from America he was sent directly to Ireland, where he covered 56 mares at a fee of IR35,000gns before being despatched for a second 1987 season in Australia. Coolmore reduced his fee to IR25,000gns in 1989, but for some reason it advanced again to IR30,000gns for 1990. There was profit for breeders in only about half of his first crop of auctioned yearlings, but among them were several real stars. Many regarded his 370,000gns colt out of Flame of Tara as the best yearling seen in 1989. The consensus view of his stock as a whole was that there might be soundness problems, but that those who stayed sound could be very good indeed. Whether or not they have an optimum distance we shall discover in 1991.

# Law Society

IN their heyday at the Keeneland Sales, Robert Sangster and partners rarely invested at the top of the market in colts other than those by either Northern Dancer or one of his sons. In 1983 they broadened their horizons for once. True, they were – luckily – underbidders on the $10.2 million disaster Snaafi Dancer (who never ran) and they did waste $4.25 million on Foxboro (last in his only race), who were both by Northern Dancer. However, they did venture boldly into less familiar territory, giving $1.65 million for Gold Meridian (by Seattle Slew), the amazing sum of $2.6 million for Side Chapel (by Raja Baba, a sire with a bad record in Europe), and $2.7 million for Law Society (by Alleged). Gold Meridian was at least useful, winning three of his six races and finishing second at Group 3 level; Side Chapel proved pathetic, picking up his only win when opposed by three worse maidens at Phoenix Park; Law Society won the Irish Derby, and by the end of his third season at Coolmore, the breeders who had used his services had effectively paid for him and the two failures as well.

Law Society, bred by Will Farish and William Kilroy, was a grand individual as a yearling, with more quality than most of his sire's stock. Even Khalid Abdullah, who had an aversion to outlandish prices, allowed himself to be persuaded (by James Delahooke) that here was one to whom normal limits should not apply, and it was his bid of $2.6 million which proved second-best. The colt flew off to Ballydoyle, to be trained in the environment where his sire had flourished five and six years ago, and Vincent O'Brien did not take long to learn that he had ability. The hope had been that, as his dam Bold Bikini had previously produced a high-class American two-year-old (Strike Your Colors) from a mating with Alleged's sire Hoist the Flag, Law Society might prove more precocious than Alleged had been; such was indeed the case.

O'Brien had Law Society out in mid-August, already forward enough to win an 11-runner maiden in promising style. A fortnight later the colt was a Pattern winner, comfortably disposing of Kamakura in the Anglesey Stakes on The Curragh. When he followed up two weeks after that with a smooth win over Concert Hall in the National Stakes at the same course, he was most people's idea of the best two-year-old in Ireland. He had only one more run that season, and in that he established that he was probably as good as anything in England too. He did not win the Dewhurst Stakes, but he probably would have done if he had managed to keep a straight course; under the severest pressure he had ever felt, and in close combat with two worthy foes, he hung right, left, then right again, ultimately yielding victory to Kala Dancer by a head. The two-year-old championship of Europe went with that photo-finish verdict.

Law Society was only briefly active in his second season, taking in four races between early May and late July, all of them over a mile and a half. He was slow to come to hand in the spring, and O'Brien wisely would not rush him. He sent him first to Chester, where he won the Vase and attracted less attention than was his due because his chief rival, Miller's Mate, fractured a cannon bone early in the straight. Law Society had been going to beat him anyway. The Derby was different; there was never a moment when he was going to beat Slip Anchor, who led every step of the way, but his second place was worthy enough, for all that he was defeated by seven lengths. He did beat the rest by six lengths and more.

Slip Anchor was not in the field for the Irish Derby, and Law Society duly made the most of it – albeit in a manner not quite according to plan. The firm ground at The Curragh brought out some eccentric behaviour in several of the runners. Law Society's pacemaker, Outrider, failed to take the lead until about the time he was supposed to drop back; Mouktar, winner of the Prix du Jockey-Club and a warm second favourite, unexpectedly charged off in front; horses were drifting around, getting in each other's way, for most of the race. Law Society met some traffic trouble en route and veered right himself over a furlong out, but, hard driven by Pat Eddery, he got up to beat Theatrical by half a length. His quickening powers were well in evidence that day, but they were missing at Ascot in the King George VI & Queen Elizabeth Stakes. The competition was stronger, and in a fast-run race on firm ground he was simply run off his legs; he finished fourth behind

*Law Society is driven out to defeat Theatrical in the Irish Sweeps Derby at The Curragh.*

Petoski, Oh So Sharp and Rainbow Quest.

A plan to run Law Society in the Phoenix Champion Stakes had to be abandoned after an injury to his off-fore in a gallop at Ballydoyle, and news of his retirement was not long delayed. It was a sad end to the career of one who had always impressed for his robust, healthy appearance. He had undoubtedly been a good racehorse, and would have seemed a good Derby winner if Slip Anchor had stayed in his box that day. He clearly did not have his sire's capacity to lie up with – or set – the pace in a strongly run mile-and-a-half race; nor did he boast such remarkable acceleration. Nevertheless, he was one of the same type, and the best son of Alleged seen to date.

The respect Law Society commanded was best exemplified by the support he received in his first season from those closely identified with Ballydoyle and Coolmore. There was clearly a belief – which Sangster and O'Brien shared with many others – that here was the top-class outcross needed for their abundance of Northern Dancer-line mares who were proving difficult to mate. Unfortunately, and in common with virtually all Coolmore stallions, he was priced and was allocated his quota of mares with the objective of balancing his stud's books, rather than with a view to giving him the best opportunity to make his name as a sire. He covered 68 mares in his first season, and his fee was IR60,000gns. There were 53 foals; 35 of them went to auction as yearlings, and 28 fetched less than the fee – among them fillies out of sale-topping mares Dunette and Tenea, and a colt who was a half-brother to Shirley Heights. The story was much the same in the second year, when his fee was reduced to IR40,000gns – 66 mares covered, 52 foals, 36 auction yearlings, 20 of them sold at a loss.

Law Society's fee was cut every year down to 1990, when it stood at IR20,000gns, one-third of what it had been at the outset. His story provides an excellent example of the madness in the modern era, illustrating stallion management designed to satisfy bankers, not breeders. The latter are too short-sighted to see that the policy works against their interests; they have lost money on the horse – and interest in him – by the time he descends to a sensible fee, and the industry complains about another stallion who has not come up to expectations. In a lot of cases, if old-style management techniques had been in force, those expectations would have been realized.

In 1990 Law Society was fighting for his credibility in the market-place when he should have been consolidating a useful start with his first crop of two-year-olds. He had a Pattern winner in Endless Joy (bred by Vincent O'Brien), and several others ran with promise. Had his initial fee been what it should have been, the industry would have been talking him up on the basis of those results, instead of wondering whether he could survive commercially.

## Racing record

| Year | Starts | Wins | 2nd | 3rd | 4th | £ |
|------|--------|------|-----|-----|-----|------|
| 1984 | 4 | 3 | 1 | - | - | 57,135 |
| 1985 | 4 | 2 | 1 | - | 1 | 253,172 |
| | 8 | 5 | 2 | - | 1 | 310,307 |

## Principal wins

| 1984 | Anglesey Stakes-Gr3 |
|------|---------------------|
| | National Stakes-Gr2 |
| 1985 | Chester Vase-Gr3 |
| | Irish Derby-Gr1 |

## Principal progeny

**1987**

b f ENDLESS JOY (ex La Joyeuse, by Northern Dancer)
   1989   Killavullen Stakes-Gr3

## LAW SOCIETY    (bay, 1982)

| | | | |
|---|---|---|---|
| Alleged (b 1974) | Hoist the Flag | Tom Rolfe | Ribot |
| | | | Pocahontas |
| | | Wavy Navy | War Admiral |
| | | | Triomphe |
| | Princess Pout | Prince John | Princequillo |
| | | | Not Afraid |
| | | Determined Lady | Determine |
| | | | Tumbling |
| Bold Bikini (b 1969) | Boldnesian | Bold Ruler | Nasrullah |
| | | | Miss Disco |
| | | Alanesian | Polynesian |
| | | | Alablue |
| | Ran-Tan | Summer Tan | Heliopolis |
| | | | Miss Zibby |
| | | Mehrabi | Migoli |
| | | | Majideh |

# Lomond

WHEN the Ballydoyle stable thrived famously – between the mid-1970s and the mid-1980s – there were three key figures with clearly defined roles in the operation. Robert Sangster was the fellow with the flair and enterprise, the ideal front man for the empire. John Magnier supplied the calculating business brain, perhaps the sharpest in the industry. To Vincent O'Brien fell the task of ensuring that the other two had something worthwhile on which to exercise their talents. He was the one with the responsibility for selecting the raw material, identifying the young stock which he felt he could develop into champions, and the one entrusted with the completion of the job. Moreover, he was not the others' employee, but a full partner, with the same financial commitment as them in all the horses he chose and trained.

At different times there were others involved, most notably the Greek shipping tycoon Stavros Niarchos, with whom links were forged largely on account of their frequently acting against each other's interests in the yearling market. That relationship ended, according to Niarchos, because decisions were being taken by the 'great triumvirate' without proper consultation, but he was a man used to doing his own thing in business, never really suited to a partnership operation, particularly one in which his partners contributed virtually 100 per cent of the expertise. The subsequent launch of Classic Thoroughbreds, the public company which came to own all the Ballydoyle horses, effectively made the Sangster-Magnier-O'Brien expertise available to a much wider group of individuals; it reaffirmed the trio's established roles, and they became the largest shareholders in an enterprise which – predictably – has found it hard to overcome the loss of market dominance and the power to buy the young stock it wants.

Nevertheless, the Ballydoyle triumvirate enjoyed many great triumphs, succeeding because each fulfilled his own role superbly and let the others get on with theirs. The one notable exception to the rule concerned Lomond. Demarcation lines were crossed in his case, yet to the ultimate benefit of all three. In 1980 Sangster and Magnier attended the November Sales at Keeneland, while O'Brien remained at

home. Sangster was probably going to buy some mares on his own account, and there was a chance that the partners would also invest in the mare market. What O'Brien did not expect, and was alarmed to receive, was a phone call from Magnier to the effect that Sangster had undertaken, on behalf of the trio, to buy a foal he had seen in a private deal for $1.5 million. At first the trainer simply did not want to know; so far as he was concerned, Sangster could do what he liked with his own money, but it was not his place to buy a foal for the partnership, even if it was by Northern Dancer out of the dam of Seattle Slew. Sangster might be able to read a pedigree, up to a point, but he would not know a good foal if he saw one, less still one which might have faults that even O'Brien's special skills could not correct. Calls went back and forth across the Atlantic, with O'Brien seeking all manner of assurances about the colt's conformation, development, bearing, action, temperament and every other factor that he would have taken into account in an on-the-spot inspection. Only when Sangster and Magnier had begun to think that the whole exercise had been more bother than it was worth did O'Brien give his all-clear to proceed with the deal.

Lomond did not prove himself a great racehorse, losing more races than he won. However, he did win a classic, and he provided Robert Sangster with a deal of amusement over the time when he had exceeded his brief – and had done so to the profit of all concerned. The colt, a much smaller, neater specimen than his illustrious half-brother, had only two outings as a two-year-old. He ran first in a 21-runner maiden at The Curragh, was obviously expected to win, and duly did so by six lengths. Victory was again taken for granted in the National Stakes over the same course a month later, but this time his effort petered out and he was beaten into third place behind his stable companion Glenstal. The form was unbelievable in view of what Lomond had been doing at home, and a reason was soon found; he was suffering from a throat infection.

According to the official Irish handicapper, there were six two-year-olds better than Lomond in his own stable, headed by Danzatore and Caerleon. It seemed that Danzatore would be the chief Ballydoyle hope for the 2000 Guineas, that Caerleon would go for the Derby, and that Lomond – along with the others – would find a suitable niche somewhere along the way. O'Brien was clearly unsure about what Lomond would become, and before the season began he entered him in the King's Stand Stakes, England's number one five-furlong sprint race. With many options still open to him, Lomond began as a three-year-old in the Gladness Stakes at The Curragh, and he beat second-class older horses comfortably. He was supposed to reappear in the Group 3 Tetrarch Stakes two weeks later, but in the interim there were other developments. Danzatore, the Guineas favourite, worked badly – so badly that he had apparently completely lost his form. There was no point in running him at Newmarket, and if Ballydoyle was to be represented, the obvious candidate now was Lomond. The change of plan was confirmed only a week before the classic, but the public's respect for the O'Brien stable resulted in the colt's becoming a well-supported market fancy.

Lomond won the Guineas with remarkable ease. Beautifully ridden by Pat Eddery, he progressed smoothly to take the lead from Gorytus inside the final furlong, then was driven along for a two-length victory over the late-challenging Tolomeo. His dominance that day could hardly have been more emphatic, but he was never to look so good again. In the Irish 2000 he met some trouble in running, but

was out of it well in time to beat Wassl if he had been good enough; he was not. He took his chance in the Derby, and whether or not he stayed the distance seemed irrelevant, as he was never a factor at any stage and had only five behind him at the finish. He was then brought back to a mile for the Sussex Stakes and was equipped with blinkers, but he made no show there either; to all intents and purposes he had emulated Danzatore, losing interest in racing. The decision to retire him was inevitable.

The story of Lomond at stud is the familiar Coolmore one of excessive fees and excessive books, with the attendant risks of over-supply in the market and swift breeder disillusionment. He spent his first three seasons at IR65,000gns, covering more than 190 mares in that period. Of the 143 foals they produced, 102 were sold as yearlings, 53 of them for less than the fee. After his fourth season at IR60,000gns there were three individual Pattern winners among the first crop of two-year-olds, which caused his fee to be raised to IR100,000gns for the 1988 season and ensured that owner-breeders formed a higher proportion of his patrons. Only two years on, his official price was IR30,000gns but nominations could be had for as little as IR25,000gns, with a live foal concession thrown in.

Lomond got the remarkable total of six individual Pattern winners from his first crop, five of them fillies. The only colt was the ill-fated Kneller, who

*Lomond, an emphatic winner of the 2000 Guineas but never to look so good thereafter.*

## Racing record

| Year | Starts | Wins | 2nd | 3rd | 4th | £ |
|------|--------|------|-----|-----|-----|-----|
| 1982 | 2 | 1 | - | 1 | - | 3,620 |
| 1983 | 5 | 2 | 1 | - | - | 95,562 |
| | 7 | 3 | 1 | 1 | - | 99,182 |

## Principal win

1983   2000 Guineas Stakes-Gr1

## Principal progeny

### 1985

b f ASHAYER (ex Good Lassie, by Moulton)
1987   Prix Marcel Boussac-Gr1
1988   Prix de Psyche-Gr3
b f DARK LOMOND (ex Arkadina, by Ribot)
1988   Pretty Polly Stakes-Gr2
Irish St Leger-Gr1
b f FLUTTER AWAY (ex Flying Bid, by Auction Ring)
1987   Railway Stakes-Gr3
Moyglare Stud Stakes-Gr1
b f INCHMURRIN (ex On Show, by Welsh Pageant)
1988   Child Stakes-Gr2
ch c KNELLER (ex Fruition, by Rheingold)
1988   Doncaster Cup-Gr3
Jockey Club Cup-Gr3
b f LOMOND BLOSSOM (ex December Blossom, by Condorcet)
1987   Killavullen Stakes-Gr3

### 1986

b c CITIDANCER (ex Mrs McArdy, by Tribal Chief)
1989   Ballymacoy Stakes-Gr3

## LOMOND (bay, 1980)

| | | | Nearco | Pharos |
|---|---|---|---|---|
| | | Nearctic | | Nogara |
| | | | Lady Angela | Hyperion |
| Northern Dancer | | | | Sister Sarah |
| (b 1961) | | | Native Dancer | Polynesian |
| | Natalma | | | Geisha |
| | | | Almahmoud | Mahmoud |
| | | | | Arbitrator |
| | | | Round Table | Princequillo |
| | | Poker | | Knight's Daughter |
| | | | Glamour | Nasrullah |
| My Charmer | | | | Striking |
| (b 1969) | | | Jet Action | Jet Pilot |
| | | | | Busher |
| | Fair Charmer | | | Alsab |
| | | | Myrtle Charm | Crepe Myrtle |

b c GREAT LAKES (ex Costly Wave, by Caro)
1990   Gladness Stakes-Gr3
b f OCZY CZARNIE (ex Gracious Lassie, by Kalamoun)
1988   Prix du Calvados-Gr3
Prix de la Salamandre-Gr1
1989   Pucker Up Stakes-Gr3

### 1987

ch c DUCK AND DIVE (ex Avec l'Amour, by Realm)
1990   Greenlands Stakes-Gr3

promised to become the outstanding stayer of his crop, but had to be put down late in his second season because of a rupture of the caecum. Most of the Lomond colts have proved disappointing and the sire has undoubtedly been responsible for spreading unsoundness, often in the joints and feet. There has also been a suspicion that trainers have judged them badly, getting at them early instead of giving them time, and failing to allow them opportunities over longer distances. It already seems certain, though, that Lomond is not going to attain the status of a major Northern Dancer stallion.

# Lord Gayle

THE careers of Lord Gayle, as racehorse and as sire, might well be cited as illustrations of the rewards to be gained from the virtues of patience and perseverance. He had to cross the Atlantic three times and then leave his adopted country in order to register an important victory on the racecourse. As a stallion he had to battle against the odds, as all cheap stallions do, and after he had earned his retirement, a colt from his fourteenth crop penned the perfect postscript with a win in the richest race in Europe.

Lord Gayle was bred by Taylor Hardin, a Virginia-based Anglophile who loved to visit the December Sales in Newmarket and to take home a choice filly or broodmare if he could. With an almighty dollar to aid his cause, he generally succeeded. In 1958 he took home the highest-priced filly of the week, a three-year-old called Sticky Case who had won six races, had been beaten a head in the important Falmouth Stakes, and, for good measure, had an excellent pedigree; her sire and maternal grandsire had been stud champions, and her dam was a half-sister to Honeyway, another sire of note.

Hardin soon found himself in profit over the deal; he sent Sticky Case in her first season to the great Native Dancer, and he sold the offspring, a filly, to Eddie Taylor for $60,000. Two years later he had another good yearling out of the mare, this time a colt; he came from the first full crop of the fast horse Sir Gaylord, and he, too, went to the Saratoga Sales. His buyer there was Newmarket trainer Fred (Sam) Armstrong, who made his successful $40,000 bid on behalf of Reginald Webster, an owner with the rare distinction of having had classic winners to his credit on both sides of the Atlantic. Martial had won him the 2000 Guineas in 1960, and a couple of months before his purchase of Lord Gayle, Amberoid had landed the Belmont Stakes for him. What this newly elected member of the New York Jockey Club had never had was a horse who carried his colours to victories in three different countries. That was to come.

Lord Gayle was the most expensive of six yearlings bought by Armstrong at Saratoga that year, and when they arrived at Newmarket – less than a fortnight after the sale – he looked the pick of the bunch, a well-grown colt of abundant quality. Looks were one thing; getting the locomotive parts to function was quite another matter. Armstrong had niggling little problems with him throughout his two-year-old season, eventually deciding to leave him alone while he concentrated on training Petingo, that year's top English-based juvenile. In the following spring Webster decided he might just as well have the colt back home, and away he went, apparently growing out of his problems as the year went on. By August Lord Gayle was not just running, but winning, twice over seven furlongs at the Saratoga meeting held in conjunction with the sales. As Webster had bought a couple of yearlings there, destined for Armstrong's stable, it now seemed to make sense to send Lord Gayle back with them. Sir Gaylord's stock were suited to Europe, if Sir Ivor was anything to go by, and Armstrong (father-in-law of Sir Ivor's jockey, Lester Piggott) was naturally delighted to have a second opportunity with the colt.

As luck would have it, no sooner had Lord Gayle returned to Newmarket – in September 1968 – than he became unsound again. It was tendon trouble, and it was serious – serious enough to ensure that his English debut would be delayed until 1970. By that time Sir Gaylord had had a second star European performer in Habitat, and there was intense frustration at St Gatien Stables over the enforced inactivity of one who had always promised so much. The long wait proved well worthwhile. Lord Gayle had a tremendous season as a five-year-old, racing nine times and collecting six victories; furthermore his campaign extended from the first day of the season to the last, and he won at both ends. He bowed out as sound as a bell.

He began by beating the useful Chebs Lad over seven furlongs at Doncaster, ran unplaced (for the only time in his career) over the inadequate distance of six furlongs at Nottingham, then carried top weight to victory in a handicap at Teesside Park, again over seven. Only third in the Magnet Cup over an extended ten furlongs, he dropped back to a mile for wins in two of the best-contested handicaps in the North. He equalled the Redcar course record in the William Hill Gold Cup, and in the Ripon Rowels he had top weight of 9st 10lb. A trip to France for the Prix La Rochette yielded a third place behind the top-

*Lord Gayle at the Irish National Stud where he was always popular with breeders.*

class performer Dictus, and he underlined his progress with a smooth win, after making all the running, in the Mitre Stakes at Ascot. That game effort proved Lord Gayle's ability to stay ten furlongs, but for his final race Armstrong brought him back to a mile and sent him out against the best competition he had ever encountered in the Prix Perth at Saint-Cloud. Regular rider Lester Piggott cried off the trip, imagining he was going to win the Haydock Sprint Cup on Balidar that day; he was wrong, and Bill Williamson was right to accept the invitation to deputize. The Australian obtained a ready response when he asked him to quicken a quarter of a mile from home, and Lord Gayle won with total authority by two lengths.

A well-made horse, fashionably bred and not far removed from the top class, Lord Gayle was the type to appeal to Irish breeders when he stood his first season in 1971 at £850 on 'no foal, no fee' terms. When his first yearlings averaged around nine times his fee, he understandably became more popular still. Nine individual winners from 20 runners was also not bad for the first season's representation of a horse who himself had not appeared as a two-year-old. What he lacked for a while was a high-class performer, and by the time he had his first Pattern winner – Yankee Gold in the Ballymoss Stakes – his fertility had dipped from satisfactory to well below par. Nevertheless, he was getting results, and the sensible switch to live-foal terms meant that breeders did not lose interest in him.

Over the first few years Lord Gayle earned respect with a fair quota of winners, but there seemed to be nothing of genuine top class unless it was his fourth-crop daughter Blondy, an exceptional filly in Venezuela, whatever that might signify. Most of his stock seemed to want at least a mile, and few excelled as juveniles. Then along came Blue Wind to change a few perceptions. A IR5,600gns yearling, she became a IR180,000gns two-year-old, having in the meantime won the Group 3 Silken Glider Stakes. At three she ran away with the Oaks, added the Irish Oaks, and suddenly Lord Gayle had moved out of the run-of-the-mill category where many had placed him.

Low fertility figures were always a hindrance, and it was never going to be his destiny to sire a profusion of big winners, but his stock gained in demand and the occasional high-class performer was his best advertisement. Perversely, he got a lot of pretty fillies who turned out to be moderate, and his uglier representatives seemed to be the best runners. He continued to cover at the Irish National Stud until 1987, but then, from a reduced book of only eight mares, he got just three in foal. In retirement he achieved his best results at home and abroad in 1989, when Carroll House won the Arc de Triomphe and Executive Perk was one of the best of his crop in Ireland.

Always intelligently managed, Lord Gayle was a grand servant to both his stud and his adopted nation's breeders; he did a lot of people a good turn in his time.

## Racing record

| Year | Starts | Wins | 2nd | 3rd | 4th | £ |
|------|--------|------|-----|-----|-----|------|
| 1967 | 0 | | | | | |
| 1968 | 4 | 2 | - | 2 | - | 4,052 |
| 1969 | 0 | | | | | |
| 1970 | 9 | 6 | - | 2 | - | 19,430 |
| | 13 | 8 | - | 4 | - | 23,482 |

## Principal win

1970   Prix Perth

## Principal progeny

**1972**
gr c YANKEE GOLD (ex Ceol an Oir, by Vimy)
    1976   Ballymoss Stakes-Gr2
        Royal Whip Stakes-Gr3
    1977   Ballymoss Stakes-Gr2

**1973**
b f LADY SINGER (ex Ceol an Oir, by Vimy)
    1976   Pretty Polly Stakes-Gr2

**1974**
br c ARISTOCRACY (ex Roxboro, by Sheshoon)
    1977   Whitehall Stakes-Gr3
b c LORDEDAW (ex Umgeni Poort, by Botticelli)
    1977   Tetrarch Stakes-Gr3

**1975**
br c STRONG GALE (ex Sterntau, by Tamerlane)
    1981   Grosser Preis von Dortmund-Gr3

**1978**
ch f BLUE WIND (ex Azurine, by Chamossaire)
    1980   Silken Glider Stakes-Gr3
    1981   Oaks Stakes-Gr1
        Irish Oaks-Gr1

**1980**
br c ARCTIC LORD (ex Arctic Chimes, by Arctic Slave)
    1984   Blandford Stakes-Gr2
ch g EVENING M'LORD (ex Evening Slipper, by Above Suspicion)
    1983   Ballymoss Stakes-Gr2
    1984   Sierra Nevada Handicap [Div.1]-Gr3
b c GAY LEMUR (ex Coming-of-Age, by Majority Blue)
    1984   John Porter Stakes-Gr3
        Jockey Club Stakes-Gr2
        St Simon Stakes-Gr3
br c ISAAK BABEL (ex Ilsebill, by Birkhahn)
    1983   Premio Lazio-Gr3

# LORD GAYLE                    (bay, 1965)

| | | | |
|---|---|---|---|
| Sir Gaylord (b 1959) | Turn-to | Royal Charger | Nearco / Sun Princess |
| | | Source Sucree | Admiral Drake / Lavendula |
| | Somethingroyal | Princequillo | Prince Rose / Cosquilla |
| | | Imperatrice | Caruso / Cinquepace |
| Sticky Case (ch 1958) | Court Martial | Fair Trial | Fairway / Lady Juror |
| | | Instantaneous | Hurry On / Picture |
| | Run Honey | Hyperion | Gainsborough / Selene |
| | | Honey Buzzard | Papyrus / Lady Peregrine |

**1981**
gr f DESIRABLE (ex Balidaress, by Balidar)
    1983   Cheveley Park Stakes-Gr1

**1982**
ch c LORD DUKE (ex All Ours, by Northfields)
    1985   Gallinule Stakes-Gr2

**1983**
ch f GAYLE GAL (ex Best Gal, by Bonne Noel)
    1985   Moyglare Stud Stakes-Gr1

**1984**
b c LORD AMERICO (ex Hynictus, by Val de Loir)
    1987   Premio Lazio-Gr3

**1985**
ch c CARROLL HOUSE (ex Tuna, by Silver Shark)
    1988   Furstenberg Rennen-Gr3
        Grosser Preis von Baden-Gr1
    1989   Princess of Wales's Stakes-Gr2
        Phoenix Champion Stakes-Gr1
        Prix de l'Arc de Triomphe-Gr1
b c EXECUTIVE PERK (ex Areola, by Kythnos)
    1988   Ballymacoy Stakes-Gr3
    1989   Concorde Stakes-Gr3

# Lyphard

AIRLIE Stud owner Tim Rogers seemed to be on a high in the autumn of 1969. In October he bought and successfully syndicated the champion European miler Habitat. In November, as one of the small band of European horsemen with the intelligence to see what was happening in the Thoroughbred world and with the courage to act on it, he ventured to the Keeneland Fall Sales and bought himself a colt-foal by Northern Dancer for $35,000. Whether or not the purchase of Habitat worked out in the long run, that second deal had to represent something of a coup. Northern Dancer was the sire of Nijinsky, certainly the best two-year-old in Europe, and if Nijinsky was to do what was expected of him in 1970, the Rogers colt, out of a stakes-winning mare by Court Martial, was bound to be worth a fortune.

Of course, Nijinsky's role in the piece would be crucial, but as the drama of the new season unfolded, it was as though Tim Rogers, rather than Vincent O'Brien, had written his script. As for the way the big, powerful colt delivered his lines, well, he was just magnificent – the first Triple Crown in 35 years, a cantering victory in the 'King George', still unbeaten, with the Arc de Triomphe yet to come, two days after the sale of Rogers' colt. Even Nijinsky's kid brother Minsky had got into the act and performed well, winning the Railway Stakes and Beresford Stakes. The stage was set for at least a Newmarket October Sale record, maybe something even more momentous.

As the time for lot 821's appearance drew nigh, an air of expectancy filled the Tattersalls arena. Speculation as to who would buy the colt had been reduced to thoughts of who could possibly afford to buy him, and the obvious favourite had to be Charles Engelhard, the owner of Nijinsky and Minsky. His manager, David McCall, would be around somewhere, and in his customary manner he would bob out from his usual spot near the left door to make the clinching bid. Lady Beaverbrook, who would presumably take her seat in a minute, was likely to give McCall a run for his money, and the other likeliest contenders had to be David Robinson's agent, Lord Harrington, and Marcos Lemos, both of them prodigious supporters of the market.

At last the great moment came. The colt made his entrance and a hush descended. The auctioneer made the introductions, and the bidding began. It was Arpad Plesch. Then Alec Head. Then Plesch again. Then Head again. One of these fellows would drop out in a minute, and sure enough, after two or three more exchanges between the pair, Plesch was beaten. Who would be next? Lady B. seemed to be missing. There was no sign of Lemos. Harrington sat motionless. If McCall was going to bob out, he was leaving it late. You could have heard a pin drop, but the sound, unmistakably, was that of a hammer. '15,000gns – Alec Head'. Tim Rogers had lost money.

Of course, it had to be said that the colt did not have the commanding presence of Nijinsky, nor even the rugged muscularity of Minsky. He was, not to put too fine a point on it, small. Still, Northern Dancer had been small, so insignificant-looking as a yearling that he could not find a buyer at the modest reserve of $25,000. Disappointment at the sales did not mean that disappointment on the racecourse was bound to follow. When a horse sells cheaply to Joe Bloggs, it is reasonable to assume that there is something radically wrong with it, but when the buyer is the greatest horseman in Europe, it may well be that he has simply outsmarted everyone else.

Alec Head turned his acquisition over to Mme Pierre Wertheimer, to whom he was virtually private trainer at the time, and she gave him the name Lyphard. As a two-year-old he was clearly good, but not so good that he seemed to be a champion in the making. Outpaced on his debut over five furlongs, he improved for the opportunity of racing at or around a mile. He won a maiden at Maisons-Laffitte by five lengths, and the more important Prix Hérod at Longchamp by two, on the latter occasion producing a really impressive turn of foot to clinch the issue. His last start of the year was his first in Pattern company, and he started at odds-on, but for some reason his accelerator failed to function and he came home a modest seventh behind the filly First Bloom. The official French handicapper rightly reckoned that Lyphard was better than that, rating him only 6lb below the top of his class, Hard to Beat.

It was Head's belief that Lyphard would make a cracking middle-distance three-year-old, while his other star Riverman would excel over a mile. That was the way he planned their campaigns, but in the summer he switched their roles. With an Olivier and a Gielgud in his cast, a director can do that sort of thing and get away with it; Head certainly did. Lyphard's first three outings were at around ten furlongs. He ran away with the Prix Lagrange at Maisons-Laffitte, then trounced Sukawa and four others in the Group 2 Prix Daru. He was then supposed to win the Group 1 Prix Lupin, and his jockey was widely blamed for his failure to do so. Freddie Head, the trainer's son, sat over-confidently at the back, brought him with a tremendous rush to dispute the lead a furlong and a half from home, then felt him die in his hands. He finished fourth, three lengths behind Hard to Beat, and seemed distinctly unlucky.

The displeasure Freddie Head incurred that day at Longchamp turned out to be as nothing compared with the derision he received from the Epsom crowd a few weeks later. Lyphard started co-second favourite for the Derby, failed to negotiate Tattenham Corner, and only the outer rail kept him from careering into the fairground. In the circumstances it was amazing that he was able to beat seven of his 21 rivals; he lost a vast amount of ground. Still, the Irish Derby soon proved that Lyphard was not a mile-and-a-half horse anyway. He was tried in blinkers, which may have helped his cornering, but they could not give him stamina he did not own. His effort quickly petered out after he had held a prominent position at the two-furlong pole.

Alec Head ditched the blinkers and pitched him in with the toughest group of milers seen in many years. There was no Brigadier Gerard among them, but they were an evenly-matched and intensely competitive class, scarcely less formidable for the fact that Riverman had now dropped out. In the Prix Jacques le Marois Lyphard got home by the skin of his teeth from the 2000 Guineas winner High Top, storming home with a terrific run from the rear. In the Prix du Moulin those tactics were repeated, but either Freddie Head's timing was at fault or he simply under-estimated Sallust; the colt's dramatic acceleration brought him from next to last to second in the straight, but could not quite be sustained close home. The jockey risked criticism again in the Prix de la Forêt, run over only seven furlongs, when Lyphard was left with a lot of ground to retrieve in the last quarter-mile. This time the ploy worked to perfection, the electrifying burst which carried him past Martinmas to a clear victory providing a stunning advertisement for the colt's remarkable gear-change.

Lyphard retired after the Forêt and was installed at the Haras d'Etreham in Normandy. He still was not big, but he was strong, especially impressive behind the saddle, and if it was true that horses with exceptional finishing speed made the best stallions, he was clearly going to the top. He did, and he wasted little time about it.

Thanks to Pharly, he was the leading first-season sire in France; thanks to Durtal, he was the leading first-season sire in Britain too. After those results, all the top breeders in Europe wanted to get to him, but if they did not make it in 1977, they were not to get another chance. Lyphard had just five seasons at Etreham, and before the fifth was over it was announced that he had been sold to John Gaines, who at that time was collecting stallions as some people collect stamps. From the buyer's angle it was quite a gamble, based on the results of one crop's performance in about one season and one month. Europeans could – and did – regret the sale, but they had no means of knowing just what manner of sire was leaving and what manner of stock he was leaving behind him. All in due time, they discovered.

In the course of his five seasons in France, Lyphard got 22 individual winners of 47 European Pattern winners, with four winners of 14 American Graded Stakes for good measure. He sired champion two-year-olds and champion three-year-olds, he got a winner of the Arc de Triomphe, and he twice headed the sires' list in France. He was Northern Dancer's most faithful agent in Europe, getting comparable stock with comparable aptitudes, and in the matter of quality among his fillies, he did not have to defer to his father. He was a phenomenon, and Europe let him go, followed within months by Blushing Groom, Caro and The Minstrel.

Lyphard had a disease-restricted first season at Gainesway. The resultant crop numbered only 29 and contained nothing of note, but it was merely a brief hiatus in a career of otherwise unbroken brilliance. The big winners kept coming, and though as time wore on it seemed that those who excelled on dirt were very much in the minority, the constant flow of his stock to Europe ensured that his status was maintained. In his tenth crop there were two grass champions, Manila in the States and Dancing Brave on this side of the Atlantic, and in the latter he had a son with his own devastating acceleration, capable of carrying it beyond his own limit of stamina. Courtesy of Manila, he was able to add the 1986 North American sires' championship to the titles he won in France in 1978 and 1979.

Having started in the States as a $60,000 stallion, Lyphard rose to a peak of $275,000 in

*Lyphard, who has consistently sired winners of the highest class.*

1985. He could be used in 1990 at $80,000 without guarantee of a foal, but the live-foal price of $125,000 seemed the better bet, with his fertility not what it used to be. He has never been a horse to get flashy 'lookers', yet while none of his stock would win in a show-ring and some have quite unsightly defects of conformation, his record as a sire of soundness is probably unmatched in the annals of the Thoroughbred. Anyone who owned a physically untrainable Lyphard had the consolation of a rarity of museum-exhibit status. Almost everything by him has got to the races, a factor which has been crucial to his success.

To date the performance of his sire sons is mixed. Pharly proved a poor deputy for him at Etreham and has continued to disappoint in England, while Monteverdi's record in the States prompted his export to Venezuela. The short-lived Lypheor was possibly going to be good. Bellypha (now in Japan), Lyphard's Wish and Al Nasr have all had their moments without quite managing to become established. There are numerous younger horses, several of them currently fashionable and with the potential to change the picture over the next few years. Meanwhile, the Lyphard fillies are already proving highly successful broodmares.

## LYPHARD (bay, 1969)

| | | | |
|---|---|---|---|
| Northern Dancer (b 1961) | Nearctic | Nearco | Pharos / Nogara |
| | | Lady Angela | Hyperion / Sister Sarah |
| | Natalma | Native Dancer | Polynesian / Geisha |
| | | Almahmoud | Mahmoud / Arbitrator |
| Goofed (ch 1960) | Court Martial | Fair Trial | Fairway / Lady Juror |
| | | Instantaneous | Hurry On / Picture |
| | Barra | Formor | Ksar / Formose |
| | | La Favorite | Biribi / La Pompadour |

### Racing record

| Year | Starts | Wins | 2nd | 3rd | 4th | FR |
|---|---|---|---|---|---|---|
| 1971 | 4 | 2 | - | - | 1 | 85,784 |
| 1972 | 8 | 4 | 1 | - | 1 | 934,455 |
| | 12 | 6 | 1 | - | 2 | 1,020,239 |

## Principal wins

1972    Prix Daru-Gr2
        Prix Jacques le Marois-Gr1
        Prix de la Foret-Gr1

## Principal progeny

**1974**

b f DURTAL (ex Derna, by Sunny Boy)
    1976    Cheveley Park Stakes-Gr1
    1977    Fred Darling Stakes-Gr3
ch c PHARLY (ex Comely, by Boran)
    1976    Prix de la Foret-Gr1
    1977    Prix Lupin-Gr1
            Prix du Rond Point-Gr3
            Prix du Moulin de Longchamp-Gr1
b c PRESIDENT (ex Peisquiera, by Free Man)
    1977    Prix de Guiche-Gr3

**1975**

b f CALDERINA (ex Cendres Bleues, by Charlottesville)
    1978    Prix de Sandringham-Gr3
            Prix de Malleret-Gr2
    1979    Gallorette Handicap-Gr3
b f DANCING MAID (ex Morana, by Val de Loir)
    1978    Prix Vanteaux-Gr3
            Poule d'Essai des Pouliches-Gr1
            Prix Chloe-Gr3
            Prix Vermeille-Gr1
gr c IRON RULER (ex Lindera, by Linacre)
    1979    Goldene Peitsche-Gr3
b c LYPHEOR (ex Klaizia, by Sing Sing)
    1978    Prix Quincey-Gr3
ch f NORTH SEA (ex Rough Sea, by Herbager)
    1978    Prix de Flore-Gr3
b f REINE DE SABA (ex Sirya, by Sicambre)
    1978    Prix Saint-Alary-Gr1
            Prix de Diane-Gr1

**1976**

gr c BELLYPHA (ex Belga, by Le Fabuleux)
    1978    Prix Thomas Bryon-Gr3
    1979    Prix de la Jonchere-Gr3
            Prix Daphnis-Gr3
            Prix Quincey-Gr3
b c LYPHARD'S WISH (ex Sally's Wish, by Sensitivo)
    1979    Craven Stakes-Gr3
            Dante Stakes-Gr3
    1980    United Nations Handicap-Gr1
b f SINGAPORE GIRL (ex Cheftaine, by Tanerko)
    1979    Prix Maurice de Nieuil-Gr2
b f THREE TROIKAS (ex Three Roses, by Dual)
    1979    Prix Vanteaux-Gr3
            Poule d'Essai des Pouliches-Gr1
            Prix Saint-Alary-Gr1
            Prix Vermeille-Gr1
            Prix de l'Arc de Triomphe-Gr1
    1980    Prix d'Harcourt-Gr2

**1977**

b f BENICIA (ex Bashi, by Stupendous)
    1980    Prix de Flore-Gr3

b f CHAIN BRACELET (ex Chain, by Herbager)
    1981    Bed o' Roses Handicap-Gr3
            Top Flight Handicap-Gr1
            Shuvee Handicap-Gr2
ch c MONTEVERDI (ex Janina, by Match)
    1979    National Stakes-Gr2
            Dewhurst Stakes-Gr1

**1978**

b c AL NASR (ex Caretta, by Caro)
    1981    Prix La Force-Gr3
            Prix de la Cote Normande-Gr3
    1982    Prix Exbury-Gr3
            Prix Dollar-Gr2
            Prix d'Ispahan-Gr1
b/br c EUCLID (ex Lucky for Me, by Appiani)
    1980    Beresford Stakes-Gr2
b c GHADEER (ex Swanilda, by Habitat)
    1981    Premio Carlo Porta-Gr3
ch c LYDIAN (ex Miss Manon, by Bon Mot)
    1981    Prix Noailles-Gr2
            Gran Premio di Milano-Gr1
            Grosser Preis von Berlin-Gr1
b f PHYDILLA (ex Godzilla, by Gyr)
    1980    Prix Eclipse-Gr3
    1981    Prix Quincey-Gr3
b f SANGUE (ex Prodice, by Prominer)
    1981    Prix de Psyche-Gr3
    1982    Yerba Buena Handicap-Gr2
            Beverly Hills Handicap-Gr2
            Vanity Handicap-Gr1
    1983    Santa Monica Handicap [Div.2]-Gr2
            Chula Vista Handicap-Gr3
            Ramona Handicap-Gr2
            Golden Harvest Handicap-Gr3
            Yellow Ribbon Invitational Stakes-Gr1
            Matriarch Stakes-Gr1

**1980**

b c ALZAO (ex Lady Rebecca, by Sir Ivor)
    1984    Premio Ellington-Gr3
b c AU POINT (ex Quillo Queen, by Princequillo)
    1983    Dwyer Stakes-Gr1
b c ESPRIT DU NORD (ex Rajput Princess, by Prince Taj)
    1983    Preis von Europa-Gr1
    1984    Gran Premio di Milano-Gr1
b c LEGEND OF FRANCE (ex Lupe, by Primera)
    1984    Earl of Sefton Stakes-Gr3
b c LYPHARD'S SPECIAL (ex My Bupers, by Bupers)
    1983    September Stakes-Gr3
ch f SABIN (ex Beaconaire, by Vaguely Noble)
    1983    Saranac Stakes-Gr2
            New York Handicap-Gr2
            Sheepshead Bay Handicap-Gr2
            Boiling Springs Handicap-Gr3
    1984    La Prevoyante Handicap [Div.1]-Gr3
            Black Helen Handicap-Gr2
            Orchid Handicap-Gr2
            Gamely Handicap-Gr1
            Sheepshead Bay Handicap-Gr2
            Matchmaker Stakes-Gr2
            Yellow Ribbon Invitational Stakes-Gr1
    1985    La Prevoyante Handicap [Div.2]-Gr3

**1981**

b c DAHAR (ex Dahlia, by Vaguely Noble)
    1984    Prix Lupin-Gr1
    1985    San Gabriel Handicap-Gr3
              San Marcos Handicap-Gr3
              Century Handicap-Gr1
    1986    San Luis Rey Stakes-Gr1
              San Juan Capistrano Handicap-Gr1
ch c ENDS WELL (ex Late Bloomer, by Stage Door Johnny)
    1984    Rutgers Handicap [Div.2]-Gr2
    1985    United Nations Handicap-Gr1
    1986    Michigan Mile & One-Eighth Handicap-Gr2
              Hawthorne Gold Cup Handicap-Gr2
ch c SICYOS (ex Sigy, by Habitat)
    1983    Prix d'Arenberg-Gr3
    1984    Prix de Saint-Georges-Gr3
ch c VACARME (ex Virunga, by Sodium)
    1983    Mill Reef Stakes-Gr2

**1982**

b c HERALDISTE (ex Heiress, by Habitat)
    1985    Prix Quincey-Gr3
b/br h PROUD DEBONAIR (ex Proud Delta, by Delta Judge)
    1987    Grey Lag Handicap-Gr3

**1983**

b c DANCING BRAVE (ex Navajo Princess, by Drone)
    1986    Craven Stakes-Gr3
              2000 Guineas Stakes-Gr1
              Eclipse Stakes-Gr1
              King George VI & Queen Elizabeth Stakes-Gr1
              Select Stakes-Gr3
              Prix de l'Arc de Triomphe-Gr1
b c LESOTHO (ex Sealy, by Filiberto)
    1987    La Coupe-Gr3
    1988    La Coupe-Gr3

b c MANILA (ex Dona Ysidra, by Le Fabuleux)
    1986    Cinema Handicap-Gr2
              Lexington Stakes-Gr2
              United Nations Handicap-Gr1
              New Jersey Turf Classic Stakes-Gr3
              Turf Classic Stakes-Gr1
              Breeders' Cup Turf Stakes-Gr1
    1987    United Nations Handicap-Gr1
              Arlington Million Stakes-Gr1
b/br c STORM ON THE LOOSE (ex That's a Kennedy, by Kennedy Road)
    1986    Laurel Turf Cup Handicap [Div.2]-Gr3
    1987    Royal Palm Handicap-Gr3

**1984**

b c MAZILIER (ex Marie Curie, by Exbury)
    1989    San Simeon Handicap-Gr3
b f TENUE DE SOIREE (ex River Rose, by Riverman)
    1987    Prix de Saint-Georges-Gr3
              Prix du Gros Chene-Gr3

**1985**

b f ANDALEEB (ex Bag of Tunes, by Herbager)
    1988    Lancashire Oaks-Gr3
b f RIVIERE D'OR (ex Gold River, by Riverman)
    1987    Prix d'Aumale-Gr3
    1988    Prix Vanteaux-Gr3
              Prix Saint-Alary-Gr1

**1986**

b f ENSCONSE (ex Carefully Hidden, by Caro)
    1989    Nell Gwyn Stakes-Gr3
              Irish 1000 Guineas-Gr1
ch f PEARL BRACELET (ex Perlee, by Margouillat)
    1989    Poule d'Essai des Pouliches-Gr1

**1987**

ch c FUNAMBULE (ex Sonoma, by Habitat)
    1989    Prix des Chenes-Gr3
    1990    Prix du Palais Royal-Gr3

# Mill Reef

A LOT of people turned up at Salisbury on 13 May 1970 in the expectation of seeing a future classic winner. They all departed convinced that they had. The only change there had been between the prospect and the confirmation was the identity of the horse concerned.

What Fireside Chat had achieved on his debut at Newmarket a fortnight earlier was nothing short of amazing. He had fallen out of his stall, lost at least a dozen lengths, then passed all of his 26 rivals in four furlongs, continued to go away in the fifth, and won by four lengths. It was no wonder that he started at odds of 2/9 for the Salisbury Stakes, and no wonder that he had already been backed to win next year's 2000 Guineas. This time when the stalls opened he was away alertly, soon chasing a little bay colt in Paul Mellon's colours. Give Fireside Chat his due, he did not give up the chase, but even Lester Piggott accepted that it was a forlorn hope inside the final furlong, and the upstart flashed by the post, four lengths clear, still full of running.

Mill Reef was headline news next morning, and he was to remain in the public eye for the rest of his life. Better than that, he was a horse the public took to its heart; he stirred imaginations with his displays of class and courage on the racecourse, combining with – if only once competing with – Brigadier Gerard to establish an era of affluence in terms of talent on the Turf. In the early 70s it could truly be said that the British racegoer had never had it so good.

Mill Reef came from the fourth crop of Never Bend and was the first runner in England by the sire, a classy and headstrong horse whose seven efforts to win beyond nine furlongs produced seven of his ten defeats. His idea of racing was to run himself into the ground, and after he had failed to last home in the Kentucky Derby (second) and the Preakness Stakes (third) his owner finally abandoned his ambitious plan to run against Relko and the rest in the 1963 Epsom Derby. Even so, Never Bend had excellent credentials for stud and he was already doing well with his runners in the States when Ian Balding took delivery of Mill Reef, the second produce of Milan Mill, a Princequillo mare who had damaged a hind leg as a foal and had been taken out of training after a single

– unplaced – start as a two-year-old.

After his brilliant debut performance, Mill Reef was brilliant again at Royal Ascot, though his opposition in the Coventry Stakes really was not worthy of the occasion. Having won in a canter there by eight lengths, he ventured to France for the Prix Robert Papin and such was his reputation that his short-head defeat by My Swallow was regarded by many as a catastrophe. By the end of the season, with My Swallow unbeaten in seven starts and the first-ever laureate of the French juvenile 'Quadruple Crown', the result could be seen in a different perspective. Mill Reef also saw out the remainder of his season without a loss. He was never off the bit at any stage of York's Gimcrack Stakes, winning by ten lengths; he took a long time to subdue Hecla in the Imperial Stakes at Kempton, but ultimately won going away; and in the Dewhurst Stakes he was given no sort of test, outclassing his only two rivals. As My Swallow had done nothing wrong since their encounter at Maisons-Laffitte, Mill Reef almost had to be rated 1lb below him in the Free Handicap. Third on the list, also by a 1lb margin, was the Middle Park Stakes winner, Brigadier Gerard.

During the winter there was much speculation over the 2000 Guineas prospects of this trio, with acknowledgements also to the champion Irish two-year-old Minsky, a full brother to Nijinsky. There was equally fascinating debate over whether Mill Reef would have sufficient stamina for the Derby, and when it was referred to his sire's owner-breeder, Harry Guggenheim, his reply was: 'I'll not live to see the day when a son of Never Bend wins the Derby.' The remark was presumably meant to be unequivocal; it turned out to be exactly the opposite. Guggenheim fulfilled the prophecy by dying in January 1971. In March Ian Balding went on record as saying that Epsom would definitely figure on Mill Reef's agenda.

The colt began at three with an impressive four-length win in the Group 3 Greenham Stakes at Newbury, a performance which ensured that he would start as favourite for the Guineas. In the classic, Geoff Lewis rode the perfect race to beat My Swallow, but no sooner had Mill Reef settled that old quarrel than along came Brigadier Gerard to beat them both, unquestionably the best horse on the day. If it seemed improbable that Britain could have two great champions at once, it was now at least possible. The proof came soon enough.

Mill Reef never once looked like being beaten again in 1971. In the Derby it was obvious at Tattenham Corner that only lack of stamina could prevent him from winning. Linden Tree, to his credit, made him display his staying power, but when Lewis got at him he dug in, wore that rival down, and won with authority by two lengths. In the Eclipse he was faced by an apparently formidable rival in Caro, who had recently come into his own as a four-year-old and was ideally suited to ten furlongs. Mill Reef rose to the challenge. A quarter of a mile out it seemed likely to be a close-run race, but the younger colt then shifted into overdrive and opened a four-length margin. Opposed by nothing of Caro's class in the King George VI & Queen Elizabeth Stakes, Mill Reef had to win, and it was just a matter of how he would accomplish it. The answer was immaculately. He came into the straight on the bridle, quickened on demand, and burst clear to beat Ortis by six lengths.

Although the previous three Derby winners – Sir Ivor, Blakeney and Nijinsky – had all been beaten in the Arc de Triomphe, nobody had any doubts that Mill Reef would stop the rot. He did so with another superlative display, accelerating brilliantly under pressure and setting a course record as he beat Pistol Packer by three lengths. It seemed that all he had left to do was to gain his revenge over Brigadier Gerard as a four-year-old; unfortunately, though neither ever ducked the other, the re-match everyone hoped to see was never to take place.

The ten who turned out to oppose Mill Reef and his pacemaker in the 1972 Prix Ganay were not good, as the odds of 1/10 about the favourite signified. Whether there was ever another horse who could have made them look quite so bad as he did that day at Longchamp is another matter. If anything, he looked better than ever as he strolled home by ten lengths. His gloriously fluent action, which he would exhibit whatever the ground conditions, was never displayed more memorably.

The Coronation Cup was different. He was again a virtually unbackable favourite, and the odds seemed right as he quickened to draw up to Homeric a furlong and a half out, then edged in front. The well-rehearsed script called for him to burst clear, but he did not, and plainly could not. Lewis showed him the

*Mill Reef in his paddock at the National Stud – a horse of superb balance and quality.*

whip and had to ride hard just to preserve a neck advantage.

Mill Reef had missed a couple of gallops because of wet weather and Balding's confidence that he could win albeit short of peak fitness was barely borne out. It was the last stroke of luck the trainer was to have with the colt. He picked up a virus and had to miss both the Eclipse and the 'King George'. Brigadier Gerard won both. Back in training and working well, Mill Reef was aimed at the Benson & Hedges Gold Cup, where he was set to meet the Brigadier and Roberto, the latest Derby winner. Then a hock swelled up and put paid to that plan. Worse was to come. No sooner had Paul Mellon decided that because the colt had missed so much of this season he would be kept in training as a five-year-old, than Mill Reef fractured his near foreleg in a canter at Kingsclere. His career was over, and for a while his life seemed in danger. The only hope of saving him for a stud career was a successful outcome to an operation never previously performed in Britain. To the relief of a nation, the outcome was a total success.

Mill Reef went to the National Stud, and because of his injury was restricted to 21 mares in his first season. Only a dozen foals resulted and among his most celebrated mates Bleu Azur and Highest Hopes proved barren, while Humble Duty and Park Top slipped. It was remarkable that he was covering at all, something less than a disaster that the only Pattern winner to emerge from the crop was the one-paced Millionaire.

Such is the time-lag between a covering season and the three-year-old campaign of those conceived in it that it can be difficult to monitor the progress of a young horse like Mill Reef. It was good that he was able to accept a full book of mares in 1974, but by the spring of 1978 there was little evidence to suggest that he was going to prove a significant sire. On the contrary, it was clear that he had suffered another disaster in 1977, when he contracted contagious equine metritis and had got only nine mares in foal. The picture was to change dramatically. Mill Reef ended 1978 as champion sire, having got the winners of all three major European Derbys. From that mini-crop conceived in 1977 came Fairy Footsteps, another classic winner, and the horse who was unbeaten away from home for three seasons, Glint of Gold. His six visits to the Continent brought six Group 1 victories.

After Acamas and Shirley Heights had proved their worth, there was no looking back for Mill Reef. He was, quite simply, the best sire in England, the most regular and reliable supplier of top-class horses to the British breeding industry. He was also the source of substantial income for the National Stud, thanks to the syndication deal effected after his first season by which the Horserace Betting Levy Board became owners of eight shares. Paul Mellon retained the same number in a contract which valued the horse at £2 million, considerably less than he would have been worth in America. Over ten years he rose from a share price of £50,000 to a nomination price of £100,000, and he was due to stand for that six-figure sum again in 1986 when he was struck down with a heart condition. Rapid deterioration made his destruction inevitable on 2 February that year.

Death did not bring an end to the Mill Reef success story. In 1987 he was champion sire for the second time, thanks to his best-ever son, Reference Point. In 1988 he had the 2000 Guineas winner in Doyoun. In 1989, with his last crop of three-year-olds at the races, he had more individual Pattern winners than any other sire. Overall, his stock were characteristically better at three than at two; most were happy to go 12 furlongs and many needed that distance, Fairy Footsteps proving the most remarkable exception to the rule. He got nothing as precocious as himself, nothing capable of such startling acceleration, and nothing which could really have been said to have emulated him as an all-rounder. The truly great horses do not reproduce themselves; the best we can hope is that they will distribute some of their best qualities to a large number of their progeny. Mill Reef did that.

Nobody can doubt Mill Reef's status among the great sires of the recent past, but a devil's advocate may yet point to some negative features in his record. Along with ability, he sometimes transmitted unsoundness and mental problems; plenty of his stock were delicate and difficult to train. A horse of superb balance and quality himself, he sometimes overdid the refinement in his progeny, who tended to be very light of bone. It is remarkable that his one really successful stallion son is Shirley Heights, a horse about as untypical of him as Nijinsky is of Northern Dancer. Many of Mill Reef's other sons have seemed to lack masculinity and much of their stock has proved soft. Acamas was infertile, so had an excuse, but such as Main Reef, Milford, Glint of Gold, Diamond Shoal, Pas de Seul, Wassl and (so far) Simply Great have made no impression as sires. Numerous Mill Reef horses have stood in Australia, all with poor results; only Japan appears to have succeeded with them. It is possible to be a great sire without making a great impact on the breed, and it is beginning to look as though that might be Mill Reef's destiny.

## Racing record

| Year | Starts | Wins | 2nd | 3rd | 4th | £ |
|------|--------|------|-----|-----|-----|---|
| 1970 | 6 | 5 | 1 | - | - | 37,123 |
| 1971 | 6 | 5 | 1 | - | - | 235,914 |
| 1972 | 2 | 2 | - | - | - | 42,226 |
| | 14 | 12 | 2 | - | - | 315,263 |

## Principal wins

| 1970 | Coventry Stakes |
|------|-----------------|
| | Gimcrack Stakes |
| | Imperial Stakes |
| | Dewhurst Stakes |
| 1971 | Greenham Stakes-Gr3 |
| | Derby Stakes-Gr1 |
| | Eclipse Stakes-Gr1 |
| | King George VI & Queen Elizabeth Stakes-Gr1 |
| | Prix de l'Arc de Triomphe-Gr1 |
| 1972 | Prix Ganay-Gr1 |
| | Coronation Cup-Gr1 |

## Principal progeny

**1974**

br c MILLIONAIRE (ex State Pension, by Only for Life)
  1977   Queen's Vase-Gr3

**1975**

b c ACAMAS (ex Licata, by Abdos)
  1978   Prix Lupin-Gr1
         Prix du Jockey-Club-Gr1
b f IDLE WATERS (ex Midsummertime, by Midsummer Night)
  1978   Park Hill Stakes-Gr2
b c SHIRLEY HEIGHTS (ex Hardiemma, by Hardicanute)
  1977   Royal Lodge Stakes-Gr2
  1978   Dante Stakes-Gr3
         Derby Stakes-Gr1
         Irish Derby-Gr1

**1976**

ch c MAIN REEF (ex Lovely Light, by Henry the Seventh)
  1978   July Stakes-Gr3
  1979   Cumberland Lodge Stakes-Gr3
         St Simon Stakes-Gr3
ch c MILFORD (ex Highclere, by Queen's Hussar)
  1979   White Rose Stakes-Gr3
         Lingfield Derby Trial Stakes-Gr3
         Princess of Wales's Stakes-Gr2

**1977**

b c SCOUTING MILLER (ex Scout Girl, by New Chapter)
  1982   Premio Ellington-Gr3

**1978**

b f FAIRY FOOTSTEPS (ex Glass Slipper, by Relko)
  1981   Nell Gwyn Stakes-Gr3
         1000 Guineas Stakes-Gr1
b c GLINT OF GOLD (ex Crown Treasure, by Graustark)
  1980   Gran Criterium-Gr1
  1981   Derby Italiano-Gr1
         Grand Prix de Paris-Gr1
         Great Voltigeur Stakes-Gr2
         Preis von Europa-Gr1
  1982   John Porter Stakes-Gr2
         Grand Prix de Saint-Cloud-Gr1
         Grosser Preis von Baden-Gr1

## MILL REEF                                      (bay, 1968)

| | | | |
|---|---|---|---|
| **Never Bend** (b 1960) | Nasrullah | Nearco | Pharos / Nogara |
| | | Mumtaz Begum | Blenheim / Mumtaz Mahal |
| | Lalun | Djeddah | Djebel / Djezima |
| | | Be Faithful | Bimelech / Bloodroot |
| **Milan Mill** (b 1962) | Princequillo | Prince Rose | Rose Prince / Indolence |
| | | Cosquilla | Papyrus / Quick Thought |
| | Virginia Water | Count Fleet | Reigh Count / Quickly |
| | | Red Ray | Hyperion / Infra Red |

**1979**

b c DIAMOND SHOAL (ex Crown Treasure, by Graustark)
  1983   John Porter Stakes-Gr2
         Grand Prix d'Evry-Gr2
         Gran Premio di Milano-Gr1
         Grand Prix de Saint-Cloud-Gr1
         Grosser Preis von Baden-Gr1
gr f DIONE (ex La Speroana, by Roan Rocket)
  1982   Prix de l'Opera-Gr2
b c PAS DE SEUL (ex Thereby, by Star Moss)
  1981   Prix Eclipse-Gr3
  1982   Hungerford Stakes-Gr3
         Prix de la Foret-Gr1
b c SIMPLY GREAT (ex Seneca, by Chaparral)
  1982   Dante Stakes-Gr2

**1980**

br c GARDE ROYALE (ex Royal Way, by Sicambre)
  1984   La Coupe-Gr3
         Prix Jean de Chaudenay-Gr2
ch f GREEN REEF (ex Infra Green, by Laser Light)
  1983   Prix de Psyche-Gr3
b c MILLE BALLES (ex Elezinha, by Tourangeau)
  1984   Prix Exbury-Gr3
         Prix Messidor-Gr3
b c SOUTH ATLANTIC (ex Arkadina, by Ribot)
  1983   Blandford Stakes-Gr2
b c WASSL (ex Hayloft, by Tudor Melody)
  1983   Greenham Stakes-Gr3
         Irish 2000 Guineas-Gr1
  1984   Lockinge Stakes-Gr3 [dead-heat]

**1981**

ch c KING OF CLUBS (ex Queen Pot, by Buckpasser)
  1984   Premio Nearco-Gr3
         Premio Vittorio di Capua-Gr2
         Premio Ribot-Gr2
  1985   Earl of Sefton Stakes-Gr3
         Premio Emilio Turati-Gr1
         Premio Federico Tesio-Gr2

b c LASHKARI (ex Larannda, by Right Royal)
    1984    Prix du Conseil de Paris-Gr2
             Breeders' Cup Turf Stakes-Gr1
ch c MAROONED (ex Short Rations, by Lorenzaccio)
    1986    N.E. Manion Cup Handicap-Gr3
             Chairman's Handicap-Gr3
             Sydney Cup Handicap-Gr1
ch f PARIS ROYAL (ex Place d'Etoile, by Kythnos)
    1984    Oaks d'Italia-Gr1
b f SANDY ISLAND (ex Sayonara, by Birkhahn)
    1984    Lancashire Oaks-Gr3

### 1982

b c BIG REEF (ex Lady Habitat, by Habitat)
    1986    Premio Federico Tesio-Gr2
    1987    Premio Aprile-Gr3

### 1983

b f FLEUR ROYALE (ex Sweet Mimosa, by Le Levanstell)
    1986    Pretty Polly Stakes-Gr2
b f GULL NOOK (ex Bempton, by Blakeney)
    1986    Ribblesdale Stakes-Gr2
b c VERARDI (ex Val d'Erica, by Ashmore)
    1987    Premio Ambrosiano-Gr3

### 1984

ch c ENTITLED (ex Lady Capulet, by Sir Ivor)
    1987    Desmond Stakes-Gr3
ch c IBN BEY (ex Rosia Bay, by High Top)
    1987    Gran Premio d'Italia-Gr1
    1988    Grand Prix de Deauville-Gr2
    1989    Prix Maurice de Nieuil-Gr2
             Geoffrey Freer Stakes-Gr2
             Preis von Europa Gr1
ch f MILLIGRAM (ex One in a Million, by Rarity)
    1987    Coronation Stakes-Gr2
             Waterford Crystal Mile-Gr2
             Queen Elizabeth II Stakes-Gr1

b c REFERENCE POINT (ex Home on the Range, by Habitat)
    1986    Futurity Stakes-Gr1
    1987    Dante Stakes-Gr2
             Derby Stakes-Gr1
             King George VI & Queen Elizabeth Stakes-Gr1
             Great Voltigeur Stakes-Gr2
             St Leger Stakes-Gr1

ch c ROSE REEF (ex Rose Bowl, by Habitat)
    1989    Gladness Stakes-Gr3

ch c STAR LIFT (ex Seneca, by Chaparral)
    1988    Prix Royal-Oak-Gr1
    1989    Prix d'Harcourt-Gr2
             Grand Prix d'Evry-Gr2
             Prix Foy-Gr3

### 1985

br c DOYOUN (ex Dumka, by Kashmir)
    1988    Craven Stakes-Gr3
             2000 Guineas Stakes-Gr1

### 1986

b c ALONG ALL (ex All Along, by Targowice)
    1988    Prix des Chenes-Gr3
    1989    Prix Greffulhe-Gr2

b f BEHERA (ex Borushka, by Bustino)
    1989    Prix Penelope-Gr3
             Prix Saint-Alary-Gr1

ch c CREATOR (ex Chalon, by Habitat)
    1989    Prix Guillaume d'Ornano-Gr2
             Prix Dollar-Gr2
    1990    Prix d'Harcourt-Gr2
             Prix Ganay-Gr1
             Prix d'Ispahan-Gr1

b c SIERRA STAR (ex New Chant, by New Providence)
    1989    St Leger Italiano-Gr3

# Mr Prospector

NOBODY needs to be a breeder of racehorses to know that products of the same mating are often more remarkable for their differences than for their similarities. Most people who have children are aware of the fact, and those with a lot of children realize something of the vast potential for variation that exists in the pairing of one male with one female. The Thoroughbred breeder tends to forget that. Although it seemed like a good idea to mate mare X with stallion Y last year, when he sees that the outcome is a cripple, he is unlikely to repeat the mating. On the other hand, if he likes the first result, he may well try it again, and when he gets a cripple the second time around, he cannot understand why. He takes one good result as proof that the mating works, one bad result as proof that it does not.

Gold Digger had seven foals by Raise a Native, and it was lucky that Mother Nature decreed that they came in the order they did. The last four were all so unsound that they could not be dragged to the racetrack. The third had a breathing problem and managed only one win. The first also won only once and broke down as a two-year-old, but it was because he looked a good sort when he was born that the mating was tried a second time. The outcome of that union was Mr Prospector, the white sheep of his family and the most successful active sire in the world today.

Raise a Native was a flying machine, but one who was grounded after only four flights on account of mechanical problems. His racing career was over by mid-July of his two-year-old season, by which time he had won once over three furlongs at Hialeah and three times at Aqueduct, twice over five furlongs, the last over five and a half. It was anybody's guess how good he was, and the official handicapper guessed that he was the best of his generation, 3lb better than a certain Northern Dancer, for example. Whatever, Raise a Native went off to Spendthrift Farm in Kentucky to spread class, speed and unsoundness, often as a package, among the Thoroughbred population. Mr Prospector had a good, tough dam – a winner ten times from 35 starts and runner-up in the Kentucky Oaks – who might have helped him out in the soundness department, but she did no more for him than for his four brothers and two sisters.

She was unable to prevent him being unsound, but at least she did not inhibit – and may even have contributed to – the expression of class and speed.

Bred by Spendthrift's owner, Leslie Combs, Mr Prospector was the top-priced yearling at Keeneland in 1971, fetching $220,000 from Butch Savin, a Connecticut businessman who also owned a stud in Florida. In due course he sent his colt off to trainer Jimmy Croll and awaited good news. For a depressingly long period, he received bad news; every time Mr Prospector worked, he became shin-sore. He never did race as a two-year-old. In February 1973, things looked up. He made his debut in a six-furlong maiden at Hialeah and won by 12 lengths; two weeks later he ran in an allowance race over seven furlongs and won that by nearly six lengths. He had to miss the Grade 3 Hutcheson Stakes because of a slight fever, but no matter. He moved across town to Gulfstream Park and won a six-furlong allowance race there, setting a track record which is still intact 17 years later. Suddenly he seemed like a Derby contender and he was shipped to Kentucky to prove the point. He did the opposite. He finished third in the Calumet Purse at Keeneland, evidently failing to last the eight and a half furlongs. He tried a mile in the Derby Trial at Churchill Downs, was outstayed again, and hobbled back to the barn with a chipped bone in his off-fore fetlock. That was enough to keep him out of action until February 1974.

Croll brought him back in good shape for an allowance event at Gulfstream Park, and he covered the six furlongs in quick time, winning by five lengths. It was high time Mr Prospector became a stakes-winner, and his trainer did not care where he had to go to make it happen. He took him to New York and saw him finish third in the Paumonok Handicap at Aqueduct. Then it was back to Miami, where the good local sprinter Lonetree gave him 1lb and beat him comfortably in the Royal Poinciana. A trip to New Jersey did the trick. There, with top weight in the company of useful sprinters, he took the six-furlong Whirlaway Handicap at Garden State Park, in track-record time. Mr Prospector was getting better, and at Belmont he won for the third time as a four-year-old, taking a six-furlong allowance race by three lengths.

Getting better was one thing, getting over-ambitious was something else. He took on Horse of the Year Forego in the seven-furlong Carter Handicap, and the champion ran away from him, giving him 5lb into the bargain. He then showed that he could no more cope with eight and a half furlongs on turf than on dirt, being beaten a long way by horses of no real account. When he reverted to his true metier, he provided proof that he was a much improved sprinter. In the Gravesend Handicap at Aqueduct he was a five-length winner over Infuriator, with his old rival Lonetree, now getting 5lb, back in third. In the Firecracker Handicap, the Fourth of July feature at Liberty Bell Park in Philadelphia, he all but became a Grade 3 winner, losing by a nose to Barbizon Streak, who was receiving 10lb. Unfortunately, Mr Prospector did not stay sound enough to get another chance. On 26 July, in a work-out at Monmouth Park, he fractured a sesamoid and his career was over. Four days earlier, his yearling brother Kentucky Gold (the one who developed the respiratory problem) had been sold at Keeneland for a world-record $625,000.

It is hard to assess Mr Prospector's merits as a runner. According to the *Daily Racing Form* handicapper he was the best six-furlong horse in America in 1974, though the standard that year was not what it had been in most recent seasons. His rating was based largely on his performance in the Gravesend Handicap, when he beat the best sprinters in New York, and as he was still on the upgrade at the time of his retirement, he might have earned greater respect if he had still been around in the autumn for the Fall Highweight Handicap. However, he was fragile, and he was always going to fall apart at some time.

Butch Savin took Mr Prospector to Florida, installed him at his Aisco Farm, and accepted bookings at $7500 with a live-foal concession. The horse was well bred, he stood just about 16 hands, and he had a good, powerful rear end on him. If the local mares would forgive him his generally plain appearance, and the fact that he turned his off-fore out markedly, he might have a deal to offer them. The question was, what would they have to offer him? It was hard to make the grade as a stallion in Florida, where only In Reality had done consistently well and earned national acclaim in recent years. The basic problem was that there was not enough class in the Sunshine State broodmare band.

Mr Prospector did not care whether his mares were reckoned to have class or not. He just set about putting some class into their foals, and did it to some effect. His first crop amounted to no more than 28,

but there were four stakes winners among them, including It's In the Air, who was named co-champion two-year-old filly of 1978. Thanks to her, he was America's leading first-crop sire, much to the embarrassment of the fashionable Kentucky set. In 1979 he became the nation's leading sire of two-year-olds, aided by a large second crop of 51 foals which eventually yielded 11 individual stakes winners. If he could get such results from Florida mares, what would he achieve with real chances?

By 1980, when his third crop reached the races, Mr Prospector's fee had risen to $40,000, which was realistic for a horse of his merit but not for one in his location. He had become too big for his adopted state. Butch Savin contacted Seth Hancock at Claiborne Farm and asked if he would be interested in taking the new sire sensation to Kentucky. It did not take long to arrange a deal, and before Mr Prospector had completed his sixth Florida season it was announced that his seventh would be spent at Claiborne. By the time he got there he was already looking like a gilt-edged investment, and it would eventually emerge that he had got a total of 50 stakes-winners from his six years at Aisco Farm, including horses of championship calibre like Hello Gorgeous, Conquistador Cielo and Gold Beauty, all out of mares who would not have been allowed near a fashionable stallion in Kentucky.

Some sires do not get better results from matings with better mares, but Mr Prospector was no chance-bred horse and it was always a good bet that his record would improve. Sure enough, the mares who came to him at $100,000 in 1981 and 1982 produced him outstanding performers on both sides of the Atlantic, and as the fee rose, to a peak of $325,000 in 1986, the quantity of quality in his progeny kept growing. In 1987 he headed the North American sires' table with record earnings of $5,877,385, and in 1988 he raised the record to $8,986,790. Relatively ordinary results achieved by his 1989 three-year-olds dragged him down to sixth place in that season's table, but he did have the champion two-year-olds of both Europe (Machiavellian) and America (Rhythm) in his team, lending support to the view that another phenomenal year was in store for 1990. The depth of quality in his mare books for the last five seasons is probably unsurpassed in the history of the breed; his success is not about to end, nor even abate.

Mr Prospector's impact has been tremendous, most particularly as a source of brilliant speed and precocity. Plenty of his stock do train on, a number can cope with a mile and a quarter, and the odd one lasts 12 furlongs, but as a rule they like the first mile

*Mr Prospector, a source of brilliant speed and precocity.*

best. It must be said, though, that not even his keenest supporter would credit him with a contribution to the beauty of the Thoroughbred population. His stock come in all shapes and sizes, and they come with physical faults which most judges would regard as unacceptable in the progeny of any normal stallion. They are plain about the head, they have crooked legs – many, like their sire, turn their off-fore out – and they have small feet. For a long time there was a prejudice against them in Europe, where a number had proved disappointing, and though their record here is now much better, it still seems that their feet do not take well to firm ground and undulating surfaces in England; they are happier on the constantly watered courses in France.

Some of Mr Prospector's sons are already showing merit as sires, most notably Fappiano, who headed the first-crop sires and juvenile sires in 1985 and actually ranked three places above his sire on the 1989 general list. In the latter year he also showed signs of making a breakthrough in Europe. Among the other sons conceived in Florida, Miswaki has enjoyed a modicum of success, but Hello Gorgeous and Conquistador Cielo, both out of mares from plebeian backgrounds, have proved ghastly failures. More positively, several sons of limited racing

| MR PROSPECTOR | | | (bay, 1970) |
|---|---|---|---|
| Raise a Native (ch 1961) | Native Dancer | Polynesian | Unbreakable Black Polly |
| | | Geisha | Discovery Miyako |
| | Raise You | Case Ace | Teddy Sweetheart |
| | | Lady Glory | American Flag Beloved |
| Gold Digger (b 1962) | Nashua | Nasrullah | Nearco Mumtaz Begum |
| | | Segula | Johnstown Sekhmet |
| | Sequence | Count Fleet | Reigh Count Quickly |
| | | Miss Dogwood | Bull Dog Myrtlewood |

distinction are proving capable of getting good performers, both in the States and abroad. That was a feature for which Northern Dancer was noted from an early stage. No bounds are set in the extent of Mr Prospector's influence as a new century approaches.

## Racing record

| Year | Starts | Wins | 2nd | 3rd | 4th | $ |
|------|--------|------|-----|-----|-----|---|
| 1972 | 0 | | | | | |
| 1973 | 5 | 3 | 1 | 1 | - | 17,725 |
| 1974 | 9 | 4 | 3 | 1 | 1 | 94,446 |
| | 14 | 7 | 4 | 2 | 1 | 112,171 |

## Principal wins

1974    Whirlaway Handicap
        Gravesend Handicap

## Principal progeny

### 1976

b f IT'S IN THE AIR (ex A Wind Is Rising, by Francis S.)
    1978    Arlington-Washington Lassie Stakes-Gr2
            Oak Leaf Stakes-Gr2
    1979    Vanity Handicap-Gr1
            Alabama Stakes-Gr1
            Delaware Oaks-Gr1
            Ruffian Handicap-Gr1
    1980    El Encino Stakes-Gr3
            Vanity Handicap-Gr1

### 1977

b c FAPPIANO (ex Killaloe, by Dr Fager)
    1980    Discovery Handicap-Gr3
    1981    Metropolitan Handicap-Gr1
b/br c GOLD STAGE (ex Stage Princess, by Cornish Prince)
    1979    Breeders' Futurity-Gr2
ch c HELLO GORGEOUS (ex Bonny Jet, by Jet Jewel)
    1979    Royal Lodge Stakes-Gr2
            Futurity Stakes-Gr1
    1980    Dante Stakes-Gr2

### 1978

ch c MISWAKI (ex Hopespringseternal, by Buckpasser)
    1980    Prix de la Salamandre-Gr1
b f SEEKER'S GOLD (ex I Understand, by Dr Fager)
    1982    Lightning Handicap-Gr3
    1984    Liverpool City Cup Handicap-Gr3

### 1979

b c CONQUISTADOR CIELO (ex K D Princess, by Bold Commander)
    1981    Saratoga Special Stakes-Gr2
    1982    Metropolitan Handicap-Gr1
            Belmont Stakes-Gr1
            Dwyer Stakes-Gr2
            Jim Dandy Stakes-Gr3
b/br c DISTINCTIVE PRO (ex Well Done, by Distinctive)
    1982    Hutcheson Stakes-Gr3
b/br c FAST GOLD (ex Flack Attack, by Ack Ack)
    1982    Paterson Handicap-Gr2
    1983    Excelsior Handicap-Gr2
b f GOLD BEAUTY (ex Stick to Beauty, by Illustrious)
    1982    Test Stakes-Gr2
            Fall Highweight Handicap-Gr2
    1983    True North Handicap-Gr3
b f VAIN GOLD (ex Chancy Dance, by Bold Reason)
    1981    Gardenia Stakes-Gr3

### 1980

ch c EILLO (ex Barbs Dancer, by Northern Dancer)
    1984    Breeders' Cup Sprint Stakes-Gr1
b c PROCLAIM (ex Maybellene, by Fleet Nasrullah)
    1983    Salisbury 2000 Guineas Trial Stakes-Gr3
b/br c STRIKE GOLD (ex Newchance Lady, by Roi Dagobert)
    1983    Bay Shore Stakes-Gr3
b f WIDAAD (ex Attache Case, by Diplomat Way)
    1982    Queen Mary Stakes-Gr2

### 1981

b f OPTIMISTIC LASS (ex Loveliest, by Tibaldo)
    1984    Musidora Stakes-Gr3
            Nassau Stakes-Gr2
br c PROCIDA (ex With Distinction, by Distinctive)
    1983    Criterium de Maisons-Laffitte-Gr2
    1984    Prix de la Foret-Gr1
            Hollywood Derby [Div.1]-Gr1
b f PROSKONA (ex Konafa, by Damascus)
    1984    Prix de Seine-et-Oise-Gr3
            Premio Umbria-Gr2
b f WITWATERSRAND (ex Sleek Belle, by Vaguely Noble)
    1984    Pucker Up Stakes [Div.1]-Gr3

### 1982

b c DAMISTER (ex Batucada, by Roman Line)
    1985    Classic Trial Stakes-Gr3
            Dante Stakes-Gr2
            Great Voltigeur Stakes-Gr2
br c GOLD CREST (ex Northernette, by Northern Dancer)
    1984    Beresford Stakes-Gr2
b c TANK'S PROSPECT (ex Midnight Pumpkin, by Pretense)
    1985    El Camino Real Derby-Gr3
            Arkansas Derby-Gr1
            Preakness Stakes-Gr1

### 1983

ch c GOLD ALERT (ex Croquis, by Arts and Letters)
    1987    Eclipse Handicap-Gr3
            Dominion Day Handicap-Gr3
ch c MOGAMBO (ex Lakeville Miss, by Rainy Lake)
    1985    Champagne Stakes-Gr1
    1986    Gotham Stakes-Gr2
b/br f SCOOT (ex Northernette, by Northern Dancer)
    1986    Flower Bowl Handicap-Gr1 [dead-heat]
ch c WOODMAN (ex Playmate, by Buckpasser)
    1985    Anglesey Stakes-Gr3
            Curragh Futurity Stakes-Gr3

### 1984

ch c AFLEET (ex Polite Lady, by Venetian Jester)
    1987    Jerome Handicap-Gr1
            Pennsylvania Derby-Gr2
    1988    Toboggan Handicap-Gr3
gr f AT RISK (ex Misgivings, by Cyane)
    1986    Rockfel Stakes-Gr3
b f CHIC SHIRINE (ex Too Chic, by Blushing Groom)
    1987    Ashland Stakes-Gr1
b c GONE WEST (ex Secrettame, by Secretariat)
    1987    Gotham Stakes-Gr2
            Withers Stakes-Gr2
            Dwyer Stakes-Gr1

b c GULCH (ex Jameela, by Rambunctious)
    1986    Tremont Stakes-Gr3
              Saratoga Special Stakes-Gr2
              Hopeful Stakes-Gr1
              Futurity Stakes-Gr1
    1987    Bay Shore Stakes-Gr2
              Wood Memorial Stakes-Gr1
              Metropolitan Handicap-Gr1
    1988    Potrero Grande Handicap-Gr3
              Carter Handicap-Gr1
              Metropolitan Handicap-Gr1
              Breeders' Cup Sprint Stakes-Gr1
ch c HOMEBUILDER (ex Smart Heiress, by Vaguely Noble)
    1988    Ben Ali Handicap-Gr3
              Fayette Handicap-Gr2
    1989    Baltimore Breeders' Cup Handicap-Gr3
ch c JADE HUNTER (ex Jadana, by Pharly)
    1988    Donn Handicap-Gr1
              Gulfstream Park Handicap-Gr1
ch c MINING (ex I Pass, by Buckpasser)
    1988    Vosburgh Stakes-Gr1

### 1985

b f BLUE JEAN BABY (ex Jones Time Machine, by Current Concept)
    1987    Sorority Stakes-Gr2
b/br f CLASSIC CROWN (ex Six Crowns, by Secretariat)
    1987    Frizette Stakes-Gr1
    1988    Gazelle Handicap-Gr1
ch c FORTY NINER (ex File, by Tom Rolfe)
    1987    Sanford Stakes-Gr2
              Futurity Stakes-Gr1
              Champagne Stakes-Gr1
              Breeders' Futurity-Gr2
    1988    Fountain of Youth Stakes-Gr2
              Haskell Invitational Handicap-Gr1
              Travers Stakes-Gr1
ch f OVER ALL (ex Full Tigress, by El Tigre Grande)
    1987    Landaluce Stakes-Gr3
              Schuylerville Stakes-Gr2
              Adirondack Stakes-Gr2
              Spinaway Stakes-Gr1
              Matron Stakes-Gr1

b f RAVINELLA (ex Really Lucky, by Northern Dancer)
    1987    Prix d'Arenberg-Gr3
              Cheveley Park Stakes-Gr1
    1988    1000 Guineas Stakes-Gr1
              Poule d'Essai des Pouliches-Gr1
b c SEEKING THE GOLD (ex Con Game, by Buckpasser)
    1988    Peter Pan Stakes-Gr2
              Dwyer Stakes-Gr1
              Super Derby-Gr1

### 1986

b c EBROS (ex Scuff, by Forli)
    1989    Round Table Stakes-Gr2
b/br f FANTASTIC FIND (ex Blitey, by Riva Ridge)
    1990    Hempstead Handicap-Gr1
ch f GILD (ex Veroushka, by Nijinsky)
    1988    Gardenia Stakes-Gr2
b c GOLD SEAM (ex Ballare, by Nijinsky)
    1989    Kiveton Park Stakes-Gr3
b c IDABEL (ex Impetuous Gal, by Briartic)
    1990    Ark-La-Tex Handicap-Gr3
br f TERSA (ex Peacefully, by Jacinto)
    1988    Prix du Bois-Gr3
              Prix Morny-Gr1

### 1987

ch c CARSON CITY (ex Blushing Promise, by Blushing Groom)
    1989    Sapling Stakes-Gr2
b f GOLDEN REEF (ex Virginia Reef, by Mill Reef)
    1989    Schuylerville Stakes-Gr2
b c JADE ROBBERY (ex Number, by Nijinsky)
    1989    Grand Criterium-Gr1
b c MACHIAVELLIAN (ex Coup de Folie, by Halo)
    1989    Prix Morny-Gr1
              Prix de la Salamandre-Gr1
b c RHYTHM (ex Dance Number, by Northern Dancer)
    1989    Breeders' Cup Juvenile Stakes-Gr1
    1990    Colin Stakes-Gr3

# Mummy's Pet

BEAUTY is in the eye of the beholder, they say, and sometimes the beholder may be in a minority of one. The anonymous writer who called Mummy's Pet a 'handsome individual' in the 1970 volume of *Racehorses* was either alone in his opinion or had been looking at the wrong horse. Even Mummy's Pet's best friends – and he made many good friends on account of the excellent results he achieved both on the racecourse and at stud – would never have called him handsome, and those most closely connected with him, with most reason to be kind about him, felt bound to be brutally honest about his defects.

He was tall and narrow, light of bone, with excessively long pasterns; he was over at the knee, he turned his toes out, and his hind-leg conformation was atrocious, with bent hocks set away from him. If you were to go in serious search of good points, you might have commended his heart room and his measurement from hip to hock, but most judges would already have turned away from an eyesore who looked a disgrace to his breed. It was no wonder that stud advertisements for Mummy's Pet did not feature the usual posed portrait; for years he was depicted being led across a field in longish grass in a shot which cleverly concealed his faults.

To appreciate Mummy's Pet, you had to see him move, and in that respect it was fortunate that he was bred and offered for sale in a country where it is the practice to walk horses around a ring rather than – as in America and many other nations – have them stand still for the appraisal of the onlookers. When Mummy's Pet made his delayed auction appearance at Tattersalls (having missed an earlier date because of a skin infection) in the 1969 December Sales, nobody could miss his bad points. However, nobody goes to a yearling sale expecting to find perfection; anyone who did would never buy a horse. The business is all about weighing good points against bad points, determining whether defects in some areas might be compensated for by more agreeable features elsewhere. The vastly experienced bloodstock agent Jack Doyle was on hand at Newmarket that day. As always he had clients for the precocious sprinting types which were his speciality, and he was attracted by the pedigree of Mummy's

Pet, which was all speed on both sides. The colt had been bred by Tim Holland-Martin's Overbury Stud, a renowned source of fast horses, and he came from its fastest family. It did not take Doyle long to establish that the yearling was a dreadful specimen. It was not just that he had faults in so many departments; he also was not made in the mould of the sprinter he was supposed to be. For all that, Doyle waited for Mummy's Pet to come into the ring, and suddenly he found himself prepared to forgive him everything. This young horse defied the weaknesses of his construction. He walked around the ring in about ten strides, moving sweetly and rhythmically. Doyle waved his catalogue, and bought him for 6000gns.

The agent was lucky that his client, a Hungarian bullion dealer called Lorant Goldschlager, had never owned a horse before and was about as conversant with the horse business as Doyle was with the international bullion market. Assured by the good judge who had bought him that he had a nice horse, and reassured by his trainer, John Sutcliffe, who professed to like him, Goldschlager was happy. As it turned out, he had every reason to be.

Mummy's Pet won his first three races. On his debut at Kempton he was a little slow to start, but soon caught up and had far too much speed for his modest rivals. Two weeks later he took the Hyperion Stakes at Ascot, again winning well while also confirming the message of his pedigree, that he would never want to go beyond six furlongs. At Doncaster he met stiffer competition in the Norfolk Stakes (later renamed the Flying Childers Stakes), but he underlined his progress in a smooth victory over Fireside Chat, the colt who had been runner-up on the occasion of Mill Reef's debut. The run of success stopped there, but only because he was asked to do the impossible in his last two races of the year. He finished second to Brigadier Gerard, probably the horse of the decade, in the Middle Park Stakes, and he was second again in the Cornwallis Stakes, beaten by Cawston's Pride, the fastest juvenile filly seen in Britain for many years.

In his second season Mummy's Pet was better than ever on his good days, but he was less consistent than as a two-year-old; all his races were over five furlongs. He had to struggle to overcome Pisces in the Sceptre Stakes at Kempton, and then ran unaccountably badly in the Group 3 Palace House Stakes at Newmarket. A week later, sporting a pair of blinkers for the first time, he won the Queen Elizabeth Handicap at Kempton under 9st 7lb in brilliant style, and before the month of May was out he was a Pattern winner, having made all and gamely accounted for Artaxerxes. By now the blinkers were deemed essential, but they did not help him to win again. He made the running in the King's Stand Stakes, but Swing Easy caught him and ran away from him in the final furlong. York was to prove more disappointing than Ascot, as he was never able to establish a clear lead in the Nunthorpe Stakes and finally faded into seventh place. Plans to run Mummy's Pet in the Prix de l'Abbaye were promptly abandoned.

Lorant Goldschlager had been repaid almost threefold through the prize money earned by his first horse. Between the King's Stand and the Nunthorpe he realized that appreciating asset, selling Mummy's Pet for a six-figure sum to David Gibson, who planned to syndicate him to stand at his Barleythorpe Stud. Gibson was committed to the deal by the time of the York defeat, an event which did not aid the sale of shares priced at 4000gns, and he had to persuade his friends Robert Percival and Tom Warner to make substantial investments when others were reluctant to come forward. The horse never was properly syndicated and it was not long before

the three owned the whole horse between them.

Mummy's Pet began at an official fee of £1000, though many nominations were sold at a discount and he had to take numerous inferior mares. Not surprisingly, his stock did not appeal in the sale-ring and it was crucially important to him that his early runners won races. They did; they won plenty of races. Of 15 runners in his first season, five won ten races; in his second crop he had ten two-year-old winners of 19 races. These were not high-class horses, but they did credit to a relatively cheap stallion who had been sent indifferent mares. Their bad hocks did not stop them winning, so perhaps trainers did have a good case for buying his yearlings, and perhaps breeders would be justified in entrusting him with better mares. Things began to look up.

In 1978 he was the leading sire in Britain and Ireland in terms of number of overall individual winners, individual two-year-old winners, two-year-old races won, and two-year-old earnings. There had to be something about him, even though he had yet to sire a Pattern winner.

Inevitably, the Pattern winners came, and with the better patronage, a general improvement in the performance of his stock. To quantity of winners, which was never a problem, he added quality, and before long he was acknowledged as Britain's prime source of speed and precocity. If he had his limitations, that was not necessarily a drawback.

*Mummy's Pet, a prolific sire of two-year-old winners.*

When you bred a Mummy's Pet, or bought one, you knew what you were going to get, and in an era when sprinting lines had died, either through neglect or natural exhaustion, he was the one reliable speed sire around. Eventually his fee rose to £14,000, and breeders were glad to pay it. Remarkably, all his Pattern winners were colts, and none was able to win at Group 1 level. He did, though, have a couple of good filly winners abroad in Miss Welsh, a noted performer in Brazil, and Teacher's Pet in America. His colt Mister Wonderful, only Group 3 standard here, eventually won a Grade 1 handicap in California.

Mummy's Pet was always highly strung and late in his stud life he became increasingly temperamental, occasionally subject to fits. He finally became a danger to his handlers and had to be destroyed on 22 September 1986. To date most of his sons at stud have had to start in the same modest way as Mummy's Pet himself, and they have not made the breakthrough that he achieved. A particular disappointment has been Precocious, an unbeaten horse whose career was halted by a knee injury which seemed merely unfortunate at the time. More recent developments suggest that there was an inherent weakness, as knee problems have been prevalent in Precocious's stock. Hopes for the succession now rest with Colmore Row in Ireland and Reprimand (who was probably his sire's best son and was endowed with rather more stamina than most), a recruit to the ranks of National Stud stallions in 1990.

## Racing record

| Year | Starts | Wins | 2nd | 3rd | 4th | £ |
|------|--------|------|-----|-----|-----|------|
| 1970 | 5 | 3 | 2 | - | - | 10,851 |
| 1971 | 6 | 3 | 1 | - | - | 6,314 |
| | 11 | 6 | 3 | - | - | 17,165 |

## Principal wins

1970   Norfolk Stakes
1971   Temple Stakes-Gr3

## Principal progeny

**1977**
br c RUNNETT (ex Rennet, by King's Bench)
    1981    Matt Gallagher Sprint Stakes-Gr3
            Haydock Sprint Cup-Gr2
b f TEACHER'S PET (ex Moben, by Counsel)
    1982    Suwannee River Handicap [Div.2]-Gr3

**1978**
b c CHUMMY'S SPECIAL (ex Go Too, by Goldhill)
    1980    Norfolk Stakes-Gr3
b c TINA'S PET (ex Merry Weather, by Will Somers)
    1982    King George Stakes-Gr3
            Goldene Peitsche-Gr3

**1979**
b c MUMMY'S GAME (ex Final Game, by Pardao)
    1982    Temple Stakes-Gr3

**1980**
b c ARAGON (ex Ica, by Great Nephew)
    1983    Prix de la Jonchere-Gr3

**1981**
b c PETORIUS (ex The Stork, by Club House)
    1983    Cornwallis Stakes-Gr3
    1984    Temple Stakes-Gr3 [dead-heat]

## MUMMY'S PET (bay, 1968)

| | | | |
|---|---|---|---|
| Sing Sing (b 1957) | Tudor Minstrel | Owen Tudor | Hyperion / Mary Tudor |
| | | Sansonnet | Sansovino / Lady Juror |
| | Agin the Law | Portlaw | Beresford / Portree |
| | | Revolte | Xandover / Sheba |
| Money for Nothing (br 1962) | Grey Sovereign | Nasrullah | Nearco / Mumtaz Begum |
| | | Kong | Baytown / Clang |
| | Sweet Nothings | Honeyway | Fairway / Honey Buzzard |
| | | Farthing Damages | Fair Trial / Futility |

b c PRECOCIOUS (ex Mrs Moss, by Reform)
    1983    Norfolk Stakes-Gr3
            Molecomb Stakes-Gr3
            Gimcrack Stakes-Gr2

**1983**
b c MISTER WONDERFUL (ex Baffle, by Petingo)
    1986    Criterion Stakes-Gr3
    1989    American Handicap-Gr1
b c TREASURE KAY (ex Welsh Blossom, by Welsh Saint)
    1987    Temple Stakes-Gr3

**1985**
b c COLMORE ROW (ex Front Row, by Epaulette)
    1987    Norfolk Stakes-Gr3
b c REPRIMAND (ex Just You Wait, by Nonoalco)
    1987    Gimcrack Stakes-Gr2
    1989    Earl of Sefton Stakes-Gr3
            Trusthouse Forte Mile-Gr2

# Nijinsky

IT takes all the fun out of having a lot of money if other people will not let you spend it. Charlie Engelhard found that frustrating in the summer of 1968. First he went to Keeneland to buy a half-sister to his dual classic winners Ribocco and Ribero, bid a world-record price for her and was dissuaded from going beyond $400,000 by his manager, David McCall, who reckoned that enough was enough. He, the platinum king, was made to yield to a *nouveau riche* supermarket chain owner. Next he sent Vincent O'Brien to Windfields Farm in Canada to inspect a colt by his favourite stallion Ribot, whose stock had suddenly become scarce in the auction market. Back came the report, 'Don't buy him. He has a crooked leg.' This was too much. Still, he consoled himself, that was what advisers were for. Maybe he would go ahead and buy the colt that O'Brien had liked at Windfields, the one by Northern Dancer. Yes, all right, if that was the way it had to be, instead of Reine Enchanteur (who won one little race) and Northern Monarch (who won two) he would make do with Nijinsky.

Engelhard had to bid a Canadian record price of $84,000 to buy Nijinsky at Woodbine, and he sent him to Ballydoyle along with the one Ribot colt he had been able to buy, the $81,000 Saratoga purchase Riboprince. O'Brien also took delivery of the crooked-legged Northern Monarch, whom Windfields boss Eddie Taylor had decided to keep rather than sell. On arrival, Nijinsky proved to be the awkward one. Used to a diet of nuts, he refused to touch oats – until a supply of nuts was procured, by which time he had become very fond of oats. He did not like to leave his box, and when he could be made to he would rear up and cause a fuss. He did not like having a man on his back. He sweated, he fretted, and he made it clear that did not fancy the idea of cantering at all. For months he was the problem child in the Ballydoyle nursery, but gradually the patience and understanding of O'Brien's staff won his confidence. He was always going to be a nervous type, but once he had accepted the routine he would co-operate, and by May he had given his handlers an inkling of what he would become.

Nijinsky started five times as a two-year-old, partnered by Liam Ward in four outings on The Curragh and by Lester Piggott on his only excursion to England. In July he won the Erne Stakes, toying with another newcomer called Everyday while beating him by half a length. In August he had Northern Monarch for company – briefly – in the Railway Stakes, but it was the locally-bred Decies who made sure that he raced in earnest for the first time. Decies set a good gallop and Ward was obliged to set Nijinsky alight. An electrifying burst of speed settled the issue and the margin was five lengths. Two weeks later he met Everyday (an eight-length winner at Naas in the meantime) again in the Anglesey Stakes and had to concede 7lb. Nijinsky trounced him once more, this time by three lengths. Decies came back for a second tilt at him in the Beresford Stakes, and gave him something like a contest. Nijinsky won comfortably in the end, by three-quarters of a length, but Ward was obliged to roust him up a bit to make him assert his authority.

Both Everyday and Decies had registered high-class form in their other races, so nobody was now blind to Nijinsky's merit. When the plan to send him for the Dewhurst Stakes was announced, connections of the best two-year-olds in England declined the invitation to a rout. The English defence was pathetic, but it would scarcely have mattered what was fielded against him that day. Nijinsky was a commanding sight, in physical development and performance, and he powered to his inevitable victory in brilliant style. There was no doubting the identity of the best two-year-old in Europe.

Nijinsky was always going to win the 2000 Guineas; no other possibility existed. He returned in April, limbering up with a smooth victory over Deep Run and Prince Tenderfoot in the seven-furlong Gladness Stakes at The Curragh, then duly completed the first classic formality, quickening to order and pulling clear impressively. As the season wore on it became clear that the best of the beaten Guineas horses were sprinters rather than milers, but that did not make Nijinsky's performance less remarkable. He had far too much pace for them, and could have used it to win at any stage. Not everybody was convinced that Nijinsky would win the Derby, and the two basic queries – whether he would stay and whether he could beat Gyr – added up to his starting at odds-against for the first time in his life. As he was an early product of his sire and his dam, who were both apparently best at ten furlongs, there was a shortage of evidence on the stamina question. As for Gyr, well, he did have a formidable reputation in France, and Etienne Pollet had postponed his retirement for a year in order to win a second Derby with this highly-strung son of his first, Sea-Bird.

Unbeknown to the public, a potentially more serious threat to a Nijinsky Derby victory was the attack of colic he suffered on the eve of the race, but that crisis was soon over and there were no signs of anything untoward on the day. Nijinsky was brilliant, sweeping majestically past Gyr at the furlong pole to prove that he was every bit as good at 12 furlongs as he had been at a mile. Back home at The Curragh he had much less to do than at Epsom and Liam Ward enjoyed an armchair ride in the Irish Derby, with Piggott this time second on Meadowville. A month later came the most impressive moment of Nijinsky's career, when he cruised past Blakeney, the previous year's Derby winner, still in a canter, en route to an effortless victory in the King George VI & Queen Elizabeth Stakes.

An attack of ringworm in August put the brake on Nijinsky's work for a while, but it did not prevent his date with destiny in the St Leger. Still on the bridle, he pulled his way to the front two furlongs from home, and though Meadowville came at him and challenged hard, the first Triple Crown in 35 years was never seriously at risk. Had he finished with racing after Doncaster, as Bahram had done in 1935, many might have concluded that Nijinsky was truly the Horse of the Century. It was unthinkable that within 12 months there would be, in training in England, not one but two colts with higher racing reputations.

Nijinsky was finished with winning after Doncaster. He should have won the Arc de Triomphe, and came to win it with his familiar, tremendous run, but he had come from too far behind, and no sooner was his head in front than Sassafras fought back. It was a new experience to find a competitor still resisting him at this stage of the proceedings, and to feel the crack of his rider's whip. Crucially, Nijinsky edged to the left when to have kept straight might still have saved the day. Sassafras beat him by a head. Only 13 days later he tried to erase that memory, but the huge throng who gathered at Newmarket for the farewell celebrations in the Champion Stakes were to be sadly disappointed. As he left the paddock he became warm and on edge; at the start he boiled over into a muck sweat. He had taken enough, and he showed

as much in the race. When Piggott asked him to go and challenge Lorenzaccio he declined, and it was by only a neck that the weary campaigner retained second place over Hotfoot.

Only a fortnight earlier Nijinsky had seemed like the Horse of the Century; now he had to depart to Claiborne Farm as a fallen hero, instead of an unbeaten champion, a two-time loser. Nevertheless, nobody in America was going to regard him as anything other than a great racehorse, worthy of the best opportunities as a stallion. The odd defeat was par for any horse's course, and Nijinsky's genes – the only currency he would use in his new career – remained exactly what they were when he was unbeaten. What had happened at Longchamp and Newmarket could not alter the fact that here was an exceptional physical specimen, massive at 16.3 hands, yet astonishingly sound and light on his feet, able to produce instant acceleration at the end of a race over any distance.

Horses of Nijinsky's stature do not reproduce themselves. Such as Sea-Bird, Brigadier Gerard, Tudor Minstrel, Abernant, Ribot, Mill Reef, Vaguely Noble and Alleged have all proved that, and Dancing Brave will be another example. The best that we are entitled to hope is that such giants will raise the level of merit in the population by getting a high proportion of superior runners. Nijinsky has surpassed all those mentioned above in his capacity to get numerous runners within a few pounds of his own calibre. He has been a better sire of racehorses than Northern Dancer. His greatness at stud matches his greatness on the racecourse.

Nijinsky was syndicated, between his 'King George' and St Leger triumphs, for a world-record $5.44 million, being divided into 32 shares at $170,000. Charlie Engelhard retained ten, though he was to die soon after the horse began covering. His first book of mares was perhaps more notable for relations to champions than for champions themselves, but he was a newcomer in an intensely competitive business, pitted against horses who were already proven progenitors. His chance with the champions would come, if he were to make a success of his new role.

Success came just as soon as it could. His first runner in England, Silky, won on her debut. His first runner in the States, Copernica, and his first in France, Green Dancer, did the same. By the end of 1974 Nijinsky was champion first-season sire in Britain, thanks to Green Dancer's victory in the Observer Gold Cup. The assumption that if they were good at two, they would be better still at three proved correct. Green Dancer won twice more at

Group 1 level, and Caucasus won the Irish St Leger. Nijinsky never looked back.

From the start it was apparent that he could get runners suitable for racing on both sides of the Atlantic, and from all but two of his first 16 crops there have been winners of both Pattern Races and Graded Stakes; there has never been a crop without one or the other. He ranks second only to his sire in number of individual stakes winners and seems set to take over the number one spot some time in 1991; his ratio of stakes winners to foals is also among the best of this or any era.

While he remains the best all-round stallion son of his sire, it seems important to note that he is by no means a typical Northern Dancer horse, his stock rarely typical of the Northern Dancer-line horses as exemplified by the Lyphards, the Danzigs and the Nureyevs. Nijinsky is a one-off, a full hand taller than his sire and appreciably bigger than most of his sire's progeny; as a racehorse he looked different, and displayed different aptitudes, from the other Northern Dancers, and as a sire he has not conformed to the accepted N.D. pattern. To all intents and purposes he is not a Northern Dancer; he is Nijinsky, and his progeny are Nijinskys rather than Northern Dancer-line horses.

His stock are generally big, the majority being over 16 hands, ranging up to the 17.2-hand Quiet Fling, but he has never yet got a son who could match his own commanding physique. They tend to be plainer, some to the point of ugliness, and he has had his quota of over-big specimens, straight in the shoulder, unsound and slow into the bargain. Remarkably, one or two of that sort, notably Whiskey Road in Australia, have sired handsome stock, with the good shoulders characteristic of the Northern Dancer breed.

The Nijinskys are not precocious. They come to themselves in the second half of their first season, and they peak at three – or later, if they get the chance. In their maturity a mile is their minimum, and it is a rare one – like Kings Lake or Shadeed – who would not rather go at least a mile and a quarter. A rarer one still is Dancing Spree, who came back from a win in the ten-furlong Suburban Handicap to take the Breeders' Cup Sprint over six furlongs. Like Mill Reef, another whose ability to last the Derby course was doubted, Nijinsky has proved himself to be primarily an influence for stamina, which is why he has figured more often among the top ten sires in Britain and Ireland (six times) than in America (three). In 1986 he topped the British list and ranked fourth in the States, thanks to his unique feat of siring Epsom (Shahrastani) and Kentucky

*Nijinsky after winning the St Leger and thus achieving the first Triple Crown for 35 years.*

(Ferdinand) Derby winners in the same crop. That pair were also instrumental in dispelling the irrational idea that Nijinsky's chesnuts were inferior to his bays.

Nijinsky's fee, 'only' $80,000 in 1979, rose by stages to $450,000 in 1984, when he provided an appropriate response with a tally of nine Pattern or Graded winners from the resultant foals. Commercially, they did not fare so well; nine of the 17 sold at auction did not cover the service cost. Still, though it is no kind of achievement to have a yearling son whom two people mistakenly believe to be worth $13 million, it is a fact that Seattle Dancer (from a crop conceived for $250,000) made Nijinsky the sire of the horse who, it is hoped, will remain the highest-priced auction Thoroughbred for all time. As well as his notoriety, Seattle Dancer also had some brief moments of fame, winning a couple of Group 2 events in Ireland before a hasty exit to stud.

The fact that Nijinsky's fifteenth crop was the first to have produced no three-year-old Pattern or Graded winner might have been taken as a sign that his powers were finally beginning to wane, but that impression was promptly contradicted by a sixteenth crop which gave him his best-ever score with two-year-olds – two Graded winners in North America and two Pattern winners in Ireland. That rise coincided with the sixth consecutive reduction in his fee, which was down to $115,000 for his twentieth stud season in 1990.

With so much success over so long a period with his runners, Nijinsky might have been expected to be well established as a sire of sires by now. He has done a good deal better than Habitat in that respect, and among his 80-odd sons now at stud he has many more than Mill Reef with 'breeder-credibility', but he does not have a counterpart to Mill Reef's Shirley Heights. The fact is often used as a stick with which to beat Nijinsky, especially on account of the contrast with the record of Northern Dancer's other sons. There have been some particularly disappointing failures, most notably the unsound and undefeated Derby winner Golden Fleece, whose early death seemed a tragedy at the time but, in view of the subsequent showing of his runners, must have saved breeders an enormous amount of money and enabled their mares to find better opportunities elsewhere. There is a prejudice against Nijinsky horses, which is inevitably working against his long-term influence, but there is still time for perceptions to change. A move in his favour may well occur before long.

## Racing record

| Year | Starts | Wins | 2nd | 3rd | 4th | £ |
|------|--------|------|-----|-----|-----|---|
| 1969 | 5 | 5 | - | - | - | 20,017 |
| 1970 | 8 | 6 | 2 | - | - | 262,206 |
| | 13 | 11 | 2 | - | - | 282,223 |

## Principal wins

| | | |
|---|---|---|
| 1969 | Railway Stakes | |
| | Anglesey Stakes | |
| | Beresford Stakes | |
| | Dewhurst Stakes | |
| 1970 | Gladness Stakes | |
| | 2000 Guineas Stakes | |
| | Derby Stakes | |
| | Irish Derby | |
| | King George VI & Queen Elizabeth Stakes | |
| | St Leger Stakes | |

## Principal progeny

**1972**

bc CAUCASUS (ex Quill, by Princequillo)
  1975  Irish St Leger-Gr1
  1976  Sunset Handicap-Gr1
        Manhattan Handicap-Gr2
  1977  Arcadia Handicap-Gr3
        San Luis Rey Stakes-Gr1
b c DANCING CHAMP (ex Mrs Peterkin, by Tom Fool)
  1975  Woodlawn Stakes [Div.1]-Gr3
  1976  Massachusetts Handicap-Gr2

## NIJINSKY (bay, 1967)

| | | | |
|---|---|---|---|
| **Northern Dancer** (b 1961) | Nearctic | Nearco | Pharos |
| | | | Nogara |
| | | Lady Angela | Hyperion |
| | | | Sister Sarah |
| | Natalma | Native Dancer | Polynesian |
| | | | Geisha |
| | | Almahmoud | Mahmoud |
| | | | Arbitrator |
| **Flaming Page** (b 1959) | Bull Page | Bull Lea | Bull Dog |
| | | | Rose Leaves |
| | | Our Page | Blue Larkspur |
| | | | Occult |
| | Flaring Top | Menow | Pharamond |
| | | | Alcibiades |
| | | Flaming Top | Omaha |
| | | | Firetop |

b c GREEN DANCER (ex Green Valley, by Val de Loir)
  1974  Observer Gold Cup-Gr1
  1975  Poule d'Essai des Poulains-Gr1
        Prix Lupin-Gr1
b f LIGHTED GLORY (ex Lighted Lamp, by Sir Gaylord)
  1975  Prix de Flore-Gr3
b c QUIET FLING (ex Peace, by Klairon)
  1976  John Porter Stakes-Gr2
        Coronation Cup-Gr1

b f SUMMERTIME PROMISE (ex Prides Promise, by Crozier)
    1977    Gallorette Handicap-Gr3

### 1973

b f AFRICAN DANCER (ex Miba, by Ballymoss)
    1976    Cheshire Oaks-Gr3
            Park Hill Stakes-Gr2
b c BRIGHT FINISH (ex Lacquer, by Shantung)
    1976    Jockey Club Cup-Gr3
    1977    Yorkshire Cup-Gr2
b f JAVAMINE (ex Dusky Evening, by Tim Tam)
    1976    Long Island Handicap-Gr3
            Knickerbocker Handicap [Div.1]-Gr3
    1977    Diana Handicap-Gr2
            Arlington Matron Handicap-Gr2
ch f NIJANA (ex Prodana Neviesta, by Reneged)
    1975    Schuylerville Stakes-Gr3

### 1974

b c LUCKY SOVEREIGN (ex Sovereign, by Pardao)
    1977    Dante Stakes-Gr3
ch c PAS DE DEUX (ex So Chic, by Nasrullah)
    1978    Prix du Palais Royal-Gr3
b c UPPER NILE (ex Rosetta Stone, by Round Table)
    1978    Nassau County Handicap-Gr3
            Suburban Handicap-Gr1
b c VALINSKY (ex Valoris, by Tiziano)
    1977    Geoffrey Freer Stakes-Gr2

### 1975

b f CHERRY HINTON (ex Popkins, by Romulus)
    1977    Fillies' Mile-Gr3
br c ILE DE BOURBON (ex Roseliere, by Misti)
    1978    King Edward VII Stakes-Gr2
            King George VI & Queen Elizabeth Stakes-Gr1
            Geoffrey Freer Stakes-Gr2
    1979    Coronation Cup-Gr1
ch c NIZON (ex Exit Smiling, by Stage Door Johnny)
    1978    Prix du Lys-Gr3
            Prix de Lutece-Gr3
            Premio Roma-Gr1
b c STRADAVINSKY (ex Seximee, by Hasty Road)
    1978    Whitehall Stakes-Gr3
b f SUMMER FLING (ex Fast Approach, by First Landing)
    1978    Open Fire Stakes [Div.2]-Gr3
ch f TERPSICHORIST (ex Glad Rags, by High Hat)
    1978    Long Island Handicap-Gr3
    1979    Sheepshead Bay Handicap-Gr2

### 1976

ch c CZARAVICH (ex Black Satin, by Linacre)
    1979    Withers Stakes-Gr2
            Jerome Handicap-Gr2
    1980    Carter Handicap-Gr2
            Metropolitan Handicap-Gr1
b c NINISKI (ex Virginia Hills, by Tom Rolfe)
    1979    Geoffrey Freer Stakes-Gr2
            Irish St Leger-Gr1
            Prix Royal-Oak-Gr1
    1980    John Porter Stakes-Gr2
            Ormonde Stakes-Gr3

### 1977

b c MUSCOVITE (ex Alyne Que, by Raise a Native)
    1980    Whitehall Stakes-Gr3
ch c NICE HAVRAIS (ex Shoubra, by Bon Mot)
    1980    Prix de Fontainebleau-Gr3

b c NIGHT ALERT (ex Moment of Truth, by Matador)
    1980    Gladness Stakes-Gr3
            Prix Jean Prat-Gr2
b f PRINCESSE LIDA (ex Princesse Lee, by Habitat)
    1979    Prix Morny-Gr1
            Prix de la Salamandre-Gr1
b c SHINING FINISH (ex Lacquer, by Shantung)
    1980    St Simon Stakes-Gr3

### 1978

b f BALLETOMANE (ex Nanticious, by Nantallah)
    1981    Princess Stakes-Gr3
b f DE LA ROSE (ex Rosetta Stone, by Round Table)
    1981    Saranac Stakes-Gr3
            Long Branch Stakes-Gr3
            Diana Handicap-Gr2
            Athenia Handicap-Gr3
            E.P. Taylor Stakes-Gr3
            Hollywood Derby [Div.1]-Gr1
b c KINGS LAKE (ex Fish-Bar, by Baldric)
    1981    Irish 2000 Guineas-Gr1
            Sussex Stakes-Gr1
            Joe McGrath Memorial Stakes-Gr1
ch f LEAP LIVELY (ex Quilloquick, by Graustark)
    1980    Fillies' Mile-Gr3
    1981    Oaks Trial Stakes-Gr3
ch c NIJINSKY'S SECRET (ex Secret Beauty, by Raise a Native)
    1982    Tidal Handicap-Gr2
    1983    Bougainvillea Handicap [Div.1]-Gr2
            Hialeah Turf Cup Stakes-Gr1
            King Edward Gold Cup Handicap-Gr3
    1984    W.L.McKnight Handicap [Div.2]-Gr2
            Hialeah Turf Cup Handicap-Gr1

### 1979

b c GOLDEN FLEECE (ex Exotic Treat, by Vaguely Noble)
    1982    Ballymoss Stakes-Gr2
            Nijinsky Stakes-Gr2
            Derby Stakes-Gr1
b c HOSTAGE (ex Entente, by Val de Loir)
    1982    Arkansas Derby-Gr1
b c KHATANGO (ex Penny Flight, by Damascus)
    1982    Seneca Handicap-Gr3
    1983    Dixie Handicap-Gr2
b f NUMBER (ex Special, by Forli)
    1982    First Flight Handicap-Gr3
            Firenze Handicap-Gr2
    1983    Hempstead Handicap-Gr2
b c PEACETIME (ex Peace, by Klairon)
    1982    Classic Trial Stakes-Gr3
b f ROSE CRESCENT (ex Roseliere, by Misti)
    1983    Athenia Handicap-Gr3

### 1980

ch c BEAUDELAIRE (ex Bitty Girl, by Habitat)
    1983    Prix Maurice de Gheest-Gr2
ch f BEMISSED (ex Bemis Heights, by Herbager)
    1982    Miss Grillo Stakes-Gr3
            Selima Stakes-Gr1
b c BROGAN (ex Drumtop, by Round Table)
    1983    Prix Berteux-Gr3
b c CAERLEON (ex Foreseer, by Round Table)
    1982    Anglesey Stakes-Gr3
    1983    Prix du Jockey-Club-Gr1
            Benson & Hedges Gold Cup-Gr1
b c GORYTUS (ex Glad Rags, by High Hat)
    1982    Champagne Stakes-Gr2

b c SOLFORD (ex Fairness, by Cavan)
    1983    Prix du Lys-Gr3
             Eclipse Stakes-Gr1
b c VAL DANSEUR (ex Green Valley, by Val de Loir)
    1986    Golden Gate Handicap-Gr2 [dead-heat]
             Rolling Green Handicap-Gr3

### 1981

b c EMPIRE GLORY (ex Spearfish, by Round Table)
    1984    Royal Whip Stakes-Gr3
b f KEY DANCER (ex Key Partner, by Key to the Mint)
    1984    Athenia Handicap-Gr3
    1985    Matchmaker Stakes-Gr2
b c NAGURSKI (ex Deceit, by Prince John)
    1984    Woodlawn Stakes-Gr3
b c TIGHTS (ex Dancealot, by Round Table)
    1984    Silver Screen Handicap-Gr2
             La Jolla Mile Stakes-Gr3
             Volante Handicap-Gr3
b f VIDALIA (ex Waya, by Faraway Son)
    1983    Criterium Femminile-Gr3
b c VISION (ex Foreseer, by Round Table)
    1983    Pilgrim Stakes [Div.2]-Gr3
    1984    Secretariat Stakes-Gr1
b c WESTERN SYMPHONY (ex Millicent, by Cornish Prince)
    1983    Larkspur Stakes-Gr3

### 1982

b f DUTY DANCE (ex Discipline, by Princequillo)
    1986    Beaugay Handicap-Gr3
             Diana Handicap-Gr2
b c FIRE OF LIFE (ex Spark of Life, by Key to the Mint)
    1985    St Leger Italiano-Gr2
    1986    Premio Roma-Gr1
b f FOLK ART (ex Homespun, by Round Table)
    1984    Oak Leaf Stakes-Gr1
b c GALLANT ARCHER (ex Belle of Dodge Me, by Creme Dela Creme)
    1986    Louisiana Downs Handicap-Gr3
b c MOSCOW BALLET (ex Millicent, by Cornish Prince)
    1984    Railway Stakes-Gr3
b c SHADEED (ex Continual, by Damascus)
    1985    Craven Stakes-Gr3
             2000 Guineas-Gr1
             Queen Elizabeth II Stakes-Gr2

### 1983

b c DANCE OF LIFE (ex Spring Is Here, by In Reality)
    1986    Man o' War Stakes-Gr1
    1987    Fort Marcy Handicap [Div.1]-Gr3
             Tidal Handicap-Gr2
ch c FERDINAND (ex Banja Luka, by Double Jay)
    1986    Kentucky Derby-Gr1
             Malibu Stakes-Gr2
    1987    Hollywood Gold Cup Handicap-Gr1
             Goodwood Handicap-Gr3
             Breeders' Cup Classic Stakes-Gr1
b c FRED ASTAIRE (ex Late Bloomer, by Stage Door Johnny)
    1986    Rutgers Handicap [Div.1]-Gr2
b c MANZOTTI (ex Shufleur, by Tom Rolfe)
    1988    John B. Campbell Handicap-Gr3
             Trenton Handicap-Gr3
             Canterbury Cup Handicap-Gr3
ch c SHAHRASTANI (ex Shademah, by Thatch)
    1986    Classic Trial Stakes-Gr3
             Dante Stakes-Gr2
             Derby Stakes-Gr1
             Irish Derby-Gr1

### 1984

ch f DANCING ALL NIGHT (ex Blitey, by Riva Ridge)
    1988    Long Island Handicap-Gr2
b f HELENSKA (ex In the Offing, by Hoist the Flag)
    1988    Vineland Handicap-Gr3
b c MERCE CUNNINGHAM (ex Foreseer, by Round Table)
    1988    Prix Maurice de Nieuil-Gr2
b c SEATTLE DANCER (ex My Charmer, by Poker)
    1987    Irish Derby Trial Stakes-Gr2
             Gallinule Stakes-Gr2
b c SWORD DANCE (ex Rosa Mundi, by Secretariat)
    1988    Del Mar Invitational Handicap-Gr2

### 1985

b f BANKER'S LADY (ex Impetuous Gal, by Briartic)
    1988    Long Look Handicap-Gr2
             Ladies Handicap-Gr2
    1989    Bed o' Roses Handicap-Gr2
             Top Flight Handicap-Gr1
             Shuvee Handicap-Gr1
ch c DANCING SPREE (ex Blitey, by Riva Ridge)
    1989    True North Handicap-Gr2
             Suburban Handicap-Gr1
             Breeders' Cup Sprint Stakes-Gr1
    1990    Carter Handicap-Gr1
b f JEANNE JONES (ex Beautiful Glass, by Pass the Glass)
    1988    Fantasy Stakes-Gr1
b c LAKE COMO (ex La Dame du Lac, by Round Table)
    1987    Anglesey Stakes-Gr3
b f LOVE YOU BY HEART (ex Queen's Paradise, by Summer Tan)
    1988    Nijana Stakes [Div.2]-Gr3
             Queen Elizabeth II Challenge Cup Stakes-Gr2
    1989    Suwannee River Handicap [Div.1]-Gr3
             Black Helen Handicap-Gr2
             Sheepshead Bay Handicap-Gr2
b f MAPLEJINSKY (ex Gold Beauty, by Mr Prospector)
    1988    Monmouth Oaks-Gr1
             Alabama Stakes-Gr1
b c MISTER MODESTY (ex Dearly Precious, by Dr Fager)
    1989    Pennsylvania Governor's Cup Handicap-Gr3
ch f MYSTERY RAYS (ex Rare Mint, by Key to the Mint)
    1988    Prix Fille de l'Air-Gr3
             Prix Minerve-Gr3
b f NIKISHKA (ex Bendara, by Never Bend)
    1989    Las Palmas Handicap-Gr2

### 1986

b c CLASSIC FAME (ex Family Fame, by Droll Role)
    1988    National Stakes-Gr1
             Beresford Stakes-Gr2
b f CONNIE'S GIFT (ex Connie Knows, by Buckpasser)
    1990    Louisville Breeders' Cup Handicap-Gr2
b c ROYAL ACADEMY (ex Crimson Saint, by Crimson Satan)
    1990    Tetrarch Stakes-Gr3

### 1987

ch f SAVINA (ex Wedding Reception, by Round Table)
    1989    Miss Grillo Stakes-Gr3
b c SINGLE COMBAT (ex La Dame du Lac, by Round Table)
    1989    Anglesey Stakes-Gr3
ch c SKY CLASSIC (ex No Class, by Nodouble)
    1989    Summer Stakes-Gr3
             Grey Stakes-Gr3
ch c VICTORY PIPER (ex Arisen, by Mr Prospector)
    1989    Beresford Stakes-Gr2

# Niniski

TOWARDS the end of the 1960s only one non-American supporter had both the inclination and the necessary funds to become involved in the upper echelons of the US yearling market. Lady Beaverbrook, widow of the press baron, was on her own, a pioneer where, not so many years hence, many would have to follow in search of the horses who seemed to be able to out-run everything that the European defenders could put up against them. Sadly, she did not obtain much in the way of reward for her efforts, proving especially unfortunate with some extremely expensive sons of Sea-Bird, and when she finally achieved her target of an English classic winner – Bustino – it came from a reasonably priced product of an English stud. Nevertheless, Lady B. persevered in America, always seeking colts with stamina by classic stallions, more often at Saratoga than at Keeneland, and in 1977 her persistence paid off. For $90,000 she bought a son of Nijinsky who not only won her two Group 1 races, but also became the sire of two other colts who raced to fame in her popular brown and green colours.

Much the best thing that could be said about Niniski's pedigree was Nijinsky. The colt's dam, Virginia Hills, had won only a nine-furlong maiden race as a three-year-old from 15 efforts, and the closest connection she could claim to anything of quality was that her paternal grandsire and maternal grand-dam had been the parents of Riboccare, a game but somewhat one-paced winner of the Jockey Club Cup. At least there was every reason to believe that he would stay.

Niniski went into training with Dick Hern, who knew a prospective stayer when he saw one and knew not to rush him. As a two-year-old the colt was so backward that his trainer decided to leave him pretty much to his own devices, taking him to the racecourse just once, for educational purposes. He ran twelfth in a field of 23 for a Newbury maiden, and that was as much as was expected. What Lady Beaverbrook expected of her three-year-old colts was that they should contest the classics, most especially the Derby and St Leger, so Hern got down to more serious work with him in the following spring, although he had, in Troy and Milford, two supposedly much brighter prospects.

The colt began propitiously at three, winning a mile maiden at Newmarket from 27 others, and he then ran a close second in a minor event at York. He was not going to win a Derby on that form, but he ran anyway because that was what Lady Beaverbrook wanted, and his ninth place behind Troy was not at all bad; at least he beat Milford. Another stable companion, More Light, proved a stumbling-block in Goodwood's Gordon Stakes, but he battled hard and went under by only three-quarters of a length. He was obviously on the upgrade, and he was probably as good as any stayer who was not trained in his own yard. In the Geoffrey Freer Stakes, his first race in open company and his first beyond 12 furlongs, he proved the point, progressing under hard driving from Willie Carson and winning with authority from M–Lolshan, who had been third in the 1978 St Leger.

Niniski was not up to winning his St Leger, but he gave it his best shot, forging clear in the straight and trying to sap his rivals' stamina. The ploy disposed of his English foes, but the French-trained pair Son of Love and Soleil Noir were too strong for him in the last furlong. Still, there were compensations – and Group 1 honours – yet to be won in the Irish and French St Legers, and Niniski now came into his own. The opposition at The Curragh was well below true classic standard, and Niniski's ten-length romp made that point emphatically. At Longchamp, in the Prix Royal-Oak (opened to older horses for the first time), the field was better, but there was nothing as good as the pair who had beaten him at Doncaster, and Niniski beat the best of them, Anifa, by a length and a half in the style of a resolute stayer.

In his third season Niniski began by revealing an apparently new dimension to his talents, showing good acceleration to come from an unpromising position and win the John Porter Stakes by three lengths from Morse Code. He then made heavy weather of what had seemed to be a relatively easy task in the Ormonde Stakes, and it was downhill all the way thereafter. He had his revenge over Soleil Noir in the Coronation Cup, but never looked like catching all-the-way winner Sea Chimes. That was his third consecutive race on firm ground, and he did not seem to appreciate it. He was not seen again until the autumn, and even then was barely sighted - thirteenth in the Arc de Triomphe, sixth in the Royal-Oak, the latter on the soft ground he was supposed to favour.

Niniski was syndicated to stand at Kirsten Rausing's Lanwades Stud in Newmarket, his fee set at £5000, and the 'knowing ones' in the industry wondered who it was who could have talked such a shrewd horsewoman into standing a late-developing, one-paced horse by a stallion whose sons were not doing well at stud, and who was bound to get stock ill-equipped for racing in the modern era. They began to have second thoughts when Kala Dancer won the Dewhurst Stakes, was named champion two-year-old and earned Niniski the first-season sires' title, beating no less a rival than Kris.

Kala Dancer went wrong as a three-year-old, breaking blood vessels, but along came his contemporaries Kiliniski and Petoski with prestige victories to change many perceptions of their sire. Niniski's fee, which had edged up to £6000 in his fourth season and had been pushed to £14,000 in his fifth, now rocketed to £40,000. It was a move which entailed long-term risk, but in the short term promised to procure a higher class of mare while maximizing income at the opportune moment. As it turned out, 15 of 20 auctioned yearlings from that crop fetched less than the cost of the nomination. The fee was reduced in each of the four following seasons and in 1990 (before the most expensively produced crop had raced as three-year-olds) was down to £12,500. That was in spite of the fact that Lady Beaverbrook, after her great triumph with Petoski, had enjoyed a second wonderful win with a Niniski product, in Minster Son's St Leger.

It is rare for any stallion to get a runner of higher class than himself, and Niniski has earned respect for his ability to do that. His problem has been that for a while it cost breeders too much to discover that he does not manage it very often, and that the market will not trust him to manage it on a regular basis. He is tending now to get the stayers he was always expected to get, and though he may not be the glamour sire he once aspired to be, he may yet establish himself as a consistent source of stamina, valuable to British breeders.

*Niniski quickens well to defeat Morse Code and Torus (right) in the John Porter Stakes at Newbury.*

## Racing record

| Year | Starts | Wins | 2nd | 3rd | 4th | £ |
|------|--------|------|-----|-----|-----|---|
| 1978 | 1 | - | - | - | - | - |
| 1979 | 8 | 4 | 2 | 1 | - | 97,351 |
| 1980 | 5 | 2 | 1 | - | - | 41,286 |
| | 14 | 6 | 3 | 1 | - | 138,637 |

## Principal wins

| | | |
|---|---|---|
| 1979 | Geoffrey Freer Stakes-Gr2 |
| | Irish St Leger-Gr1 |
| | Prix Royal-Oak-Gr1 |
| 1980 | John Porter Stakes-Gr2 |
| | Ormonde Stakes-Gr3 |

## Principal progeny

**1982**

gr c KALA DANCER (ex Kalazero, by Kalamoun)
    1984   Dewhurst Stakes-Gr1
ch f KILINISKI (ex Kilavea, by Hawaii)
    1985   Oaks Trial Stakes-Gr3
b c PETOSKI (ex Sushila, by Petingo)
    1985   Princess of Wales's Stakes-Gr2
           King George VI & Queen Elizabeth Stakes-Gr1

**1983**

b c KADIAL (ex Khadaeen, by Lyphard)
    1988   Dixie Handicap-Gr2

## NINISKI (bay, 1976)

| | | | |
|---|---|---|---|
| Nijinsky (b 1967) | Northern Dancer | Nearctic | Nearco |
| | | | Lady Angela |
| | | Natalma | Native Dancer |
| | | | Almahmoud |
| | Flaming Page | Bull Page | Bull Lea |
| | | | Our Page |
| | | Flaring Top | Menow |
| | | | Flaming Top |
| Virginia Hills (b 1971) | Tom Rolfe | Ribot | Tenerani |
| | | | Romanella |
| | | Pocahontas | Roman |
| | | | How |
| | Ridin' Easy | Ridan | Nantallah |
| | | | Rough Shod |
| | | Easy Eight | Eight Thirty |
| | | | Your Game |

**1984**

b c SERGEYEVICH (ex Rexana, by Relko)
    1987   Goodwood Cup-Gr3
           St Leger Italiano-Gr2
    1988   Sagaro Stakes-Gr3

**1985**

ch c MINSTER SON (ex Honey Bridge, by Crepello)
    1988   Gordon Stakes-Gr3
           St Leger Stakes-Gr1

# Northern Dancer

THERE is plenty of advice available in the horse business. Most of it will cost you, and some of it might just cost you . . . well, millions in the long run. Larkin Maloney was quite a well-known owner on the Toronto racing circuit, and he knew a thing or two about horses, but he was not so sure of himself that he would want to buy a yearling without his trainer's approval. That was why he took his trainer along to Eddie Taylor's pre-priced yearling sale at Windfields in September 1962. As it happened, he found a colt there he really liked, and under the terms of the sale he could be Maloney's for $25,000 – unless anybody else wanted to bid higher. The owner could not disguise his enthusiasm, but, in all honesty, the trainer could not hide his opposite opinion. 'He's just too small, and he'll never amount to much,' he advised, 'but if you really want to spend that much, why not buy that good colt by Menetrier?' Maloney bowed to the professional's greater wisdom in such matters, and in normal circumstances he would not have been disappointed about a $25,000 investment in a stakes winner who earned $67,548. It was just a shame that the one he had really wanted to buy was Northern Dancer.

Maloney's trainer was not the only one who thought that the little colt by Nearctic out of Natalma was too little. In fact nobody would bid the asking price, so Eddie Taylor was forced to keep him. It was his own fault for producing such a late foal. When Natalma broke a bone in a knee during her training for the Kentucky Oaks, he had brought her back to the farm and pondered for too long over the question of whether an operation which might make her sound enough for further racing would be worthwhile. It was mid-June before he had decided to keep her at Windfields and the end of the month before she had been mated with Nearctic, his headstrong Nearco horse then in his first season at stud. He could hardly blame anybody who did not want to buy a runt of a yearling, born on 27 May.

Taylor turned Northern Dancer out into a paddock, hoped he might grow a bit, and trusted to the Canadian winter to toughen him up. In the following March he fetched him in, noted that he had not grown much, and sent him to his trainer, Horatio Luro, to see what he could make of him. Luro gave

him time, and did not start him until 2 August, two weeks after Raise a Native, the colt who would be named champion two-year-old, had ended his racing career and had been retired to stud. In a sense, Northern Dancer took over where Raise a Native left off. He won his maiden in fine style, by nearly seven lengths. That race, and his next two, were at Fort Erie. In the Vandal Stakes he was beaten easily, but he won the Summer Stakes, over a mile on turf, leading all the way. He ran on the grass again at Woodbine, in the Cup and Saucer Stakes, and he was the best horse at the weights, but he could not concede 11lb to Grand Garcon, a colt whom Eddie Taylor had sold for $10,000. Northern Dancer was not beaten again in 1963. He took an allowance race and the Coronation Futurity (by more than six lengths) at Woodbine, then the Carleton Stakes at Greenwood. There was not much doubt that he was the best two-year-old in Canada; he might as well try his luck south of the border. He did, and he thrashed the good colt Bupers by eight lengths in an Aqueduct allowance race as a prelude to an all-the-way win in the mile Remsen Stakes over the same track.

Northern Dancer had won seven of nine races in his first season and had been second in the other two. He was Canada's champion, and he ranked only 3lb below Raise a Native on the North American handicap. He had also acquired a quarter-crack, an injury to the hoof on his near-fore, and he underwent repairs on his trainer's farm in Georgia during December. Luro put him back into work the following month at Hialeah and ran him in a minor six-furlong race. He was never nearer than third and his jockey, who had hit him contrary to instructions, was fired. With Bill Shoemaker up he won the Flamingo Stakes, and moved on to Gulfstream Park, where he gave The Scoundrel 8lb and beat him by four lengths in a seven-furlong allowance race, repeating that result at level weights, though by only a length, in the nine-furlong Florida Derby. He had won the two best races for three-year-olds in Florida, and he was ready to go to Kentucky. The only thing to dampen the Northern Dancer camp's enthusiasm was that Shoemaker decided to abscond. He had also been riding the Californian classic hope Hill Rise, and that was the one he wanted to be on for the Triple Crown.

*Northern Dancer storms to an emphatic seven-length victory in Canada's Queen's Plate.*

Northern Dancer, he reckoned, was too immature for the task; after all, he would not actually be three years old until the week before the Belmont.

The little bay had run 13 times and had six different riders. His final change teamed him with Bill Hartack, who had already won three Kentucky Derbys with Iron Liege, Venetian Way and Decidedly, and the new partnership made a propitious start, winning the Blue Grass Stakes at Keeneland after a good tussle with Alan Adair. The Derby came next, and the backers sided with Shoemaker, making Hill Rise the odds-on favourite. Northern Dancer won, and did so in record time, leading at the turn for home and clinging tenaciously to his advantage as Hill Rise bore down on him in the last furlong. The public still preferred the Californian when the first five from the Derby renewed rivalry in the Preakness, but it was the Canadian who triumphed again, and more easily, this time with The Scoundrel as runner-up. It was Northern Dancer who was odds-on for the Belmont, and again the money was wrong. He patently did not get the distance, failing to get to Quadrangle then wearily ceding second place to Roman Brother. Still, two-thirds of the Triple Crown was not bad for a little rejected yearling, still not 15.2 hands.

Northern Dancer went home to Canada, hailed as his nation's finest Thoroughbred product, and nothing happened to spoil his party when he turned out for the Dominion's most famous race. He ran away with the Queen's Plate, beating Langcrest (another son of Nearctic) by more than seven lengths. Back he went to the States, and ten days later, in a work-out at Belmont Park, he bowed the tendon on his near-fore.

Late in the year came talk that he might return, but on second thoughts Eddie Taylor decided he would have him home. He would stand him at a fee of $10,000, with a live foal concession, and hope to get support from leading breeders south of the border. In fact, Northern Dancer's book was swiftly filled, with mares from such as Claiborne, Spendthrift, Greentree, Hurstland, Hermitage, Newstead, Nydrie – just about every prominent US stud. Among the mares from Canadian breeders was one from Larkin Maloney.

The world of Thoroughbred breeding was already beginning to change when Northern Dancer covered his first mares in February 1965. Charlie Engelhard and one or two other pioneers were already sending US yearling purchases to make an impact on racing in Britain; Ribot was already on his way to recognition as the first great intercontinental star stallion. There would have been a new and smaller, ultra-commercial world of breeding, recognizably ruled from America, even if Natalma had had her operation, gone back into training and never had a son. What Northern Dancer did was to accelerate the process, essentially to ensure that instead of evolution, there was revolution. At first he seemed just a symbol, one of the agents of change, but when the renewed and inspired O'Brien assaults on American auctions, concentrating on him, achieved their aims, the full dynamic force of the dominant Northern Dancer genes was exposed. The circumstances had never previously existed in which one horse could rule the world; few horses who ever existed would have matched the domination he has exercised.

In an earlier era, Northern Dancer would assuredly have been a national champion of comparable stature to Bull Lea or Bold Ruler, but the North American sires' title he took in 1971 was to be his only one. Nijinsky, then Lyphard and Northern Taste and Northern Gem and Broadway Dancer, earned him renown in a Europe which was having to turn to America for the quality stock needed for success at the highest level. The snowball effect of Vincent O'Brien's belief in Northern Dancer's greatness, and the proof he was able to provide with the aid of Robert Sangster's funding, was phenomenal. While Europe became the principal proving-ground for the northern hemisphere Thoroughbred, and America became the principal

| NORTHERN DANCER | | | (bay, 1961) |
|---|---|---|---|
| Nearctic (br 1954) | Nearco | Pharos | Phalaris / Scapa Flow |
| | | Nogara | Havresac / Catnip |
| | Lady Angela | Hyperion | Gainsborough / Selene |
| | | Sister Sarah | Abbots Trace / Sarita |
| Natalma (b 1957) | Native Dancer | Polynesian | Unbreakable / Black Polly |
| | | Geisha | Discovery / Miyako |
| | Almahmoud | Mahmoud | Blenheim / Mah Mahal |
| | | Arbitrator | Peace Chance / Mother Goose |

supplier in ever-rising markets, Northern Dancer became both the dominant contributor of excellence and, inevitably, the most successful commercial stallion in history. Over a 23-year period, 295 of his yearlings (from a total of 634 foals) were sold for an aggregate of $183,758,632; in ten of his last 12 years of representation – beginning with the year after The Minstrel's three-year-old triumphs – he led the sales averages. When Northern Dancer began his stud career, the world-record price for a yearling stood at $170,000; one of his sons brought $10.2 million, and a son of one of his sons fetched $13.1 million.

The reason for Northern Dancer's commercial dominance was, quite simply, his unrivalled record as a source of brilliant racing and breeding stock, both in America and, more especially, in Europe. His crops were small by the standards of his era, never greater than the 36 born in 1974, yet he got more stakes winners than any horse in history (137 at the latest count), he led the British/Irish sires' list on four occasions, and, crucially in an industry desperate for the comfort and guidance of continuity, he founded a dynasty. Because he was the supreme stallion of a new international era, that dynasty has become the most widely influential the world has ever known.

By the time his own reduced fertility resulted in his retirement from breeding in 1987, Northern Dancer had around 120 sons at stud, many of them apparently in possession of, and transmitting, the vital gene groupings so obviously important in the make-up of the successful racehorse of the modern epoch. He has active grandsons and great-grandsons too, a number of them making an impression, adding to the legend. He appears already in as remote a remove as the fifth generation in the pedigrees of some of today's prominent runners, his influence diluted, impossible to quantify. From saturation point degeneration will inevitably ensue, but meanwhile breeders will continue to look to him as the fount of what is best in the Thoroughbred.

It is difficult to say what it was that made the Northern Dancers stand apart from their contemporaries. They did not all look alike, behave alike or have common aptitudes, but the devotees of anthropomorphosis have credited many with a superior intelligence and a competitive instinct, qualities rarely associated with the horse in general or the Thoroughbred in particular. There are numerous examples who might be cited to support the view, though it would be easy to draw up quite a long list of Northern Dancer products, especially in recent years, who seemed to fall out of love with racing both early and abruptly. Few had long careers, and though that was often because their owners wanted it that way, there were many instances of the horse calling his own halt.

Whatever their feelings about the game, the Northern Dancers commonly did express brilliance and class of a high order. They raced honestly, they were generally very sound, and among them was a remarkably high proportion endowed with exceptional powers of acceleration. No other stallion of his time equipped so many of his stock with that rapid gear-change mechanism so vital to the winning of top-class races, over whatever distance, especially in Europe.

Northern Dancer served four seasons in Canada, switching to the Maryland division of Windfields Farm in 1969. In August 1970 he was syndicated at a valuation of $2.4 million, well under half the amount commanded by Nijinsky in a similar deal transacted in the same month. His fee was immediately raised from $15,000 to $25,000, and by the end of the decade it had reached six figures. Further steep rises followed, and after the staggering successes achieved by the crops foaled in 1980 (ten Pattern or Graded winners from only 26 runners) and 1981 (winners of nine Group 1 races), an unprecedented and unrepeatable peak was attained. The advertised fee for 1985 was only $250,000, but the going rate was $950,000 and it was rumoured that some breeders did pay seven figures. At the age of 26 he covered at $375,000, with no guarantee of a foal, and sadly there were only two foals. One of them, of course, became the sale-topper at Keeneland in the following year.

## Racing record

| Year | Starts | Wins | 2nd | 3rd | 4th | $ |
|------|--------|------|-----|-----|-----|---|
| 1963 | 9 | 7 | 2 | - | - | 90,635 |
| 1964 | 9 | 7 | - | 2 | - | 490,171 |
| | 18 | 14 | 2 | 2 | - | 580,806 |

## Principal wins

| 1963 | Coronation Futurity |
|------|---------------------|
| | Remsen Stakes |
| 1964 | Flamingo Stakes |
| | Florida Derby |
| | Blue Grass Stakes |
| | Kentucky Derby |
| | Preakness Stakes |
| | Queen's Plate |

## Principal progeny

### 1966

ch g DANCE ACT (ex Queen's Statute, by Le Lavandou)
  1971  Dominion Day Handicap
ch c EAGLESHAM (ex Pink Velvet, by Polynesian)
  1969  Lexington Handicap
b c ONE FOR ALL (ex Quill, by Princequillo)
  1969  Laurel Turf Cup Handicap
  1970  Pan American Handicap
        Sunset Handicap
        Canadian International Championship Stakes
ch g TRUE NORTH (ex Hill Rose, by Rosemont)
  1971  Seminole Handicap
        Widener Handicap

### 1967

b f FANFRELUCHE (ex Ciboulette, by Chop Chop)
  1970  Alabama Stakes
b c NIJINSKY (ex Flaming Page, by Bull Page)
  1969  Railway Stakes
        Anglesey Stakes
        Beresford Stakes
        Dewhurst Stakes
  1970  Gladness Stakes
        2000 Guineas Stakes
        Derby Stakes
        Irish Derby
        King George VI & Queen Elizabeth Stakes
        St Leger Stakes
ch c ZINGARI (ex Prodana Neviesta, by Reneged)
  1970  Hungerford Stakes

### 1968

ch f ALADANCER (ex Mock Orange, by Dedicate)
  1971  Linda Vista Handicap
  1972  Firenze Handicap [Div. 2]
b f ALMA NORTH (ex Spaws Arrow, by Swaps)
  1971  Open Fire Stakes [Div. 2]
        Post-Deb Stakes [Div. 1]
        Cotillion Handicap
        Pageant Handicap
  1972  Black Helen Handicap
        Vineland Handicap
  1973  Betsy Ross Handicap-Gr3
        Vineland Handicap-Gr2
        Margate Handicap-Gr3
        Matchmaker Stakes-Gr1

b f LAURIES DANCER (ex Its Ann, by Royal Gem)
    1971    Alabama Stakes
            Delaware Oaks
ch c MINSKY (ex Flaming Page, by Bull Page)
    1970    Railway Stakes
            Beresford Stakes
    1971    Gladness Stakes-Gr3
            Tetrarch Stakes-Gr3
ch c NORTHFIELDS (ex Little Hut, by Occupy)
    1971    Louisiana Derby
            Kent Stakes
            Hawthorne Derby Handicap

### 1969

b c LYPHARD (ex Goofed, by Court Martial)
    1972    Prix Daru-Gr2
            Prix Jacques le Marois-Gr1
            Prix de la Foret-Gr1
b c NICE DANCER (ex Nice Princess, by Le Beau Prince)
    1973    Dominion Day Handicap-Gr3

### 1970

gr c CHAMPAGNE CHARLIE (ex Shy Dancer, by Bolero)
    1973    Swift Stakes-Gr3
            Flintlock Stakes-Gr3
b c NORTHERN FLING (ex Impetuous Lady, by Hasty Road)
    1974    Riggs Handicap [Div.1]-Gr3
            Longfellow Handicap-Gr3
b f NORTH OF VENUS (ex Fly by Venus, by Dark Star)
    1973    Pageant Handicap [Div.2]-Gr3
            Seashore Stakes [Div.1]-Gr3

### 1971

ch f NORTHERN GEM (ex Bamboozle, by Alcide)
    1974    Fred Darling Stakes-Gr3
            Pretty Polly Stakes-Gr2
ch c NORTHERN TASTE (ex Lady Victoria, by Victoria Park)
    1973    Prix Eclipse-Gr3
            Prix Thomas Bryon-Gr3
    1974    Prix de la Foret-Gr1

### 1972

b f BROADWAY DANCER (ex Broadway Melody, by Tudor Melody)
    1974    Prix Morny-Gr1
b g DANCE D'ESPOIR (ex Julie Kate, by Hill Prince)
    1977    Knickerbocker Handicap [Div.1]-Gr3
b f DANCERS COUNTESS (ex Countess Belvane, by Ribot)
    1976    Susquehanna Handicap-Gr2
            Matchmaker Stakes-Gr1

### 1973

b c DANCE SPELL (ex Obeah, by Cyane)
    1976    Saranac Stakes-Gr2
            Jerome Handicap-Gr2
b c FAR NORTH (ex Fleur, by Victoria Park)
    1975    Prix Saint Roman-Gr3
b g GAY JITTERBUG (ex Gay Meeting, by Sir Gaylord)
    1977    Canadian Turf Handicap [Div.2]-Gr3

### 1974

ch c BE MY GUEST (ex What a Treat, by Tudor Minstrel)
    1977    Blue Riband Trial Stakes-Gr3
            Desmond Stakes-Gr3
            Goodwood Mile-Gr2
b c GIBOULEE (ex Victory Chant, by Victoria Park)
    1978    Dominion Day Handicap-Gr3
ch g MUSIC OF TIME (ex First Feather, by First Landing)
    1977    Jim Dandy Stakes-Gr3
    1979    Stuyvesant Handicap-Gr3

b f NORTHERNETTE (ex South Ocean, by New Providence)
    1977    Chrysanthemum Handicap-Gr3
    1978    Apple Blossom Handicap-Gr2
            Top Flight Handicap-Gr1
b f NORTHERN SEA (ex Sea Saga, by Sea-Bird)
    1977    Test Stakes [Div.2]-Gr3
ch c THE MINSTREL (ex Fleur, by Victoria Park)
    1976    Larkspur Stakes-Gr3
            Dewhurst Stakes-Gr1
    1977    Ascot 2000 Guineas Trial Stakes-Gr3
            Derby Stakes-Gr1
            Irish Derby-Gr1
            King George VI & Queen Elizabeth Stakes-Gr1

### 1975

ch f LA DORGA (ex Directoire, by Gun Bow)
    1978    Prix de Royaumont-Gr3
b c TRY MY BEST (ex Sex Appeal, by Buckpasser)
    1977    Larkspur Stakes-Gr3
            Dewhurst Stakes-Gr1
            Vauxhall Trial Stakes-Gr3
b f WHITE STAR LINE (ex Fast Line, by Mr Busher)
    1978    Kentucky Oaks-Gr1
            Test Stakes [Div.1]-Gr3
            Alabama Stakes-Gr1
            Delaware Oaks-Gr1

### 1976

ch f COUNTESS NORTH (ex Impetuous Lady, by Hasty Road)
    1979    Comely Stakes-Gr3
b c FABULOUS DANCER (ex Last of the Line, by The Axe)
    1979    Prix La Force-Gr3
            Prix du Lys-Gr3
b c IMPERIAL FLING (ex Royal Dilemma, by Buckpasser)
    1979    Bayerisches Zuchtrennen-Gr3
b c NORTHERN BABY (ex Two Rings, by Round Table)
    1979    Prix de la Cote Normande-Gr3
            Champion Stakes-Gr1
    1980    Prix Dollar Gr2
b f SALPINX (ex Suprina, by Vaguely Noble)
    1979    Prix du Conseil de Paris-Gr2

### 1977

b f DISCONIZ (ex Codorniz, by Cockrullah)
    1980    Princess Stakes-Gr3
b c MAGESTERIAL (ex Courting Days, by Bold Lad)
    1981    Blandford Stakes-Gr2
            Whitehall Stakes-Gr3
b c NUREYEV (ex Special, by Forli)
    1979    Prix Thomas Bryon-Gr3

### 1978

br c CRESTA RIDER (ex Thoroly Blue, by Blue Prince)
    1980    Criterium de Maisons-Laffitte-Gr2
    1981    Prix de Fontainebleau-Gr3
            Prix Jean Prat-Gr2
b c DANCE BID (ex Highest Trump, by Bold Bidder)
    1981    Tetrarch Stakes-Gr3
b f DISCORAMA (ex Obeah, by Cyane)
    1981    Gazelle Handicap-Gr2
b f NORTHERN FABLE (ex Fairway Fable, by Never Bend)
    1982    Palomar Handicap [Div.1]-Gr3
b c STORM BIRD (ex South Ocean, by New Providence)
    1980    Anglesey Stakes-Gr3
            National Stakes-Gr2
            Larkspur Stakes-Gr3
            Dewhurst Stakes-Gr1

### 1979

b f DANCE NUMBER (ex Numbered Account, by Buckpasser)
    1983    Shuvee Handicap-Gr2
                Beldame Stakes-Gr1
ch f LARIDA (ex Kittiwake, by Sea-Bird)
    1982    Hill Prince Stakes [Div.2]-Gr3
                Boiling Springs Stakes [Div.1]-Gr3
    1983    Orchid Handicap [Div.2]-Gr2
ch f WOODSTREAM (ex Rule Formi, by Forli)
    1981    Moyglare Stud Stakes-Gr2
                Cheveley Park Stakes-Gr1

### 1980

b c DANZATORE (ex Shake a Leg, by Native Dancer)
    1982    Ashford Castle Stakes-Gr3
                Beresford Stakes-Gr2
b c DIXIELAND BAND (ex Mississippi Mud, by Delta Judge)
    1983    Pennsylvania Derby-Gr2
    1984    Massachusetts Handicap-Gr2
b c GLENSTAL (ex Cloonlara, by Sir Ivor)
    1982    National Stakes-Gr2
    1983    Prix Daphnis-Gr3
b c HERO'S HONOR (ex Glowing Tribute, by Graustark)
    1984    Fort Marcy Handicap-Gr3
                Red Smith Handicap-Gr2
                Bowling Green Handicap-Gr1
                United Nations Handicap-Gr1
b c LOMOND (ex My Charmer, by Poker)
    1983    2000 Guineas Stakes-Gr1
b f MYSTERIEUSE ETOILE (ex Gulanar, by Val de Loir)
    1983    Prix de la Grotte-Gr3
ch c SALMON LEAP (ex Fish-Bar, by Baldric)
    1983    Tetrarch Stakes-Gr3
                Nijinsky Stakes-Gr2
                Whitehall Stakes-Gr3
b c SHAREEF DANCER (ex Sweet Alliance, by Sir Ivor)
    1983    King Edward VII Stakes-Gr2
                Irish Derby-Gr1
b f SPIT CURL (ex Coiffure, by Sir Gaylord)
    1983    Alabama Stakes-Gr1
ch f SULEMEIF (ex Barely Even, by Creme Dela Creme)
    1984    Suwannee River Handicap-Gr3

### 1981

b f BALLET DE FRANCE (ex Fabulous Native, by Le Fabuleux)
    1983    Park Stakes-Gr3
b c EL GRAN SENOR (ex Sex Appeal, by Buckpasser)
    1983    Railway Stakes-Gr3
                National Stakes-Gr2
                Dewhurst Stakes-Gr1
    1984    2000 Guineas Stakes-Gr1
                Irish Derby-Gr1
ch f NORTHERN TRICK (ex Trick Chick, by Prince John)
    1984    Prix de Diane-Gr1
                Prix de la Nonette-Gr3
                Prix Vermeille-Gr1
b c PINK (ex Pink Valley, by Never Bend)
    1985    Prix du Muguet-Gr3
                Prix du Chemin de Fer du Nord-Gr3
                Prix du Rond Point-Gr3
b c SADLER'S WELLS (ex Fairy Bridge, by Bold Reason)
    1983    Beresford Stakes-Gr2
    1984    Irish Derby Trial Stakes-Gr2
                Irish 2000 Guineas-Gr1
                Eclipse Stakes-Gr1
                Phoenix Champion Stakes-Gr1

b c SECRETO (ex Betty's Secret, by Secretariat)
    1984    Tetrarch Stakes-Gr3
                Derby Stakes-Gr1
b f WILD APPLAUSE (ex Glowing Tribute, by Graustark)
    1984    Comely Stakes-Gr3
                Diana Handicap-Gr2

### 1982

b c ANTHEUS (ex Apachee, by Sir Gaylord)
    1986    La Coupe de Maisons-Laffitte-Gr3
                Gran Premio del Jockey Club-Gr1
b c HERAT (ex Kashan, by Damascus)
    1986    New Orleans Handicap-Gr2
b f NORTHERN ASPEN (ex Fall Aspen, by Pretense)
    1985    Prix d'Astarte-Gr2
    1987    Gamely Handicap-Gr1
b c NORTHERN PLAIN (ex Highest Trump, by Bold Bidder)
    1985    Tetrarch Stakes-Gr3
b f SAVANNAH DANCER (ex Valoris, by Tiziano)
    1985    Del Mar Oaks-Gr2

### 1983

b c CHERCHEUR D'OR (ex Gold River, by Riverman)
    1986    Prix du Lys-Gr3
b c GLOW (ex Glisk, by Buckpasser)
    1986    Saranac Stakes-Gr2
b c TATE GALLERY (ex Fairy Bridge, by Bold Reason)
    1985    National Stakes-Gr1

### 1984

b c AJDAL (ex Native Partner, by Raise a Native)
    1986    Dewhurst Stakes-Gr1
    1987    Craven Stakes-Gr3
                July Cup-Gr1
                York Sprint Championship Stakes-Gr1
                Haydock Sprint Cup-Gr2
b c ALWASMI (ex Height of Fashion, by Bustino)
    1988    John Porter Stakes-Gr3
ch f CHAPEL OF DREAMS (ex Terlingua, by Secretariat)
    1988    Golden Poppy Handicap-Gr3
                Wilshire Handicap-Gr2
                Palomar Handicap-Gr2
b c RAMBO DANCER (ex Fair Arabella, by Chateaugay)
    1989    Red Smith Handicap-Gr2

### 1985

b f FAIRY GOLD (ex Fairy Bridge, by Bold Reason)
    1987    Debutante Stakes-Gr3
b c NABEEL DANCER (ex Prayers'n Promises, by Foolish Pleasure)
    1990    Prix du Gros Chene-Gr2
b c UNFUWAIN (ex Height of Fashion, by Bustino)
    1988    Chester Vase-Gr3
                Princess of Wales's Stakes-Gr2
    1989    John Porter Stakes-Gr3
                Jockey Club Stakes-Gr2

### 1986

ch f DIANA DANCE (ex Deceit, by Prince John)
    1989    Neuss Stutenpreis-Gr3
b c LOCAL TALENT (ex Home Love, by Vaguely Noble)
    1988    Prix La Rochette-Gr3
    1989    Prix Jean Prat-Gr1
b c WARRSHAN (ex Secret Asset, by Graustark)
    1989    Gordon Stakes-Gr3

# Nureyev

IT really was no wonder that everybody wanted to invest in the Thoroughbred industry in the early 1980s, when there were horses like Nureyev to advertise its money-making propensities. The routine appeared to be that you went to Keeneland, bought the top colt in the sale for $1.3 million, gave it about four minutes' racing and retired it before anybody really knew how good it was, put it to stud for a year to recoup your original investment, then re-sold it for $14 million before anybody could tell whether or not it was a good stallion. What other industry could produce that kind of return in four years?

In fact, the commercial successes enjoyed over Nureyev and a few others like him did attract a great deal of new money into the Thoroughbred market, which was why prices soared to idiotic and astronomical levels in 1983 and 1984. Inevitably most of it came from people and institutions who had no experience of the horse business, were unaware of the countless pitfalls, and were swiftly disenchanted. Quite a lot reckoned they had been taken for a ride, and no doubt quite a lot had. Nureyev was one of the rare ones, a horse who made a handsome profit not only for his breeder but also for the man who bought him as a yearling. He became a rarer beast still when he went on, not just to make fortunes for those who bought highly-priced shares in him at stud, but actually to sire a great number of high-class racehorses as well.

Nureyev was bred by Claiborne Farm, who had used Northern Dancer in his first stud season in Canada in 1965 and had become a shareholder in him when he was finally syndicated in 1970. In 1973 and 1975 Claiborne's owner, Seth Hancock, had used the Northern Dancer nomination for his good mare Thong, and he had sold the produce well. In 1976 he decided to send Thong's daughter, Special, which seemed a good idea for several reasons, not least that the result was likely to attract the Sangster–O'Brien party, then the dominant force in the market-place. O'Brien had won big races with Thatch, Lisadell and King Pellinore, all out of Thong. He had also bought Thong's first Northern Dancer colt, Marinsky, for $225,000, and that one had been very good, if also wayward (he savaged Relkino during the Diomed Stakes at Epsom), unlucky (he was

disqualified after a clear-cut victory in the July Cup) and ill-fated (he died of a twisted gut as a three-year-old).

If the mating seemed promising at the time, events between then and the time for the sale of the Northern Dancer colt out of Special had certainly done no harm. O'Brien had been back and paid $305,000 for the second Northern Dancer–Thong colt. Special's first two foals had both run and had retired unbeaten, the second of them, Fairy Bridge, having been a two-year-old champion in Ireland for Robert Sangster. There was also the little detail that Northern Dancer had been champion sire in Britain and Ireland for the second time in 1977. All in all, there ought to be scope for optimism, if it were not for the fact that the wretched yearling was so small.

When the colt went into the ring, Seth Hancock would have settled for $275,000; when the bidding started at only $20,000, it seemed he would have to settle for much less. About an age and a half later the bidding stopped at $1.3 million, the second-highest price for a yearling on record. Hancock had been right to think that Sangster would want the colt, but he had not imagined that somebody else would like him enough to outbid Sangster, at that or any kind of money. It was the Greek shipping tycoon Stavros Niarchos who won the battle, the first of many until he and Sangster decided to pool their resources and form what proved to be a not altogether harmonious partnership.

Nureyev went into training with Peter Walwyn at Lambourn, but left there without having raced. In the summer of 1979 Niarchos decided that he wanted his horses to be trained in France rather than England, for reasons which were never adequately explained; the British Government's iniquitous law relating to Value Added Tax on bloodstock was cited, as was the then prevalence of viruses affecting horses in the south of England. Whatever the cause, Nureyev moved to the Lamorlaye stable of François Boutin, and he had not been there long before he indicated that he could run.

Boutin had an excellent team of two-year-olds that year, and four who did not seem to be in Nureyev's class had already won Pattern races before the little Northern Dancer colt was ready for a race. The trainer decided to throw Nureyev in at the deep end, sending him out for his debut in the Group 3 Prix Thomas Bryon at Saint-Cloud against 11 others who were already winners. Nureyev came home alone. A tremendous rush brought him from last to first in a furlong, and he then drew clear to win by six lengths. That was Nureyev's only juvenile start, and it was enough to convince most observers that he was the best of his generation.

Nureyev's second season was not much longer than his first. He won the Prix Djebel at Maisons-Laffitte in a canter by six lengths, and was so impressive that the 2000 Guineas now seemed to be a formality. The public thought so, backing him down to 13/8 in the field of 15, and his jockey, Philippe Paquet, thought so too, judging by the way he calmly dropped into last place and gave the leaders a ten-length advantage. That was all well and fine, so long as Paquet proposed to use the wide open space of the Rowley Mile and his mount's superior pace in a challenge down the outside. Unfortunately, he chose to sit behind a wall of horses and wait for a gap to appear. When it became clear that no gap was going to appear in time, he created one, and one of his rivals, Posse, was almost brought down. Having infringed one section of the Turf's Highway Code, Paquet might well next have been prosecuted for speeding. Nureyev showed amazing acceleration once in the clear, joined issue with Known Fact, and in the last strides edged in front. Meanwhile, Posse had picked himself up, got his second wind, and chased hard to finish a close third.

Nureyev was a classic winner for about three-quarters of an hour. Then, to the surprise of nobody who had seen replays of the race, his number came down. He was placed last and his rider was suspended for seven days. It seemed a clear case of a worthy winning horse being penalized for the misdemeanour of his jockey as a result of an iniquitous rule, but it was arguable that Posse had been deprived of his chance of victory. Nureyev would just have to make amends in the Derby, and the public, remarkably optimistic about his prospects of staying the distance, promptly made him favourite.

Sadly we were not to discover whether Nureyev would stay a mile and a half, nor, for that matter, whether he was really the exceptional miler he appeared to be. He contracted a virus in mid-May, and it either set an endurance record or had some consequence detrimental to the colt's form. As early as August it

*Nureyev parades in front of the Newmarket stands before the 2000 Guineas in which he was disqualified.*

seemed that there was no intention of him ever running again, and nor did he. Niarchos whisked him off to his Haras de Fresnay-le-Buffard in Normandy and swiftly filled him at a fee of FR200,000.

Not content with breaking the rules on the racecourse, Nureyev proceeded to do the same at stud. A horse is not supposed to get seven Pattern winners among a first crop of only 23 foals. That is not just beyond the bounds of expectation; history says it does not happen. Nonetheless Nureyev achieved it, and he did it with a group which included everything from a precocious here-today-gone-tomorrow sprinter in Magic Mirror to a durable campaigner in Theatrical who peaked as a champion mile-and-a-half horse on grass as a five-year-old in America.

Unfortunately, long before European breeders realized how good Nureyev was, he was gone, sold to Walmac International Farm in Kentucky and syndicated there for upwards of $14 million. His second crop was conceived in the States, and from it came a 1,400,000gns yearling, Lead On Time, who won two Group 2 races in France, and an outstanding miler in Sonic Lady, a classic winner in the company of her own sex, a dual Group 1 winner at open weight-for-age. By the time that second crop reached the races, Nureyev's fee had been hoisted from $80,000 to $200,000, and it subsequently edged up to a new high of $250,000 in 1990. Only exceptional racecourse results could have justified that move when the general trend in fees has been downwards, and sure enough, Nureyev's results have become ever more impressive.

There were two outstanding international milers in Miesque and Soviet Star in the third crop, the former a winner of ten Group 1 or Grade 1 races, the latter with wins in five such events. Among Miesque's many distinctions was her unique status as a dual winner at the Breeders' Cup. In 1989 Nureyev was represented by the top-rated racehorse in Europe, Zilzal, who did not win at the Breeders' Cup but did win his every other race. With his sixth crop still only two-year-olds, the stallion registered the 50th win by one of his progeny in a Pattern race, a rate of progress far swifter than such as Habitat, Northern Dancer and Mill Reef were able to contrive. Granted longevity, he would leave their records way behind.

Longevity, though, is not something that can be guaranteed, and Nureyev is already on his 'second life'. In May 1987 he broke his off-hind leg in the area of the hock and underwent an operation which was believed to have only a 10 per cent chance of success. He came through, and was able to cover

## NUREYEV                              (bay, 1977)

| | | | Pharos |
| | | Nearco | Nogara |
| | Nearctic | | |
| | | Lady Angela | Hyperion |
| Northern Dancer | | | Sister Sarah |
| (b 1961) | | | Polynesian |
| | | Native Dancer | Geisha |
| | Natalma | | |
| | | Almahmoud | Mahmoud |
| | | | Arbitrator |
| | | | Hyperion |
| | | Aristophanes | Commotion |
| | Forli | | |
| | | Trevisa | Advocate |
| Special | | | Veneta |
| (b 1969) | | | Nasrullah |
| | | Nantallah | Shimmer |
| | Thong | | |
| | | Rough Shod | Gold Bridge |
| | | | Dalmary |

### Racing record

| Year | Starts | Wins | 2nd | 3rd | 4th | FR |
|------|--------|------|-----|-----|-----|-------|
| 1979 | 1 | 1 | - | - | - | 120,000 |
| 1980 | 2 | 1 | - | - | - | 60,000 |
| | — | — | — | — | — | — |
| | 3 | 2 | - | | - | 180,000 |

### Principal wins

1979   Prix Thomas Bryon-Gr3
1980   Prix Djebel

mares again by March 1988, covering 52 and getting 42 in foal. Since his return to Walmac after his operation, Nureyev has lived permanently indoors, in a vast barn housing his own breeding shed and a large walking ring; he is never off a lead.

Nureyev is really nothing to look at – very small, long, with poor joints, and altogether a moderate individual. His daughter Miesque is also no oil painting, while Zilzal – now at stud in Kentucky – has very bad front legs. Zilzal also seemed to have a problem of temperament, getting terribly worked up before his races, but he always raced genuinely and had brilliant speed. Although he has got a couple, in Theatrical and Alwuhush, capable of lasting 12 furlongs in good company, Nureyev is basically an influence for speed. A mile is generally as far as his progeny want to go. Among the best stallion sons of Northern Dancer, he has much more in common with Danzig than with Lyphard. The Danzigs are perhaps sounder in mind and body, the Nureyevs a shade more brilliant.

# Principal progeny

### 1982

gr f AL SYLAH (ex Noiritza, by Young Emperor)
    1985    Diadem Stakes-Gr3

ch f BREATH TAKING (ex Cap d'Antibes, by Better Boy)
    1984    Prix Eclipse-Gr3
    1985    Prix de Meautry-Gr3

ch f DEVALOIS (ex Dourdan, by Prudent)
    1985    Prix Cleopatre-Gr3
                E.P. Taylor Stakes-Gr2
    1986    Bewitch Stakes-Gr3

br c LIDHAME (ex Red Berry, by Great Nephew)
    1985    Salisbury 2000 Guineas Trial Stakes-Gr3

gr c MAGIC MIRROR (ex Turkish Treasure, by Sir Ivor)
    1984    Norfolk Stakes-Gr3

b c THEATRICAL (ex Tree of Knowledge, by Sassafras)
    1985    Irish Derby Trial Stakes-Gr2
    1987    Hialeah Turf Cup Handicap-Gr1
                Red Smith Handicap-Gr2
                Bowling Green Handicap-Gr1
                Sword Dancer Handicap-Gr1
                Turf Classic Stakes-Gr1
                Man o' War Stakes-Gr1
                Breeders' Cup Turf Stakes-Gr1

ch f VILIKAIA (ex Baracala, by Swaps)
    1985    Prix de la Porte Maillot-Gr3

### 1983

b c LEAD ON TIME (ex Alathea, by Lorenzaccio)
    1985    Criterium de Maisons-Laffitte-Gr2
    1986    Prix Maurice de Gheest-Gr2

ch f ONLY STAR (ex Rivermaid, by Riverman)
    1986    Prix de Sandringham-Gr3

b f SONIC LADY (ex Stumped, by Owen Anthony)
    1986    Nell Gwyn Stakes-Gr3
                Irish 1000 Guineas-Gr1
                Coronation Stakes-Gr2
                Child Stakes-Gr3
                Sussex Stakes-Gr1
                Prix du Moulin de Longchamp-Gr1
    1987    Child Stakes-Gr2

### 1984

b f ANNOCONNOR (ex My Nord, by Vent du Nord)
    1988    Vanity Handicap-Gr1
                Ramona Handicap-Gr1
                Las Palmas Handicap-Gr2
    1989    Rolling Green Handicap-Gr3
    1990    Santa Ana Handicap-Gr1

br c FOTITIENG (ex Dry Fly, by Mill Reef)
    1986    Prix des Chenes-Gr3

b f MIESQUE (ex Pasadoble, by Prove Out)
    1986    Prix de la Salamandre-Gr1
                Prix Marcel Boussac-Gr1

    1987    1000 Guineas Stakes-Gr1
                Poule d'Essai des Pouliches-Gr1
                Prix Jacques le Marois-Gr1
                Prix du Moulin de Longchamp-Gr1
                Breeders' Cup Mile Stakes-Gr1
    1988    Prix d'Ispahan-Gr1
                Prix Jacques le Marois-Gr1
                Breeders' Cup Mile Stakes-Gr1

b f MONA STELLA (ex Morana, by Val de Loir)
    1987    Prix de l'Opera-Gr2

b c SOVIET STAR (ex Veruschka, by Venture)
    1987    Prix de Fontainebleau-Gr3
                Poule d'Essai des Poulains-Gr1
                Sussex Stakes-Gr1
                Prix de la Foret-Gr1
    1988    Trusthouse Forte Mile-Gr2
                July Cup-Gr1
                Prix du Moulin de Longchamp-Gr1

br c STATELY DON (ex Dona Ysidra, by Le Fabuleux)
    1987    Concorde Stakes-Gr3
                Secretariat Stakes-Gr1
                Hollywood Derby [Div.2]-Gr1

### 1985

b f ACTION FRANCAISE (ex Allez France, by Sea-Bird)
    1988    Prix de Sandringham-Gr3

b c ALWUHUSH (ex Beaming Bride, by King Emperor)
    1989    Premio Presidente della Repubblica-Gr1
                Gran Premio di Milano-Gr1
                Carleton F. Burke Handicap-Gr1

br f MOVIELAND (ex Rivermaid, by Riverman)
    1987    Prix des Reservoirs-Gr3

b c PASAKOS (ex Cendres Bleues, by Charlottesville)
    1987    Prix La Rochette-Gr3

b f PATTERN STEP (ex Tipping Time, by Commanding)
    1988    Hollywood Oaks-Gr1

### 1986

b c DANCING DISSIDENT (ex Absentia, by Raise a Cup)
    1989    Temple Stakes-Gr2

b c GREAT COMMOTION (ex Alathea, by Lorenzaccio)
    1989    Beeswing Stakes-Gr3

ch f LOUVETERIE (ex Lupe, by Primera)
    1989    Prix Vanteaux-Gr3

b f NAVRATILOVNA (ex Baracala, by Swaps)
    1989    Prix d'Astarte-Gr2

ch c ZILZAL (ex French Charmer, by Le Fabuleux)
    1989    Jersey Stakes-Gr3
                Criterion Stakes-Gr3
                Sussex Stakes-Gr1
                Queen Elizabeth II Stakes-Gr1

### 1987

b f SILK SLIPPERS (ex Nalee's Fantasy, by Graustark)
    1989    Fillies' Mile-Gr2

# Persian Bold

STAFF Ingham entered racing as a shilling a week apprentice in the tough Stanley Wootton 'jockeys' academy' at Epsom at the end of World War I. He had nearly 20 years as a jockey, both on the Flat and over hurdles, and more than 30 as a trainer. His stable at Headley, in Surrey, was never the most fashionable and could never count on a ready supply of highly-bred yearlings from leading breeders; its success depended entirely on his skills of selection, preparation and judgment of form. When he died in 1977 he left over £250,000, a sure indication that he was a master of his profession.

Ingham had few equals as a judge of a yearling. He won a Cesarewitch with Chantry, whom he had bought for 35gns (and backed at 40/1!), and his eye for a potential winner remained keen to the last. In September 1976 he went to Goffs' sales in Ireland, armed with several orders, but bought only one. 'I saw several I liked, but just the one I fancied at the money,' he said. A month later he had a lung removed, and early in the New Year he was dead. His Irish purchase, for 18,000gns, was Persian Bold, who gave Ingham's son Tony a dream start to his training career. He also earned more than three times his cost, and was sold as a three-year-old for £500,000.

Persian Bold came from the seventh crop of Bold Lad, a champion two-year-old with tremendous speed who trained off quickly in his second season; in a long stud career he was far from consistent, but once in a while he sired one of really high class. The gelded Boldboy was the best from his early crops, the excellent sprinter Never So Bold, almost an afterthought, eventually best of them all. Persian Bold's dam (a useful winner in France up to nine furlongs), grand-dam and great-grand-dam were all daughters of Derby winners, suggesting that perhaps he would have more stamina than most Bold Lads, who tended to be pure sprinters and headstrong with it.

Persian Bold indicated in his first season that he was going to be more than just a sprinter. He failed in his only two efforts over five furlongs; his response to the move up to six was to win three times in a row, by five lengths in a maiden at Salisbury, by the same margin in a minor race at Kempton, and by a

length and a half over Hawkins in the Group 2 Richmond Stakes at Goodwood. Soft ground found him out in the Sirenia Stakes at Kempton, but on firm at Newmarket he was better than ever when runner-up to Formidable in the Group 1 Middle Park. The feeling was that he would prove even more effective over seven furlongs, so his young trainer gave him his final start of the season in the Group 3 Horris Hill Stakes. Unfortunately, rain came to change the going and Persian Bold, having looked a certain wide-margin winner a quarter of a mile out, became anchored in the mud. Nevertheless he came away with half the spoils, dead-heating with Derrylin for second place and sharing promotion when the winner, Roland Gardens, was disqualified.

It was clear that soft ground would prove prejudicial to Persian Bold's chance in the 2000 Guineas, and as luck would have it, that was the only occasion as a three-year-old that he was required to race on such a surface. It was not a good Guineas, and on a sounder footing he would probably have gone close to winning; as it was, he finished fifth to Roland Gardens. After the classic he failed his stamina test in the Dante Stakes at York, but came back for a couple of excellent wins over seven furlongs, first by ten lengths over Double Form in the Heron Stakes at Kempton, then by four lengths in open company in the John of Gaunt Stakes at Haydock. Persian Bold was beginning to look like a very good colt, and the public made him favourite to beat the Irish 2000 Guineas winner Jaazeiro in the St James's Palace Stakes at Royal Ascot. He did not quite make it, going down by a head, but he had his old rival Formidable six lengths behind him. Always a trier, even when circumstances were against him, he ended his career with a fourth and a second in Newmarket races three months apart. It was really asking too much of him against real speedsters in the July Cup, but his gameness shamed several who by rights should have beaten him; he looked only about three-parts fit for the Challenge Stakes after his long absence, yet he battled away and yielded only to Spence Bay.

Persian Bold was retired to Corbally Stud in County Kildare and stood his twelfth season there in 1990. He began at a fee of £4200 and has had an odd sort of career, seeming to be good, bad and indifferent at various times, on occasions even all three at once, regarded from different angles. He has always been fertile and has got a lot of good-looking foals, and in the first few years he had an abnormally high ratio of winners to runners. His fee, which had crept up to IR£7500 in his fifth year, was surprisingly doubled for his sixth, by which time his only Pattern winners had scored in weak Irish juvenile events. It rose again to IR£20,000 for no obvious reason in the next year, remaining there for three seasons, and more than half the auction yearlings from those crops did not realize profit, although he had a trio of good sons in Pennine Walk, Persian Heights and Bold Arrangement (never a Pattern winner but second in the Kentucky Derby) to represent him over the period. A reduction to IR£17,500 came in 1988 and a further drop to IR£15,000 in 1990.

In view of the racing performance of his stock – anything better than a second-class horse is a rarity – he has seemed over-priced for more than half of his career, yet his capacity to get good-looking stock and winners (of whatever calibre) has naturally made him popular with trainers. While many breeders have lost money on him since his rise to IR£20,000, a minority have prospered, with a few of his yearlings making truly extraordinary prices. In the final analysis, Persian Bold is likely to be regarded as some way inferior to his sire, good at getting winners, but – not surprisingly – incapable of getting quality performers in quantity.

It is a rare stallion who makes a habit of getting sons as good as himself. Pennine Walk, Persian Heights and Bold Arrangement, all now at stud in Ireland, will be hard pressed to make a stronger impact than their sire.

*Persian Bold, a sire with good-looking stock.*

## PERSIAN BOLD (brown, 1975)

| | | | |
|---|---|---|---|
| **Bold Lad** (b 1964) | Bold Ruler | Nasrullah | Nearco / Mumtaz Begum |
| | | Miss Disco | Discovery / Outdone |
| | Barn Pride | Democratic | Denturius / Light Fantasy |
| | | Fair Alycia | Alycidon / Fair Edwine |
| **Relkarunner** (b/br 1968) | Relko | Tanerko | Tantieme / La Divine |
| | | Relance | Relic / Polaire |
| | Running Blue | Blue Peter | Fairway / Fancy Free |
| | | Run Honey | Hyperion / Honey Buzzard |

### Racing record

| Year | Starts | Wins | 2nd | 3rd | 4th | £ |
|---|---|---|---|---|---|---|
| 1977 | 8 | 4 | 1 | 1 | - | 38,469 |
| 1978 | 8 | 2 | 2 | - | 2 | 25,304 |
| | 16 | 6 | 3 | 1 | 2 | 63,773 |

### Principal wins

| | |
|---|---|
| 1977 | Richmond Stakes-Gr2 |
| | Horris Hill Stakes-Gr3 [dead-heat] |
| 1978 | Heron Stakes |
| | John of Gaunt Stakes |

## Principal progeny

### 1980

ch f IMPUDENT MISS (ex Pavello, by Crepello)
    1982   Silken Glider Stakes-Gr3
ch f PERSIAN TIARA (ex Tarara Girl, by Major Portion)
    1984   Dixie Handicap-Gr2
           Seneca Handicap-Gr3
           Golden Harvest Handicap-Gr2
    1985   La Prevoyante Handicap [Div.1]-Gr3
           Sheepshead Bay Handicap-Gr2

### 1981

ch c KING PERSIAN (ex Naiad Queen, by Pampered King)
    1983   Phoenix Stakes-Gr1
ch c KINGS ISLAND (ex Gerardmer, by Brigadier Gerard)
    1985   Rolling Green Handicap-Gr3
           Sunset Handicap-Gr1

### 1982

b c PENNINE WALK (ex Tifrums, by Thatch)
    1985   Jersey Stakes-Gr3
    1986   Diomed Stakes-Gr3
           Queen Anne Stakes-Gr2

### 1984

b c BABA KARAM (ex Lady Pavlova, by Ballymore)
    1987   Royal Whip Stakes-Gr3
br f INANNA (ex Callixena, by Kalamoun)
    1986   Silken Glider Stakes-Gr3

### 1985

b f LLYN GWYNANT (ex Etoile des Galles, by Busted)
    1988   Matron Stakes-Gr3
    1989   Desmond Stakes-Gr3
ch c PERSIAN HEIGHTS (ex Ready and Willing, by Reliance)
    1988   St James's Palace Stakes-Gr1

### 1986

b c MARDONIUS (ex Dominica, by Zank)
    1989   Prix de Lutece-Gr3

### 1987

b c ANVARI (ex Anne Stuart, by Bolkonski)
    1990   Irish Derby Trial Stakes-Gr2

# Petoski

EVERYBODY should go to a yearling sale – once. It is fascinating to see the young horses, many of them away from home for the first time in their lives, and watch their different reactions as they are put through the routine of last-minute preparations and numerous inspections. The behaviour of sellers and buyers is also worth observing, not to mention the techniques of the various auctioneers when they conduct the all-important bidding. Nevertheless, if you do not have to be there every day, you may rest assured that what you see on one day will last you a lifetime. Those who attend for a lifetime could never fill one day with what they remember. Whole years of routine activity go by without a deposit in the memory bank. Just once in a while a transaction will stand out, and even then its significance may not be apparent until years afterwards.

In 1983 the first yearlings by Niniski came on the market. He had been a good horse, very much a staying horse, winner of the Irish St Leger and the Prix Royal-Oak for Lady Beaverbrook. When he retired he stood, initially for a £5000 fee, at Kirsten Rausing's Lanwades Stud in Newmarket. There really was no knowing how the market would take to Niniski's stock. Sons of Nijinsky had not proved successful with their runners to date, and people were beginning to tar them all with the same 'no good' brush. In addition, the yearling market generally had gone backwards in 1982, and though there were indications that this was a year for an upward swing, demand was surely going to be strongest for horses who promised to excel between a mile and 12 furlongs, and would do so early in their three-year-old careers. Niniski was by no means certain to sire horses in that category.

As it happened, Miss Rausing herself owned an outstanding Niniski colt. He was a product of her exceptionally well-bred mare Sushila, a winning daughter of champion sire Petingo out of a full sister to French champion sire Val de Loir. He had looks and he had breeding, but how was one to value him in the current market? He was to be sold in Tattersalls' Highflyer Sales, the best possible occasion, but he was not due in the ring until 406 other yearlings had gone. His place was half an hour before the end. There may be little money left; there

may be few buyers left. The colt had to be sold, and for Niniski's sake he needed to be sold well. That promised to be crucial to the stallion's commercial status.

The vendor had two important factors working for her. One was that her colt was the only one in the Highflyer Sale, which meant that he was presumed to be (he actually was) the best Niniski colt available for sale. She also had reason to hope that Lady Beaverbrook would want to buy the best available colt by her former favourite. When the first sons of her St Leger winner Bustino were offered in 1978, it was Lady B. who had bought what was supposed to be the best of them, and she had given 114,000gns for him. Miss Rausing was suitably encouraged when the British Bloodstock Agency's Chairman, Robin Hastings (who often acted for Lady Beaverbrook and had bought Niniski for her as a yearling at Saratoga), began to take a keen interest in her colt. He went to Lanwades to see him, and went back later with Lady Beaverbrook and her veterinary adviser, Bob Crowhurst.

Kirsten Rausing knew that Hastings was impressed, and he knew that she knew. They both knew that when Lady Beaverbrook wanted a horse, she bought it, except in circumstances when the price went so high that the vendor really did not have to worry about who was buying it. Hastings advised his client to buy, and she, who did not propose to attend the sale, gave the go-ahead. There did not seem to be much doubt about who would buy the colt; the only question was how much she would have to pay. The vendor would obviously place a reserve on him, and as she was no novice in the business, she was going to make sure she got a decent price for what was a genuinely nice yearling.

Hastings, with a simple instruction to buy and no limit, surveyed the colt in the ring and reckoned that at some point between 25,000 and 50,000gns he ought to get him. He was going to get him anyway, whatever the price. The auctioneer got things moving, soon passed 50,000 and, curiously, did not make the expected announcement that the colt was 'on the market', indicating that the reserve had been reached. He kept counting, yet from Hastings' vantage point there were no bidders to be seen. It looked as though the vendor had gone beyond reasonable bounds with her reserve and that he would have no option but to pay an embarrassingly high price for the colt. At some point he would have to bid, and eventually he did. The hammer came down in his favour at 90,000gns.

The agent was livid, swearing that Kirsten Rausing had 'pulled a fast one', knowing that he would have to buy and making him meet an excessive reserve, and he dreaded to think what Lady Beaverbrook would have to say on the matter. It was some time before he learned that he had not been the only bidder and that Sir Philip Oppenheimer had been competing against him. He never did find out what the reserve had been.

Some 20 months on they were all wearing smiles in the winner's enclosure at Ascot – Lady Beaverbrook, Robin Hastings and Kirsten Rausing. The owner, the buyer and the breeder were ecstatic over the victory in the King George VI & Queen Elizabeth Stakes of Petoski, none of them sparing a thought for the day at Newmarket when the sale of this colt had threatened to cause a rupture of diplomatic relations. Petoski had just won half as much again as he had cost. His buyer had acquired the cheapest horse in the sale. His breeder had probably sold him too cheaply, but what an advertisement for her stud and her stallion!

Petoski was a very good horse that day in July 1985. He showed class and courage of a high order, and if he looked all out at the finish, he was entitled to be, having thwarted, in Oh So Sharp, a filly who had just won the Oaks by six lengths from Triptych, and in Rainbow Quest, a colt who later that year would win the Arc de Triomphe. There were three other classic winners behind him as well, including the Irish Derby hero Law Society, and the only middle-distance three-year-old who could be rated above him was Slip Anchor, the wide-margin Derby victor.

Petoski was not expected to win that 'King George', but he had shown excellent form beforehand. He had been a good two-year-old, winning at Salisbury and Goodwood before his third in the Champagne Stakes at Doncaster and a solitary disappointing effort in the Royal Lodge Stakes. At three he had given Damister a run for his money in the Sandown Classic Trial and he was a decent second to Law Society in the Chester Vase. He had not run well in the Derby, but at that time none of Dick Hern's horses was running well, so he could be forgiven. Something more like the real Petoski was the one who won the Princess of Wales's Stakes, easily reversing Derby form with the Epsom fifth, Lanfranco.

Unfortunately, Petoski jarred a pastern soon after

*Petoski (nearside) comes with a storming run to beat Oh So Sharp (rails) and Rainbow Quest in the King George VI and Queen Elizabeth Stakes at Ascot.*

his great Ascot triumph and Dick Hern was unable to bring him out again that season. When he returned at four his conformation was as impressive as before, his form a pale shadow of what it had been. He ran with some credit in the Coronation Cup, but in the two races he had won majestically in 1985 he disappointed, fading abruptly into third behind Shardari in the Princess of Wales's Stakes and making no show at all in Dancing Brave's 'King George'.

Petoski was retired to the National Stud, probably a year too late in view of his loss of form. His fee was fixed at £15,000 and he had no trouble in attracting 45 mares, roughly half and half from commercial and private breeders. However, it was not a particularly distinguished book for a winner of one of Europe's top prestige races in his first season, and it was noticeable that he was neglected by many prominent studs. Only six of 23 auctioned yearlings exceeded the nomination price, and among the cheapest sold was a filly bred by Kirsten Rausing. In response to the market for his yearlings, his fee was halved for 1990, and no sooner had that announcement been made than a foal from his second crop, a half-brother to Pattern winners Kerrera and Rock City, was sold for 90,000gns at the December Sales. In spite of his good juvenile form, Petoski is still widely perceived as a staying type, but a good season with his first two-year-olds would procure him the better chances he surely deserves.

## PETOSKI (bay, 1982)

| | | | |
|---|---|---|---|
| Niniski (b 1976) | Nijinsky | Northern Dancer | Nearctic / Natalma |
| | | Flaming Page | Bull Page / Flaring Top |
| | Virginia Hills | Tom Rolfe | Ribot / Pocahontas |
| | | Ridin' Easy | Ridan / Easy Eight |
| Sushila (b 1975) | Petingo | Petition | Fair Trial / Art Paper |
| | | Alcazar | Alycidon / Quarterdeck |
| | Shenandoah | Vieux Manoir | Brantome / Vieille Maison |
| | | Vali | Sunny Boy / Her Slipper |

### Racing record

| Year | Starts | Wins | 2nd | 3rd | 4th | £ |
|---|---|---|---|---|---|---|
| 1984 | 4 | 2 | - | 1 | - | 25,657 |
| 1985 | 5 | 2 | 2 | - | - | 175,702 |
| 1986 | 3 | - | - | 2 | - | 13,848 |
| | 12 | 4 | 2 | 2 | - | 215,207 |

### Principal wins

1985    Princess of Wales's Stakes-Gr2
King George VI & Queen Elizabeth Stakes-Gr1

# Rainbow Quest

WHO would give $25.55 million for a group of 15 horses in the expectation of their winning, between them, one Group 3 race in Ireland and one Grade 1 race in America? Nobody. Yet that was the cost and the sum total of prestige prizes won by the yearling colts who raised $1 million or more at sales in North America in 1982. Their very names belong in the catalogue of the obscure – Empire Glory, Hidden Destiny, Esperanto, Solar City, Tridessus, Special Lineage, Argosy, Assail, Cantatore, Ensemble, Tapping Wood, Tocave Botta, Arranan, Hatim and Mugassas. It may be assumed that none of them realized expectations. Colt number 16 on the list, sold for $950,000, was Rainbow Quest.

The great change that came over the yearling market in the mid-1970s was the Sangster philosophy that a young well-bred colt was assessable as a stallion prospect before he ever set foot on a

*Rainbow Quest – has been well managed.*

racecourse. In the old days, you bought a yearling colt purely on its supposed potential as a racehorse. There were sufficient risks in that, and you bought with spare money which you expected to lose, while hoping that you might strike lucky. The very rare horse did win back its purchase price, and some even covered their training costs. If the gods really took to you, they just might bestow on you a big winner with residual value as a stallion, but you never so much as dreamed it would happen.

After Sangster – more particularly, after Sangster's successes with such as The Minstrel and Alleged – things were different, at least at the top end of the market. He could never make his scheme work by buying the odd horse; there had to be a bulk-buying programme, and there were bound to be a lot of failures, for which the successes would have to pay. His activity drove the market up, and those who sought to compete with him had to operate in the same way. Eventually the Arabs moved in, buying on a far greater scale than even Sangster had ever envisaged, and we had a situation in which racing became subservient to breeding, and the yearling colt had a price instead of a value.

By 1980 the cost of the top yearling colts was ten times what it had been in 1970, but they represented no better value. They still had to prove themselves on the racecourse to become prospective stallions, and their chances of doing that were even more remote than before, made slimmer chiefly by keener competition. All that the Sangster philosophy has achieved is to turn the business over to the mega-rich and leave the rest of those who seek to earn their livelihoods by it at their mercy.

Rainbow Quest did not have a value of $950,000 as a yearling, by no stretch of anyone's imagination, but that is what it cost Khalid Abdullah to buy him, on James Delahooke's advice, at the Fasig-Tipton Summer Sales. Abdullah was playing the game the way the rules had been set; he was buying in bulk in the hope of acquiring something which would give him fun at the highest level of competition and, indeed, he was the buyer of three of those in the $1 million-plus bracket mentioned above, among them the only Grade 1 winner, Hatim, who was in his fourth season as a racehorse when he won his only

*Quest for Fame, from the first crop of Rainbow Quest, wins the 1990 Derby at Epsom from Blue Stag.*

prestige event. Hatim never did quite recover his cost, even after his sale to the Irish National Stud. Rainbow Quest became an earner but Abdullah did not, as others would have done, transfer the burden of his losses on failed purchases on to the breeders who wanted to use his horse.

As some saw him at that auction in Lexington, Rainbow Quest represented more than the usual risk for a high-priced yearling. His pedigree, there was no denying, was superb; the fact that his dam was a half-sister to Abdullah's classic-placed filly Slightly Dangerous was just one of countless attractions. On the other hand, he was by no means a typical Blushing Groom, light of bone and lacking substance. His forelegs were not of the best, and altogether he had a rather fragile look about him. On his breeding he had every right to be good, but he would be good only if he were sound. The view that he would be sound could be justified by the fact that he was not a heavy horse.

Rainbow Quest was sound, and he was good. What is more, he got better as he matured and was in many ways a model racehorse, one of the very best of his crop for three consecutive seasons. Trainer Jeremy Tree sent him out first for a 30-runner maiden at Newmarket, and he won it in excellent style by a couple of lengths. He then took on 20 in a better-class event at Newbury, had to give 5lb all round, but did so with the minimum of fuss. His last run as a juvenile came in the Dewhurst

Stakes, and that put paid to his unbeaten record. He came from behind and ran on really strongly, leaving eight of his nine rivals way behind, but he did not have – and never would have – the pace of El Gran Senor, who had the race in safe keeping well before the finish.

One win from six starts is rarely the mark of a top-class horse, but that was Rainbow Quest's record as a three-year-old, and the official handicapper could still put only five above him in England and Ireland. He wanted further than a mile in the spring, so his short-head second to Lear Fan in the Craven Stakes and his fourth in the most competitive Guineas in years were eminently creditable efforts. He soon indicated that he was among the best around at 12 furlongs, staying on stoutly for third place in the Prix du Jockey-Club behind Darshaan and Sadler's Wells, then failing by only a length against El Gran Senor in the Irish Derby. By now he was long overdue for a victory, and it came in tremendous style in the Group 2 Great Voltigeur Stakes, by three lengths over Gold and Ivory. Within a few weeks El Gran Senor, Darshaan and Secreto all vanished from the scene, leaving Rainbow Quest the opportunity to take over the leadership of the middle-distance ranks in the Prix de l'Arc de Triomphe. Probably on account of the heavy ground, he fluffed that chance, turning in the only bad performance of an otherwise consistent career.

Rainbow Quest was decidedly the best four-year-old on the 1985 scene, and not just in his own distance category. He opened with a cantering win over ten furlongs in the Clive Graham Stakes at Goodwood, and had to be restrained from making too much of an exhibition of Old Country in the Coronation Cup. He did not win either the Eclipse or the King George VI & Queen Elizabeth Stakes, but it took the brilliant Pebbles to beat him at Sandown and at Ascot he was within a length of Petoski and Oh So Sharp. With a lifetime record of five wins when ridden by Pat Eddery and eight defeats when partnered by other jockeys, it was not surprising that the call went out to Eddery for the Arc de Triomphe. The partnership's record remained intact, but it might have been different if there had also been a change of jockey for Sagace. Rainbow Quest finished second, beaten a neck by Sagace at the end of a thrilling duel, but Legrix, whipping right-handed, had caused his mount to bump Rainbow Quest twice, and the Stewards reversed the order between them. As the race was run, Rainbow Quest was almost certainly prevented from finishing first, but poor Sagace may well have prevailed legitimately under a more intelligent ride.

Khalid Abdullah rightly reckoned that Rainbow Quest had done enough. He retired him to his own Juddmonte Farm in Berkshire, did not syndicate him, and gave a lesson to other stallion owners by pricing his nominations at £25,000. Here was the first horse since Brigadier Gerard and Mill Reef to have been rated at 130-plus on the Timeform scale at two, three and four years, a record of obviously exceptional merit. If £25,000 were to be accepted as the going rate for a new stallion with those qualifications – plus a superb pedigree – nobody should expect to pay more for a young horse of lesser calibre. Unfortunately few stallion owners can afford to act the Abdullah way, and some of those who can choose not to do so. Greed and/or folly are the usual reasons, but the stallion studs concerned can usually count on breeders to display the same weaknesses. Between them, they have an excellent formula for ruining stallions.

Rainbow Quest, who switched from Juddmonte to Banstead Manor in 1988, was still standing at £25,000 in his fifth season, with his first three-year-olds due to appear. The rare – virtually unique – pricing policy has made him available to a wide range of top-class mares in both the private and

| RAINBOW QUEST | | | (bay, 1981) |
|---|---|---|---|

| | | Nasrullah | Nearco / Mumtaz Begum |
| | Red God | | |
| | | Spring Run | Menow / Boola Brook |
| Blushing Groom (ch 1974) | | | |
| | | Wild Risk | Rialto / Wild Violet |
| | Runaway Bride | | |
| | | Aimee | Tudor Minstrel / Emali |
| | | Vandale | Plassy / Vanille |
| | Herbager | | |
| | | Flagette | Escamillo / Fidgette |
| I Will Follow (b 1975) | | | |
| | | Raise a Native | Native Dancer / Raise You |
| | Where You Lead | | |
| | | Noblesse | Mossborough / Duke's Delight |

### Racing record

| Year | Starts | Wins | 2nd | 3rd | 4th | £ |
|---|---|---|---|---|---|---|
| 1983 | 3 | 2 | 1 | - | - | 24,929 |
| 1984 | 6 | 1 | 2 | 1 | 1 | 98,950 |
| 1985 | 4 | 2 | 1 | 1 | - | 128,772 |
| | 13 | 5 | 4 | 2 | 1 | 252,651 |

### Principal wins

1984    Great Voltigeur Stakes-Gr2
1985    Coronation Cup-Gr1
         Prix de l'Arc de Triomphe-Gr1

### Principal progeny
**1987**
b c QUEST FOR FAME (ex Aryenne, by Green Dancer)
         1990    Derby Stakes-Gr1

commercial sectors, giving breeders the opportunity to produce a quality product for a reasonable sum. Not surprisingly, his yearlings have sold well, only three out of 33 auctioned in the first two years having fetched less than his fee; most more than doubled their costs of production. He had four individual winners out of 11 runners, one of them placed at Group 3 level, with his first two-year-olds in 1989. The steady start soon led to spectacular success, with Quest for Fame registering his sire's first Pattern victory in the 1990 Derby. Three days later Rainbow Quest's daughter, Knight's Baroness, ran third in the Oaks.

# Reference Point

BY 1986 the practice of giving supposed top-class three-year-old prospects an easy time in their first season had become so common that we had almost ceased to take much notice of the traditionally meaningful juvenile events. For eight consecutive years the Derby had been won by a colt who had not won a Pattern race at two; two of them – Teenoso and Shahrastani – had even started their second season as maidens. The old winter-warming exercise of poring over the form book in search of the next Derby winner seemed to be an outmoded pastime. Reference Point did not reverse the trend, as the two Derby winners who followed him were not fully exposed as two-year-olds, but he did represent a remarkable aberration. After his win in the Futurity, there was a more positive reason for leaving the form book on the shelf throughout the winter.

Louis Freedman came into racing in the 60s and was given the right sort of encouragement from the start. Within 18 months he had run third in Sea-Bird's Derby with I Say, won the Coronation Cup with the same colt and become so enthused about the game that he bought Lord Astor's Cliveden Stud with a view to breeding his own stock. Importantly, he went about that the right way, acquiring well-bred fillies and mares, mating them with the best stallions and constantly trying to upgrade, and, perhaps most crucially, he was quick to realize the importance of Habitat, using him regularly and keeping his daughters for the stud. Home on the Range was one of those fillies, and though she was untypical of his stock, being a late developer and reasonably well endowed in the stamina department, she was the best runner Freedman had produced from the family; she ran fourth in Condessa's Yorkshire Oaks and gave a display of considerable class and courage on her farewell appearance, when beating Star Pastures by a neck in the Group 2 Sun Chariot Stakes. On that form she was not far behind the best of her age and sex, and she was a worthy mate for any stallion. In her second stud season she visited Mill Reef.

Reference Point was touted as a potential Derby winner before he ever appeared on a racecourse, and because of that reputation he started a short-priced

*Reference Point trounces his opponents in the King George VI and Queen Elizabeth Stakes at Ascot.*

*Reference Pont wins his second classic and his fourth Group 1 race with a game victory over the persistent Mountain Kingdom in the St Leger at Doncaster.*

favourite on his debut in a quite well-contested mile event at Sandown in August. He was in need of the experience, however, and though he made up ground over the final two furlongs, he was beaten more than six lengths into third place. Three weeks later he was a different proposition in another minor race over the same course and distance. This time he jumped off, took the lead and kept improving his position, winning by eight lengths in record time. It looked a good performance, but there was no knowing how good, and Steve Cauthen preferred to partner unbeaten stable companion Suhaillie in the Futurity. He soon learned he had made a mistake. Pat Eddery took Reference Point into a clear lead, waited for the rest to sort themselves out, asked for extra pace when he sensed the first serious challenge, and that was that. The winning margin was seven lengths over Bengal Fire who, like the rest, was both outstayed and outsped by the winner. If there was a better two-year-old than Reference Point in Europe, it really had to be in hiding. The official handicappers certainly could not find one, and nobody else took the trouble to look.

There never was a proper ante-post market on the 1987 Derby. The public wanted to back Reference Point or nothing. During the winter he had an operation to clear infected sinuses and missed a lot of work. People still were not inclined to look for alternatives and gladly took offers of 4/1 before his long-delayed reappearance in the Dante Stakes at York, for which trainer Henry Cecil pronounced him no more than 80 per cent fit. He won it by only a length, and was quite hard pressed to do so, but the certainty that he would be riper on the day meant that no better than 7/4 was available now. He started at 6/4 and won the classic all the way, forging clear in the straight, coming under strong pressure when Most Welcome launched his bid, and staying on resolutely. It was a good performance from a colt who did not like the Epsom undulations, kept changing his legs and was never properly balanced.

The courageous decision to run Reference Point next against his seniors over the shorter distance of the Eclipse Stakes did not quite come off, but he lost by only three-quarters of a length to a much-improved Mtoto, who really had to work for his win. Mtoto must have been good that day; he was the only horse in England ever to overtake Reference Point. His connections thought better of taking the three-year-old on again over 12 furlongs in the 'King George' and they were no doubt right. Reference Point was never better than at Ascot, setting a cracking gallop that none of his rivals ever looked like matching, eventually trouncing the best of them, Celestial Storm, by three lengths. At York in the Great Voltigeur he won as he liked from opposition of no account, but he was not allowed to get off so lightly in the St Leger. In the long Doncaster straight Cauthen had to get at him and keep him up to his work to ward off Mountain Kingdom.

The Arc de Triomphe was all that was left, but it was not to provide the fitting finale. He set off at a breakneck pace on very firm ground, succeeding only in helping Trempolino to set a course record. His own effort was over early in the straight, but he came back slightly lame and an abscess was later discovered on one of his forefeet. He hardly needed to be looking for excuses for one failure; no horse had so obviously dominated his generation as both two- and three-year-old since Nijinsky.

Reference Point was certainly a very high-class performer, though almost certainly not so good as he was controversially assessed by *Timeform*. It would be hard to believe that he was only 2lb inferior to his sire, a much more brilliant racehorse. On the other hand, it would be wrong to devalue Reference Point's achievements because of the way he raced. Going off in front and disposing of most of the opposition early may not seem so impressive – at least to viewers on this side of the Atlantic – as coming from behind and swamping them for speed, but it is a legitimate form of racing, and he did have acceleration in addition to his ability to go a great gallop, his stamina and his tenacity. He also had an ideal racing temperament, relaxed to the point of idleness at home, saving himself for competition, and apart from that temporary sinus problem he was thoroughly sound.

Reference Point's destination for stud was decided early. He went to Dalham Hall, and Louis Freedman, far from syndicating him, retained no fewer than 28 shares. Ten per cent of the horse already belonged to an Irish-based company, Impshire Thoroughbreds, who had bought into him when he was a two-year-old. His fee was set at £70,000 and nominations were sold almost exclusively to private breeders, with members of the Maktoum family inevitably proving to be keen participants. There were no yearlings from his first crop in the 1989 auction market.

## REFERENCE POINT (bay, 1984)

| | | | |
|---|---|---|---|
| Mill Reef (b 1968) | Never Bend | Nasrullah | Nearco / Mumtaz Begum |
| | | Lalun | Djeddah / Be Faithful |
| | Milan Mill | Princequillo | Prince Rose / Cosquilla |
| | | Virginia Water | Count Fleet / Red Ray |
| Home on the Range (br 1978) | Habitat | Sir Gaylord | Turn-to / Somethingroyal |
| | | Little Hut | Occupy / Savage Beauty |
| | Great Guns | Busted | Crepello / Sans le Sou |
| | | Byblis | Grey Sovereign / Niobe |

### Racing record

| Year | Starts | Wins | 2nd | 3rd | 4th | £ |
|---|---|---|---|---|---|---|
| 1986 | 3 | 2 | - | 1 | - | 47,660 |
| 1987 | 6 | 5 | 1 | - | - | 726,708 |
| | 9 | 7 | 1 | 1 | - | 774,368 |

### Principal wins

| | |
|---|---|
| 1986 | Futurity Stakes-Gr1 |
| 1987 | Dante Stakes-Gr2 |
| | Derby Stakes-Gr1 |
| | King George VI & Queen Elizabeth Stakes-Gr1 |
| | Great Voltigeur Stakes-Gr2 |
| | St Leger Stakes-Gr1 |

There are no certainties where stallions are concerned, but the early outlook for Reference Point had to be bright. He was not the typical Mill Reef horse in appearance, and might be none the worse for that. He had more strength and scope than most, and as most of the others had not been good at stud, that supposedly stood him in good stead. He was also guaranteed first-rate patronage. One way and another, he had to be fancied to do at least as well as Shirley Heights, the only son of Mill Reef to have made the grade to date.

# Riverman

THE successes of American auction purchases in European classics of the late 1960s were alarming on two counts. It was bad enough that the produce of our own studs seemed unable to withstand the challenge; it was worse still that markets in the States were too high for our owners to go and compete in them. Lady Beaverbrook was the only one who could afford to get involved with the likes of Charlie Engelhard, Frank McMahon and John Olin, the men who tended to dominate events with their six-figure bids. Nevertheless, by 1969 there was a hard core of Europeans who reckoned that some form of retaliation must be made in America. If it could not be at the glamour end of the yearling market, it would have to be in their bargain basement. There might also be possibilities in the foal market.

The leader of these pioneers was Alec Head, former jockey, outstanding trainer, the greatest horseman of his era in Europe. In August, with his friend Comte Roland de Chambure in tow, he went to Saratoga, watched Humphrey Finney lay out $175,000 on behalf of Lady Beaverbrook for the top colt in the sale, a son of Sea-Bird, and when nobody else was looking he gave $15,000 for a filly by the unfashionable Gun Bow. Lady Beaverbrook's purchase, named Seaepic, won one race in England worth £666. Head's, named Pistol Packer, won all three Group 1 races for three-year-old fillies in France, and was second to Mill Reef in the Prix de l'Arc de Triomphe.

In November Head was back in America for the foal sales in Keeneland, along with Tim Rogers from Ireland and Margit Batthyany, who had studs in Ireland, France and Germany but raced principally in France. They had a successful week between them, picking up colts by Northern Dancer and Never Bend and a filly by Bald Eagle for an aggregate of $91,000. The colts – Lyphard and Riverman – both won Group 1 races for Head's Chantilly stable; both became champion sire in France on two occasions. The filly – San San – won a Prix de l'Arc de Triomphe.

San San and Riverman figured in a dispersal sale of Harry Guggenheim's Cain Hoy Stable, and both were by sons of Nasrullah who had been big winners for the old man. San San was by the failed sire Bald Eagle, which was why she cost only $15,000, while Riverman was by the promising Never Bend, which was why he was one of the three top colts of the week at $41,000.

The fiery Never Bend, who died when only 15, sired 60 stakes winners, a remarkable 17 per cent of all his foals, but only three of them ever seemed really important. One was J.O. Tobin, who looked great until Blushing Groom beat him, had greatness re-thrust upon him when he beat Seattle Slew, and descended into oblivion as a sire. In physical type and racing aptitude, he took after his father. Mill Reef and Riverman bore little resemblance to each other, to their sire or to J.O. Tobin. They both became huge stud successes.

Riverman, first produce of a modest two-time winner, had only two starts as a two-year-old. He ran first in the Prix Yacowlef at Deauville, a race confined to debutant(e)s, and he won it quite well, beating nothing of note. He did not win the Critérium de Maisons-Laffitte, but he did beat good runners that day and his performance clearly made him one of the best of his crop. He went under by a neck, after a keen struggle, to the tough and much more experienced Steel Pulse, and the pair left several of proven merit – headed by the consistent filly Mata Hari – five and more lengths behind. When Steel Pulse went on to finish second in the Grand Critérium and the Observer Gold Cup, it was obvious that Riverman would be a serious classic contender in 1972.

If there was a horse to beat Riverman in France as a three-year-old, he was not around when Riverman made himself available. Gift Card was his keenest adversary in the spring, but on the soft ground at Maisons-Laffitte for the Prix Montenica and on the much sounder surface at Longchamp for the Poule d'Essai des Poulains he suffered exactly the same fate, felled by the deadly late burst of the Never Bend colt, beaten by three-quarters of a length. There were numerous cast changes for the Prix Jean Prat, over nine furlongs at Chantilly, but the star of the show simply shone more brightly, producing an astonishing turn of foot when Freddie Head asked him to extend. That was all very well against other three-year-olds, but what would happen when they brought on the

*Riverman, a huge success at stud in France and in America.*

older horses? Much the same. All his opponents in the Group 1 Prix d'Ispahan were Pattern winners, but he was a different class, bursting through to beat the excellent Sharapour by two lengths.

Riverman was clearly going to be effective well beyond nine furlongs, and as it seemed that his stable companion Lyphard (in the same ownership) was not, the pair were now aimed at what had originally been each other's targets. To run against Brigadier Gerard in the King George VI & Queen Elizabeth Stakes was inevitably courting defeat, and that was what duly occurred, but it was the first time at 12 furlongs for both of them, and it turned out to be a case of something ventured, not much lost. Freddie Head, as ever, rode Riverman from the back, brought him last of nine into the straight and then asked him to accelerate. He did, and he flew, but he was never going to reach the first pair, who had long gone. The Brigadier won from Parnell by a length and a half, with Riverman five lengths away third. There were other and easier objectives at home, but Alec Head aimed for the top again, sending Riverman for a second crack at Brigadier Gerard in the Champion

Stakes. Most people looked on it as a kamikaze mission, and the result may suggest that it was. All the same, Riverman gave a sterling performance, lying rather closer to the pace this time, producing his usual fine acceleration and battling hard as well under strong pressure. He was gaining ground fast at the finish, beaten a length and a half, and the winner knew he had been in a race.

Riverman was promptly syndicated to stand at Alec Head's Haras de Quesnay, starting his stud career in the same year as Mill Reef. As there was never much doubt as to which of the pair was the better racehorse, he was often described at the outset as 'the other son of Never Bend', yet for all Mill Reef's wonderful achievements at stud, it cannot yet be certain that Riverman will ultimately be regarded as the lesser sire. However, as their careers were spent in different countries, and in different circumstances, a comparison of their records may not be wholly valid; there can be no knowing what each would have made of the other's opportunities.

For the first five of his seven seasons at Quesnay, Riverman had to compete for mares with the likes of

Luthier, Caro and Lyphard, and overall only the last-named really did better than him. When his first crop were three-year-olds, in 1977, he was sixth in the French sires' table, which was headed by Caro with Lyphard second. In the next two years he was Lyphard's runner-up, and for the following two seasons he was number one. Luthier, who had headed the list in 1976, did not return to the top until 1982, when all three of the others were already based in Kentucky.

Riverman crossed the Atlantic early in 1980, by which time he had already recorded the rare achievement of having been represented by a better horse than himself. Irish River, from his third crop, was an outstanding performer at both two and three years, a winner seven times in Group 1 company and as dominant a miler in France as Kris was in the same generation in England. Other celebrities followed swiftly, and with Detroit and Gold River came the unique feat of two Arc de Triomphe-winning fillies from the same crop. River Lady might have been another daughter of comparable class; sadly she broke a femur and had to be destroyed when she seemed to be on the point of adding the Prix de Diane to her Poule d'Essai victory.

The origins of his mates did not seem to make much difference to Riverman, who was soon as successful with American-conceived products as he had been with those sired in France. There was, of course, great demand for his stock in Europe, and many of his best commercial yearlings found their way here. None cost more, and none was better, than the wonderful mare Triptych, who even out-performed Irish River with her score of nine Group 1 wins. She cost $2.15 million and genuinely was a bargain; her earnings amounted to around £1.5 million, and she was sold, in training as a six-year-old, for $3.4 million. Sadly, like Gold River (killed by lightning) and River Lady before her, Triptych met an untimely end, hit by a truck in her Claiborne paddock while pregnant to Mr Prospector.

Riverman has got winners at all ages and over all distances. In addition to her Arc de Triomphe, Gold River won a Prix du Cadran and seemed to have any amount of stamina; by contrast, Dowsing was a specialist sprinter. During his early days in France, Riverman was blamed for a spot of knee trouble in the population, but he grew out of that reputation and is credited, for the most part, with stock who are generally well made and plenty sound enough for what is required of them. He gets his share of winners on dirt, though grass is their preferred surface.

Riverman's fee was never higher than $125,000 at Gainesway, and in 1990 it was possible to get to him for $50,000. He is by no means finished yet, but he could be said to be in need of a prominent stallion son. Irish River let him down badly, getting a lot of ugly stock, many tied-in below the knee, while Policeman, Bellman and Dunphy all squandered chances, if not of the best. Rousillon's promising start lends hope that there is better to come. Having lost three such exceptional daughters, Riverman could be excused a poor broodmare sire record, but in fact he is doing extremely well in that regard and is going to do even better before long.

## RIVERMAN (bay, 1969)

| | | | |
|---|---|---|---|
| **Never Bend** (b 1960) | Nasrullah | Nearco | Pharos / Nogara |
| | | Mumtaz Begum | Blenheim / Mumtaz Mahal |
| | Lalun | Djeddah | Djebel / Djezima |
| | | Be Faithful | Bimelech / Bloodroot |
| **River Lady** (b 1963) | Prince John | Princequillo | Prince Rose / Cosquilla |
| | | Not Afraid | Count Fleet / Banish Fear |
| | Nile Lily | Roman | Sir Gallahad / Buckup |
| | | Azalea | Sun Teddy / Coquelicot |

### Racing record

| Year | Starts | Wins | 2nd | 3rd | 4th | FR |
|---|---|---|---|---|---|---|
| 1971 | 2 | 1 | 1 | - | - | 101,633 |
| 1972 | 6 | 4 | 1 | 1 | - | 1,152,647 |
| | 8 | 5 | 2 | 1 | - | 1,254,280 |

### Principal wins

1972    Poule d'Essai des Poulains-Gr1
Prix Jean Prat-Gr2
Prix d'Ispahan-Gr1

### Principal progeny

**1974**
b c OLANTENGY (ex Trophee, by Snob)
    1977    Prix La Force-Gr3

**1975**
b c RIVER KNIGHT (ex Knighton House, by Pall Mall)
    1977    Prix La Rochette-Gr3
b c TAREK (ex Valita, by Alcide)
    1977    Criterium de Saint-Cloud-Gr2
    1979    Prix du Muguet-Gr3

## 1976

ch c IRISH RIVER (ex Irish Star, by Klairon)
    1978   Prix Morny-Gr1
           Prix de la Salamandre-Gr1
           Grand Criterium-Gr1
    1979   Prix de Fontainebleau-Gr3
           Poule d'Essai des Poulains-Gr1
           Prix d'Ispahan-Gr1
           Prix Jacques le Marois-Gr1
           Prix du Moulin de Longchamp-Gr1
br f RAMANOUCHE (ex Bubunia, by Wild Risk)
    1978   Prix Eclipse-Gr3
b f WATER LILY (ex First Bloom, by Primera)
    1980   Next Move Handicap-Gr3
ch f WATERWAY (ex Boulevard, by Pall Mall)
    1978   Prix du Calvados-Gr3

## 1977

br f DETROIT (ex Derna, by Sunny Boy)
    1980   Prix Fille de l'Air-Gr3
           Prix Chloe-Gr3
           Prix de la Nonette-Gr3
           Prix de l'Arc de Triomphe-Gr1
    1981   Prix Foy-Gr3
ch f GOLD RIVER (ex Glaneuse, by Snob)
    1980   Prix de Pomone-Gr3
           Prix Royal-Oak-Gr1
    1981   Prix Jean Prat-Gr2
           Prix du Cadran-Gr1
           Prix de l'Arc de Triomphe-Gr1
b c POLICEMAN (ex Indianapolis, by Barbare)
    1980   Prix du Jockey-Club-Gr1

## 1978

b c BELLMAN (ex Belga, by Le Fabuleux)
    1981   Prix du Lys-Gr3
           Prix Eugene Adam-Gr2
br c DUNPHY (ex Dourdan, by Prudent)
    1980   Prix des Chenes-Gr3
    1981   Prix Daphnis-Gr3
b f VOTRE ALTESSE (ex Vahinee, by Mourne)
    1980   Prix des Reservoirs-Gr3
    1981   Prix de Flore-Gr3

## 1979

ch f RIVER LADY (ex Prudent Miss, by Prudent)
    1982   Prix de la Grotte-Gr3
           Poule d'Essai des Pouliches-Gr1

## 1980

b f BELKA (ex Kalibella, by Barbare)
    1982   Prix des Reservoirs-Gr3
b c INUNDATOR (ex La Tulipe, by Hrant)
    1983   Premio d'Estate-Gr3

## 1981

b c AKABIR (ex Lypatia, by Lyphard)
    1987   Bougainvillea Handicap-Gr2
           Dixie Handicap-Gr2
b c ROUSILLON (ex Belle Dorine, by Marshua's Dancer)
    1984   Salisbury 2000 Guineas Trial Stakes-Gr3
           Waterford Crystal Mile-Gr2
    1985   Queen Anne Stakes-Gr2
           Sussex Stakes-Gr1
           Prix du Moulin de Longchamp-Gr1

## 1982

ch f KORVEYA (ex Konafa, by Damascus)
    1985   Prix Chloe-Gr3
b c MINNEAPPLE (ex Avum, by Umbrella Fella)
    1986   Seminole Handicap-Gr2
b c RIVLIA (ex Dahlia, by Vaguely Noble)
    1985   Prix de l'Esperance-Gr3
    1987   Golden Gate Handicap-Gr2
           Hollywood Invitational Handicap-Gr1
           Carleton F. Burke Handicap-Gr1
    1988   San Luis Rey Stakes-Gr1
br c SULAAFAH (ex Celerity, by Dancer's Image)
    1984   Zukunfts Rennen-Gr2
    1985   Badener Meile-Gr3
b f TRIPTYCH (ex Trillion, by Hail to Reason)
    1984   Prix Marcel Boussac-Gr1
    1985   Irish 1000 Guineas Trial Stakes-Gr3
           Irish 2000 Guineas-Gr1
    1986   La Coupe-Gr3
           Champion Stakes-Gr1
    1987   Prix Ganay-Gr1
           Coronation Cup-Gr1
           York International Stakes-Gr1
           Phoenix Champion Stakes-Gr1
           Champion Stakes-Gr1
    1988   Coronation Cup-Gr1
           Prix du Prince d'Orange-Gr3

## 1983

b/br f ADORABLE MICOL (ex Turn to Me, by Cyane)
    1987   Countess Fager Handicap-Gr3
b f BARGER (ex Trillion, by Hail to Reason)
    1986   Prix Vanteaux-Gr3
b c PILLASTER (ex Flying Buttress, by Exclusive Native)
    1985   Pilgrim Stakes-Gr3
           Remsen Stakes-Gr1
    1986   Rutgers Handicap [Div.2]-Gr2

## 1984

br c DOWSING (ex Prospector's Fire, by Mr Prospector)
    1987   Diadem Stakes-Gr3
    1988   Haydock Sprint Cup-Gr1
ch c HALF A YEAR (ex Six Months Long, by Northern Dancer)
    1987   St James's Palace Stakes-Gr2
b f RIVER MEMORIES (ex Le Vague a l'Ame, by Vaguely Noble)
    1987   Prix de Royaumont-Gr3
           Prix Maurice de Nieuil-Gr2
           Prix de Pomone-Gr2
           Canadian International Championship Stakes-Gr1
    1989   Flower Bowl Handicap-Gr1
b c WILDERNESS BOUND (ex Tammie Says Go, by Speak John)
    1986   California Juvenile Stakes-Gr3

## 1986

b c RIVER WARDEN (ex Sweet Simone, by Green Dancer)
    1989   Prix Eugene Adam-Gr2

## 1987

b f HOUSEPROUD (ex Proud Lou, by Proud Clarion)
    1990   Prix de la Grotte-Gr3
           Poule d'Essai des Pouliches-Gr1
ch f QIRMAZI (ex Cream 'n Crimson, by Vaguely Noble)
    1989   Prix de Cabourg-Gr3
    1990   Prix Vanteaux-Gr3

# Roberto

ROBERTO was named after Roberto Clemente, a star player with the Pittsburgh Pirates baseball team. It no doubt seemed appropriate at the time to John Galbreath, who owned both the horse and the team, but it did not really work out that way. Roberto the man lived the part of an American folk hero, feted for his athletic prowess, elected to his sport's Hall of Fame; he died a hero, too, in the prime of life, killed in a plane wreck while on a mercy mission to earthquake victims in Central America. Roberto the horse was a great achiever, too, but the hero's role was never for him. He did his own thing, offending and outraging the public in every expression of his art, and went to his grave – alongside Ribot – still under-appreciated, still misunderstood. If there was a 20th century human for whom he would have been a fitting namesake, perhaps it was Stravinsky.

Roberto was the product of high-class parents, with a champion two-year-old for his sire and a Coaching Club American Oaks winner for his dam, and excellent racing form was not all that Hail to Reason and Bramalea had in common. They shared nine ancestors (out of 24) in the third and fourth generations of their pedigrees. Few prominent horses of the modern era have had such an intensely inbred background as Roberto.

A leading owner–breeder in the States, where his Darby Dan Farm had been home to both Ribot and Sea-Bird, Galbreath took to sending a few of his better yearlings to Vincent O'Brien in the early 1960s. Roberto arrived at Ballydoyle late in 1970, by which time O'Brien had already won two Derbys with North American-bred colts in three years. The thought that this rather plain bay might be the third was not long in coming, and the trainer expressed the opinion that he might be the best horse he had ever handled even before he set foot on a racecourse. Nothing happened in his first three races to shatter that illusion.

All of Roberto's races in Ireland at two took place at The Curragh, the first two over six furlongs, the third over seven. He won his maiden without effort by three lengths; he took the Anglesey Stakes by six lengths, streaking clear in the final furlong; and in the National Stakes he came from four lengths behind Tall Dream at the quarter-pole, caught him at the

furlong, and stormed away to win by five lengths. This was surely a colt of the highest class. He then went to Longchamp, started at odds-on for the Grand Critérium, and was beaten more than four lengths. Even Lester Piggott was prone to the occasional error, and he did not shine here; having his first ride on the colt, he gave him too much to do in the straight, and a late surge never promised to bring him closer than fourth. The public, especially those who had already backed Roberto for the 2000 Guineas and the Derby, were inclined to blame the horse rather than the rider; the first seeds of Roberto's unpopularity were sown.

Roberto began well as a three-year-old, winning the seven-furlong Vauxhall Trial Stakes at Phoenix Park in heavy ground which really did not suit him. He was ridden there by Johnny Roe, who at that time partnered most of the O'Brien runners in Ireland and had shared in the colt's 1971 victories. As Piggott seemed to have a long-standing commitment to ride Crowned Prince in the Guineas, O'Brien booked Australian Bill Williamson for the classic, and that arrangement held firm even after it became known that Crowned Prince, ruled out by a wind infirmity, was to defect. Williamson duly rode Roberto at Newmarket, and rode him well enough, bringing him with a strong late challenge to finish second behind an ultra-game High Top.

The Derby ride on Roberto was now Williamson's, while Piggott searched high and low for a suitable conveyance. Ten days before the Derby, Williamson had a fall at Kempton Park, collecting a few cuts and bruises but suffering no major damage. He decided to rest his 49-year-old body for a week, and during that hiatus Piggott attached himself to the O'Brien second string, an apparent no-hoper called Manitoulin, owned by the wife of Roberto's owner. When John Galbreath arrived from Kentucky, almost on the eve of the Epsom meeting, he was concerned to hear that the fate of his Derby favourite lay in the hands of a man who might, or might not, be 100 per cent fit, and fancying that he knew a bit about sports injuries, he swiftly decided that this was a risk he was not prepared to take. It was now a simple matter to switch Piggott from Manitoulin to Roberto, and that was what he opted to do, while assuring the displaced

Williamson that in the event of Roberto winning, he would receive exactly the same present as Piggott. The news broke on the very day that Williamson's doctor passed him fit, and the public broke out in a fit of moral indignation.

Roberto won the Derby, by a short head in a tumultuous finish with Rheingold, thanks to a superlative exhibition of whip riding by an inspired Piggott. It was a great performance by the colt, an even greater one by the jockey, probably the finest of his career. The public hated them both for it, received the victory in silence, and revelled in a couple of wins for Williamson later in the afternoon. The circumstances surrounding Roberto's Derby may not have been cricket, and nor perhaps were they baseball. For all that, the decision to employ Piggott had made the difference between winning and losing the Derby, and his 75-year-old owner was never going to get a second chance.

Controversy and Roberto continued to be partners for the rest of his racing career. He went to The Curragh as odds-on favourite for the Irish Derby and finished seventh under Johnny Roe. He was then sent to York for the inaugural Benson & Hedges Gold Cup. Williamson was offered the mount but declined, saying that he was committed to riding in Belgium that day. Piggott preferred to join forces with Rheingold. It hardly seemed to matter who rode Roberto, as Brigadier Gerard (now unbeaten in 15 races) was in the field, but somebody had to, and the choice fell on Braulio Baeza, a Panamanian who had ridden a Kentucky Derby winner – Chateaugay – for Galbreath nine years earlier but had never even been to Europe before. Baeza took Roberto to the front,

*Roberto, whose stallion record was under-rated.*

set and maintained a cracking gallop, saw off 300/1 shot Bright Beam, and thereafter saw no other horse. Brigadier Gerard came after the leader, got to within a length, but never so much as threatened to go by. Roberto was not going to stop, and the Brigadier was not going to summon any extra pace. The pair pulled away from the rest, but in the last furlong Roberto pulled away from the supposedly invincible champion.

The margin was three lengths, the time a course record and a world record for ten and a half furlongs. It could not be said that Brigadier Gerard had failed to produce his form; he had, as he always did, and with Gold Rod and Rheingold way down the track behind him, there was the proof. This was the equine equivalent of Bob Beaman's leap at the 1968 Mexico Olympics; something that could not be done had been achieved. Not even that could make Roberto a hero. Now he was the villain who had wrecked the record of a national hero. What other heinous crimes had he in store? He ran twice more as a three-year-old, and failed to win. Hard to Beat lived up to his name in Longchamp's Prix Niel, leading all the way and holding Roberto's challenge by a length. In the Arc de Triomphe, the placings of this well-matched pair were narrowly reversed, not that seventh and eighth places mattered very much. Baeza partnered Roberto and tried to repeat the York tactics, but it was not to be; in the last quarter-mile there were others quickening all around him while he could only run on, and he was six lengths behind the winner, San San, at the line.

Roberto ran three times as a four-year-old, and on four other occasions when he was supposed to run, he did not. Because of who he was, the non-appearances caused more comment (most of it ill-informed) than the appearances. He missed his intended seasonal debut, in the Prix Ganay, because he suffered a minor injury en route to France, and he declined his last engagement, in the Champion Stakes, on account of a pulled ligament. In between he was taken out of both the Eclipse Stakes and the Benson & Hedges Gold Cup at the eleventh hour because O'Brien would not risk him on the ground. Roberto was alternately moderate, brilliant and appalling in his three 1973 efforts. He was way below par in the Nijinsky Stakes at Leopardstown, where Ballymore beat him and the ordinary Assertive was only half a length behind him. At Epsom in the Coronation Cup he gave a superb display, taking the lead early in the straight, drawing clear effortlessly, then coasting in, a winner by five lengths in near-record time. That was awesome, but next time, in the King George VI & Queen Elizabeth Stakes, the only one he could beat was a 200/1 shot employed as a pacemaker.

His record of seven wins from 14 starts is a sure indication that Roberto was inconsistent, as Derby winners go. At York as a three-year-old and at Epsom at four he was assuredly one of the world-beater variety, but he could not put on that kind of show regularly enough to satisfy many critics. The poor speechless fellow could never give his reasons, though chances were that they were physical rather than mental. Like a lot of the Hail to Reasons, he did not have the best of knees, and Ballydoyle's eminent vet Bob Griffin constantly warned of the dangers of racing him on soft ground. His knee problem was probably the cause of his tendency to hang under pressure, and perhaps even for the remarkable fact that he never won when there were right-hand bends to be negotiated.

Roberto went home to Darby Dan Farm, syndicated at a valuation of $3.2 million, and proceeded to compile a stud record that was often said to be as inconsistent as his racing record. There were times when it seemed like that, because his big winners did seem to come in fits and starts, but taken overall the allegation is unfair. He did not get the huge foal crops that many of his contemporaries had to represent them, and two or three crops seemed to be pretty void of talent. On the other hand, the good years tended to be very good, and any horse who can get a ratio of 17 per cent stakes winners to foals is an outstanding sire, whether he gets them in Roberto's stop-go style or with the regularity of a Mr Prospector.

It must also be remembered that although Roberto did get good mares consistently, he never had the quality in quantity that was fed to the most fashionable representatives of the Northern Dancer and Raise a Native tribes. Nor was he one of the most favoured sires when the Northern Dancer and Raise a Native mares went looking for mates, though he would have seemed an eminently worthy choice. In the long term his best ally was Ribot, whose descendants were numerous in the Darby Dan broodmare band.

At the height of the market madness, there was one Roberto yearling who made $4 million (he turned out to be a sprint handicapper of little consequence), but the sire was not renowned for flashy sales types. If they were plain, even a bit coarse, had good bone and a rugged look, they were probably going to be all right. Sookera, a neat and pretty one, precocious with it, came in the first crop and deceived many into believing that her type was the best; she turned out to be almost unique.

Roberto's fee reached a peak of $225,000 in 1984 and the crop conceived that year was one of the finest, though ironically the two Grade 1 winners who resulted were both bred by Darby Dan, Sunshine Forever by Galbreath himself, Brian's Time by his grandson John Phillips.

Roberto died on 2 August 1988 as a result of head injuries incurred when he was alone in his box; John Galbreath pre-deceased him by two weeks. The world is still only beginning to appreciate Roberto's impact, and it seems likely that he will continue to gain converts posthumously. His sons Silver Hawk and Kris S. have both sired top-class runners out of modest mares, and such as Darby Creek Road and Robellino have had their moments. Touching Wood was a predictable disappointment, while Lear Fan has so far tended to get good-looking stock without merit, but may yet improve. The Roberto mares are making their mark, none more so than Slightly Dangerous, dam of champion two-year-old and miler, Warning.

## ROBERTO (bay, 1969)

| | | | |
|---|---|---|---|
| Hail to Reason (br 1958) | Turn-to | Royal Charger | Nearco / Sun Princess |
| | | Source Sucree | Admiral Drake / Lavendula |
| | Nothirdchance | Blue Swords | Blue Larkspur / Flaming Swords |
| | | Galla Colors | Sir Gallahad / Rouge et Noir |
| Bramalea (b 1959) | Nashua | Nasrullah | Nearco / Mumtaz Begum |
| | | Segula | Johnstown / Sekhmet |
| | Rarelea | Bull Lea | Bull Dog / Rose Leaves |
| | | Bleebok | Blue Larkspur / Forteresse |

### Racing record

| Year | Starts | Wins | 2nd | 3rd | 4th | £ |
|---|---|---|---|---|---|---|
| 1971 | 4 | 3 | - | - | 1 | 9,900 |
| 1972 | 7 | 3 | 2 | - | - | 109,181 |
| 1973 | 3 | 1 | 1 | - | - | 12,686 |
| | — | — | — | — | — | ——— |
| | 14 | 7 | 3 | - | 1 | 131,767 |

## Principal wins

1971   Anglesey Stakes-Gr3
        National Stakes-Gr2
1972   Vauxhall Trial Stakes-Gr3
        Derby Stakes-Gr1
        Benson & Hedges Gold Cup-Gr1
1973   Coronation Cup-Gr1

## Principal progeny

### 1975

b c DARBY CREEK ROAD (ex On the Trail, by Olympia)
    1977   Saratoga Special Stakes-Gr2
b c FOOL'S PRAYER (ex Beautiful Morning, by Graustark)
    1980   Queen's County Handicap-Gr3
    1981   Nassau County Handicap-Gr3
br f SOOKERA (ex Irule, by Young Emperor)
    1977   Cheveley Park Stakes-Gr1
b c YOUNG BOB (ex Bast, by Summer Tan)
    1979   Hawthorne Gold Cup Handicap-Gr2

### 1977

ch c DON ROBERTO (ex Exit Smiling, by Stage Door Johnny)
    1982   Rolling Green Handicap-Gr3
b f LADY ROBERTA (ex Farouche, by Northern Dancer)
    1980   Honeymoon Handicap-Gr3
b g ROBSPHERE (ex Stratosphere, by Zenith)
    1982   Canadian Turf Handicap-Gr3
        Pan American Handicap-Gr2
        Dixie Handicap-Gr2

### 1978

br c CRITIQUE (ex Cambrienne, by Sicambre)
    1981   Cumberland Lodge Stakes-Gr3
    1982   Hardwicke Stakes-Gr2
        September Stakes-Gr3
b c ROBELLINO (ex Isobelline, by Pronto)
    1980   Seaton Delaval Stakes-Gr3
        Royal Lodge Stakes-Gr2

### 1979

b f IMMENSE (ex Imsodear, by Chieftain)
    1982   Little Silver Handicap-Gr3
b f MYSTICAL MOOD (ex Mystery Mood, by Night Invader)
    1981   Schuylerville Stakes-Gr3
b c REAL SHADAI (ex Desert Vixen, by In Reality)
    1982   Grand Prix de Deauville-Gr2
b c ROYAL ROBERTO (ex Princess Roycraft, by Royal Note)
    1982   Everglades Stakes-Gr3
        Lexington Handicap [Div.2]-Gr2
b c SILVER HAWK (ex Gris Vitesse, by Amerigo)
    1982   Craven Stakes-Gr3
b f SLIGHTLY DANGEROUS (ex Where You Lead, by Raise a Native)
    1982   Fred Darling Stakes-Gr3
b c TOUCHING WOOD (ex Mandera, by Vaguely Noble)
    1982   St Leger Stakes-Gr1
        Irish St Leger-Gr1

### 1980

b f RARE ROBERTA (ex Marketess, by To Market)
    1983   Prix Perth-Gr3

### 1981

b c AT TALAQ (ex My Nord, by Vent du Nord)
    1984   Grand Prix de Paris-Gr1

    1986   L.K.S. Mackinnon Stakes-Gr1
        Melbourne Cup Handicap-Gr1
    1987   C.F. Orr Stakes-Gr2
b c BOB BACK (ex Toter Back, by Carry Back)
    1983   Premio Tevere-Gr2
    1985   Premio Presidente della Repubblica-Gr1
        Prince of Wales's Stakes-Gr2
b c CAPITOL SOUTH (ex Polylady, by Polynesian)
    1983   Hopeful Stakes-Gr1
b c LEAR FAN (ex Wac, by Lt Stevens)
    1983   Champagne Stakes-Gr2
    1984   Craven Stakes-Gr3
        Prix Jacques le Marois-Gr1

### 1982

b f GAMBERTA (ex Gamba, by Gun Bow)
    1985   Prix Minerve-Gr3
b f I WANT TO BE (ex Frontonian, by Buckpasser)
    1985   Park Hill Stakes-Gr2
    1986   Meld Stakes-Gr3
b c SCRIPT OHIO (ex Grandma Lind, by Never Bend)
    1984   Young America Stakes-Gr1

### 1983

b c CELESTIAL STORM (ex Tobira Celeste, by Ribot)
    1987   Princess of Wales's Stakes-Gr2

### 1984

b c MIN ALLAH (ex Miss Cream Puff, by Creme Dela Creme)
    1989   Gran Premio Citta di Napoli-Gr3

### 1985

b c BRIAN'S TIME (ex Kelley's Day, by Graustark)
    1988   Florida Derby-Gr1
        Jim Dandy Stakes-Gr2
        Pegasus Handicap-Gr1
b c DYNAFORMER (ex Andover Way, by His Majesty)
    1988   Jersey Derby-Gr2
        Discovery Handicap-Gr2
b c SUNSHINE FOREVER (ex Outward Sunshine, by Graustark)
    1988   Hill Prince Stakes-Gr3
        Lexington Stakes-Gr2
        Man o' War Stakes-Gr1
        Turf Classic Stakes-Gr1
        Washington D.C. International Stakes-Gr1
b c TRALOS (ex Solartic, by Briartic)
    1989   Cumberland Lodge Stakes-Gr3
ch c UNDERCUT (ex Feature Price, by Quack)
    1987   Vintage Stakes-Gr3
ch c WHITE MISCHIEF (ex Arachne, by Intentionally)
    1987   Hoist the Flag Stakes [Div.2]-Gr3

### 1986

b f LEGARTO (ex Summer Legend, by Raise a Native)
    1988   Mazarine Stakes-Gr3
ch f MAMALUNA (ex Kadesh, by Lucky Mel)
    1989   Nassau Stakes-Gr2
br f TURSANAH (ex Farouche, by Northern Dancer)
    1988   Leopardstown Stakes-Gr3
b c ZALAZL (ex Salpinx, by Northern Dancer)
    1989   Great Voltigeur Stakes-Gr2

### 1987

b f SWEET ROBERTA (ex Candy Bowl, by Majestic Light)
    1989   Selima Stakes-Gr2

# Rousillon

A LOT of owners seem to think that two seasons in training is quite sufficient for a top-class horse. For Khalid Abdullah the norm is three. That was his practice with such as Known Fact, Rainbow Quest and Warning, and if he had not been talked into the sale of a half-share in Dancing Brave half-way through that colt's three-year-old career, we would no doubt have seen him in action against Reference Point and Mtoto in 1987. Rousillon was different. It was a moot point whether he really was top class in his second season and if he had not had the third we would never have been certain.

Rousillon was a product of Riverman's first American-conceived crop, whose dams were by no means of the level quality appropriate to a horse of his proven distinction as a sire in France. Of the 20 yearlings offered in 1982, nine made it into the Keeneland July catalogue and one into Saratoga, but the other ten had to take their chances in other sales, most on account of distaff pedigrees which were not top drawer. Still, at that time Fasig-Tipton's July auction was no bad place to sell; the odd first-rate pedigree/individual package would stand out there and might make more even than at Keeneland, while the occasion had a well-earned reputation as a source of top-grade runners with less than top-grade pedigrees. Rousillon's breeder could not really complain over the $100,000 bid for his colt out of a once-raced, unplaced mare from a background that was distinctly second-rate by American standards, obscure to anyone from Europe. From the buyer's point of view he was a typical James Delahooke 'nice horse' purchase and an agreeable make-weight to throw in with the flashier $950,000 Rainbow Quest, acquired from the same catalogue.

Guy Harwood ran Rousillon only three times as a two-year-old. First time out the colt created a good impression with a comfortable victory over 24 other maidens at Newmarket, and he looked better still when disposing of At Talaq and Finian's Rainbow at Goodwood. In the Royal Lodge Stakes he came up against another unbeaten youngster in Trojan Fen, and it seemed that if he were to beat him, we would know just how good he was. He did beat Trojan Fen, but he did not win, and the mystery over Rousillon's true merit lasted almost two more years. A furlong

out he had his supposed chief rival well in check and seemed certain to win easily, when he lost his rhythm, his head went up and he surrendered to Gold and Ivory. It was possible that tactics had caused his downfall, as he had been chased along by Greville Starkey to retrieve ground early in the straight, but many put the sudden capitulation down to his being ungenuine.

The knockers gathered further evidence during Rousillon's campaign at three, when his behaviour seemed to leave a lot to be desired. He won the Salisbury Guineas Trial well, and he gave another good display in the Poule d'Essai des Poulains, finishing only sixth but losing by less than he had forfeited in a tardy start. Then things began to go wrong. He appeared unwilling to go through with his effort in the Irish Guineas, throwing his head up and veering to the right when he was asked to get down to serious business. After a long rest he came back for the Goodwood Mile, again showing his sharp acceleration while also again suggesting that he was less than a ideal racehorse. He ran diagonally into Chief Singer, continued to lean on him, lost by half a length and was disqualified. When you foul your opponent, but he still manages to score and you get sent off, you do not please the fans, and Rousillon was roundly castigated for his misdemeanour. He did not manage to win them around in his two remaining races that season. In the Goodwood Mile, which he was expected to win easily, he produced nothing off the bridle and made heavy weather of beating the ordinary Prego. In the Prix de la Forêt he quickened well to lead, then hung to the left when challenged and even gave away second place near the finish.

Rousillon was a colt of obvious ability and there had to be a way of persuading him to display it without the accompaniment of wayward behaviour. Guy Harwood solved the problem by utilizing the services of Cataldi, five-length winner of the Lincoln Handicap in the first week of the season, as pacemaker for the colt in 1985. Cataldi, a confirmed front-runner, set the true, even gallops which enabled Rousillon to settle, do his jockey's bidding without having to think about it, and win without knowing he had been in a race. Such was his class that he was able to win the Queen Anne Stakes, the Sussex

*Rousillon coasts to victory in the Prix du Moulin at Longchamp from Kozana (rails) and Procida.*

Stakes and the Prix du Moulin de Longchamp, all by daylight margins. He still ran with his head in the air and his ears back, but while he was achieving results like that, those were amiable eccentricities, not proofs of his unwillingness. He assuredly was not the most competitive of racehorses, but formalized racing is unnatural and no horse's idea of fun. He expressed his thoughts on that theme, and if they were not always to man's liking, well, he did allow himself to be converted in the end. He might even have acquitted himself well in the Breeders' Cup Mile, but he had no Cataldi to help him, he missed the break, and once he had collected a clout from Tsunami Slew that abruptly halted his momentum, he understandably decided that enough was enough.

Rousillon went off to the National Stud, where he met an excellent response from both private and commercial breeders, a somewhat surprising development in view of the facts that he seemed to be a horse with only half a pedigree and was priced on the high side at £25,000, the same as Rainbow Quest. His first two auction yearling crops were not very level groups, with under half returning the fee while five brought six-figure sums, but in his second year his mares came mostly from owner-breeders. The reduction of his fee to £17,500 for 1990 seemed logical, notwithstanding a promising first season with his two-year-olds, whose 13 wins included a Group 3 race in France.

Early indications are that Rousillon is capable of getting top-class horses, though whether he will get a sufficient number of them to make a real impact as a sire is problematical. It may be that weaknesses of pedigree, conformation and character will combine to make him less than a consistent success at the highest level.

## ROUSILLON (bay, 1981)

| | | | |
|---|---|---|---|
| Riverman (b 1969) | Never Bend | Nasrullah | Nearco / Mumtaz Begum |
| | | Lalun | Djeddah / Be Faithful |
| | River Lady | Prince John | Princequillo / Not Afraid |
| | | Nile Lily | Roman / Azalea |
| Belle Dorine (b 1977) | Marshua's Dancer | Raise a Native | Native Dancer / Raise You |
| | | Marshua | Nashua / Emardee |
| | Palsy Walsy | Sea O Erin | Shannon / Chantress |
| | | Allie's Pal | War Dog / Our Cherrycote |

## Racing record

| Year | Starts | Wins | 2nd | 3rd | 4th | £ |
|---|---|---|---|---|---|---|
| 1983 | 3 | 2 | 1 | - | - | 19,289 |
| 1984 | 6 | 2 | - | 1 | - | 50,228 |
| 1985 | 4 | 3 | - | - | - | 208,844 |
| | 13 | 7 | 1 | 1 | - | 278,361 |

## Principal wins

1984    Salisbury 2000 Guineas Trial Stakes-Gr3
         Goodwood Mile-Gr2
1985    Queen Anne Stakes-Gr2
         Sussex Stakes-Gr1
         Prix du Moulin de Longchamp-Gr1

## Principal progeny

**1987**
br f AROUSAL (ex Model Girl, by Lyphard)
1989    Prix du Calvados-Gr3

# Sadler's Wells

IN some respects the arrival of the Arabs did Robert Sangster enormous long-term damage. They robbed him of his dominant role in the market-place, simply by pursuing excellence without counting the cost, and eventually they forced him to explore other avenues which never really promised to lead him back to the goals which were once so accessible. However, one by-product of Sangster's inability to compete with the Maktoums at Keeneland is that he now has, at Coolmore, what is almost certainly the best sire in Europe.

The Coolmore strategy with stallions always was, and still is, badly flawed. Management has been all about accountancy, making the business of standing expensive horses pay, generating enough money to be able to go out and buy more expensive horses, and then generate more money. According to the stud's bankers it is something that has been accomplished very well. Unfortunately, it is not a style of management that lends itself to the development of top-class stallions – at least, not when it is conducted on a grand scale, with several highly priced horses always on the farm and one or two new ones arriving every year.

Coolmore has been operated on the lines of the great Kentucky stallion stations without the Kentucky benefits of a vast pool of quality broodmares, an international yearling market and a soundly structured home-based racing industry able to absorb high-cost products. The stud has been much too big for its environment, its history one of excessive fees and over-used horses, with breeders footing the bill for a policy which did not serve their interests – though breeders, of course, have had nobody to blame but themselves in that respect.

There can be little doubt that several Coolmore-based stallions of the last dozen years would have compiled impressive, consistent records as the only, or chief, stallion on a smaller stud; where they were they could only be king for a day, as it were, while they awaited proof of their own commercial unviability or attention became focused on a new pretender to the crown. There had never been a Coolmore horse capable of sustaining his appeal, not even the admirable Be My Guest, until Sadler's Wells came along. A key factor in his prolonged reign has

been that, thanks to the market dominance established by the Maktoums, Coolmore has had nothing of major consequence worth promoting since he came.

The Coolmore partners did not even have to go out and buy Sadler's Wells. They bred him and they raced him as few top-class horses of recent years have been raced. We would learn an awful lot more about the merits of our supposed best Thoroughbreds if they were all subjected to a campaign of nine races as a three-year-old, every time at the top level, and it was because Sadler's Wells came through that rigorous examination of his talent, his temperament, his soundness and his constitution that he became, on the day that he retired, the stallion that every top breeder in Europe wanted to use.

Of course, Sadler's Wells could hardly have written himself a better pedigree, but by the end of 1984 a prospective stallion could not expect to have breeders beating a path to his door just by saying, 'I'm a Northern Dancer.' By then we had seen too many of the soft sort, the Storm Birds, the Danzatores and the Lomonds who had got fed up with the game and would not express their natural talents to order. For many people that sort would have to prove themselves again; Sadler's Wells did not have to apologize for anything he had done on the racecourse. He was all horse, toughness, honesty and class, and if he was not going to make a sire, we all might as well take up basket-weaving.

Sadler's Wells had two races as a two-year-old, and he won them both. Odds-on for a 16-runner minor race over seven furlongs at Leopardstown in September, he trotted up by six lengths. Three weeks later he had negligible competition in the Group 2 Beresford Stakes over the Curragh mile, and he treated it with disdain, scoring by six lengths again. At three he began in rather more exalted company, finishing second to his stable companion El Gran Senor in the Gladness Stakes. Then came a battling win in the ten-furlong Irish Derby Trial at Leopardstown before his switch back to a mile for the Irish 2000 Guineas. For reasons best known to himself, Pat Eddery chose to ride Capture Him, and from fourth place had an excellent view of George McGrath making just about every yard of the running

*Sadler's Wells defeats Seattle Song (right) and Princess Pati in the Phoenix Champion Stakes.*

on Sadler's Wells, who held on tenaciously in a good finish with Procida and Secreto.

After that classic triumph Sadler's Wells was sent in search of a second at Chantilly, and he went close to emulating Caerleon in the Prix du Jockey-Club, failing by only a length and a half against Darshaan. Next came the Eclipse, and the new Ballydoyle hero displayed two of his exceptional qualities, sharp acceleration to go after and overhaul the pace-making Society Boy, then courage to withstand the late challenges of Time Charter and Morcon. He was not quite up to completing the great midsummer weight-for-age double, never really offering a threat to front-running Teenoso in the 'King George', but he was a clear second-best, with three other classic winners among his victims.

Sadler's Wells at last gave a below-par performance in the Benson & Hedges Gold Cup, no

doubt as a consequence of his busy campaign, but he bounced back with a vengeance in the Phoenix Champion Stakes. Eddery had him in front at the two-furlong pole, and the colt battled on gamely for his third Group 1 win, resisting the efforts of Seattle Song by three-quarters of a length. In four victories as a three-year-old, Sadler's Wells never had a wider margin of victory; he had no soft touches that season, having to fight for every penny he earned. There were no more earnings to come. He had his day trip to Paris on the first Sunday of October, as all top horses should, but he was wearing his winter coat for the occasion and the best he could do was to outpace all the other visitors; there were seven of the French in front of him, Sagace by about 18 lengths.

One of the many assets which Sadler's Wells took to stud was his close relationship to Nureyev, who shared his sire and whose dam was grand-dam of the younger horse. Nureyev was already a highly regarded stallion, commercially very acceptable, and with a couple of Pattern winners as two-year-olds in his first crop. But Sadler's Wells had all the attributes that were lacking in Nureyev, that namby-pamby little runt who would not come out to play after he had caught a cold in May. The little runt has gone on to prove himself a tremendous sire, but it is tempting to hope that Sadler's Wells will eventually make a more lasting contribution to the breed. His stock are better tempered, much more relaxed than the Nureyevs, and they stay better. While the most prepotent of the younger Northern Dancer horses in the States are very proficient in the mile department, the true classic distance for European racing is a mile and a half, and Sadler's Wells is the best bet to supply Derby horses of the nineties.

If there is a physical fault about the Sadler's Wells stock, who are very much 'peas in a pod', it is that they all have long pasterns. To date, their reply to that has been a resounding 'So what?' It is not a fault so far as they are concerned, and the form book supports their view. There has not been a stallion in Europe in recent times who has got good-looking and classy horses with such consistency, and their early racecourse performances have confirmed his dominance of the auction scene since his retirement as a correct assessment of his importance. As it does with all its horses, Coolmore has juggled a little with Sadler's Wells' fee, but never so much as to damage his credibility. If he had not produced the goods with his first crop, that initial charge of IR125,000gns would have looked a bit sick, but instead it convinced those who used him at IR80,000gns in his fourth year that they had got a bargain. In 1990 he stood at IR150,000gns and he will go no lower in the foreseeable future.

The only worrying aspect about Sadler's Wells is the thought that he is just too good to be true. It certainly seemed unreal that from his first crop he should get the dead-heaters for first place in the Dewhurst Stakes, a third who won both the Chantilly and Curragh Derbys, and a fourth who started favourite for the Prix de l'Arc de Triomphe. If he *is* real, he might well establish himself as the best stallion ever to have stood in Ireland.

---

## Racing record

| Year | Starts | Wins | 2nd | 3rd | 4th | £ |
|------|--------|------|-----|-----|-----|---|
| 1983 | 2 | 2 | - | - | - | 28,260 |
| 1984 | 9 | 4 | 3 | - | 1 | 548,240 |
| | 11 | 6 | 3 | - | 1 | 576,500 |

## Principal wins

1983    Beresford Stakes-Gr2
1984    Irish Derby Trial Stakes-Gr2
        Irish 2000 Guineas-Gr1
        Eclipse Stakes-Gr1
        Phoenix Champion Stakes-Gr1

## Principal progeny

**1986**
b c BATSHOOF (ex Steel Habit, by Habitat)
    1990    Rogers Gold Cup-Gr2
b c BRAASHEE (ex Krakow, by Malinowski)
    1990    Ormonde Stakes-Gr3
            Yorkshire Cup-Gr2
b c DOLPOUR (ex Dumka, by Kashmir)
    1990    Gordon Richards Stakes-Gr3
b c IN THE WINGS (ex High Hawk, by Shirley Heights)
    1989    Prix du Prince d'Orange-Gr3
    1990    Coronation Cup-Gr1
b c OLD VIC (ex Cockade, by Derring-Do)
    1989    Classic Trial Stakes-Gr3
            Chester Vase-Gr3
            Prix du Jockey-Club-Gr1
            Irish Derby-Gr1
b c PRINCE OF DANCE (ex Sun Princess, by English Prince)
    1988    Champagne Stakes-Gr2
            Dewhurst Stakes-Gr1 [dead-heat]

---

## SADLER'S WELLS                    (bay, 1981)

| | | | |
|---|---|---|---|
| Northern Dancer (b 1961) | Nearctic | Nearco | Pharos / Nogara |
| | | Lady Angela | Hyperion / Sister Sarah |
| | Natalma | Native Dancer | Polynesian / Geisha |
| | | Almahmoud | Mahmoud / Arbitrator |
| Fairy Bridge (b 1975) | Bold Reason | Hail to Reason | Turn-to / Nothirdchance |
| | | Lalun | Djeddah / Be Faithful |
| | Special | Forli | Aristophanes / Trevisa |
| | | Thong | Nantallah / Rough Shod |

b c SCENIC (ex Idyllic, by Foolish Pleasure)
    1988    Dewhurst Stakes-Gr1 [dead-heat]
    1989    Scottish Classic Stakes-Gr3

**1987**
b f SALSABIL (ex Flame of Tara, by Artaius)
    1989    Prix Marcel Boussac-Gr1
    1990    Fred Darling Stakes-Gr3
            1000 Guineas Stakes-Gr1
            Oaks Stakes-Gr1

# Seattle Slew

IT is a rare enough event for a cheap yearling to develop into an outstanding racehorse, much rarer still for him then to develop into an outstanding sire. The cheapness is generally a consequence of indifferent breeding credentials or poor conformation, or both, and though he may 'out-run his pedigree' and/or cope admirably with a physical defect to make a successful athlete, those original imperfections tend to come back to haunt him. In Europe breeders are disinclined to accept good performance as proof of good pedigree, and while Americans take a much more rational line on the subject, even they prefer to trust top-class form and top-class breeding as a package. As for the conformation fault, it is one of the oldest adages in the business that even if a horse overcomes a problem on the racecourse, it is wise not to depend on his progeny following suit.

Seattle Slew was sold as a yearling for $17,500. He actually was not *that* cheap, allowing for the fact that the average price in his auction was only $10,683, but he might have been in a more fashionable catalogue. He was well under the average for the yearlings by his sire, a first-season Claiborne horse, several of whose stock were admitted to the Keeneland July catalogue. If Bold Reasoning could be fancied to make the grade at stud, as a lot of people evidently thought, his son out of a stakes-winning mare from the renowned 'black type' family of Myrtlewood ought to be worth a place in a major catalogue, and ought to be worth a fair amount of money. The trouble with the colt was that he turned his off-fore foot out at an angle of nearly 90 degrees.

That was hard luck on breeder Ben Castleman, but the buyer, Seattle resident Karen Taylor, could afford to be less concerned about her slew-footed acquisition. Corrective shoeing might well help the colt's problem, and he was a big, strong, otherwise well-made fellow who might not let it worry him anyway. She and husband Mickey sent him off to trainer Billy Turner in New York, and as early as March the dark bay youngster indicated that he could gallop. What he needed, though, was more time to develop, so Turner sent him back to the farm for a couple of months, then brought him along steadily when he returned. Seattle Slew did not run until 20 September. Within a month he had run three times, won three times, and earned himself a championship. He won his maiden by five lengths over six furlongs, took a seven-furlong allowance event easily by three and a half lengths, then ran clean away from the best New York could field against him in the Grade 1 Champagne Stakes. His margin was nearly ten lengths and his time was fast.

Seattle Slew wintered in Florida and had his first run at three in a seven-furlong allowance race at Hialeah. He trotted up by nine lengths. Then came the Grade 1 Flamingo Stakes, and he led throughout the nine furlongs to beat Giboulee by four lengths. Back in New York he won the Grade 1 Wood Memorial the same way, this time by three and a quarter lengths over Sanhedrin. Apart from the few moments after the gates opened for the Kentucky Derby, and Seattle Slew was caught flat-footed, there was never a threat that he might fail in any of the Triple Crown events. He soon retrieved the lost ground at Churchill Downs, took command with half a mile to run, and drew clear to win as he liked by a length and three-quarters from Run Dusty Run. He had the Preakness won as soon as he had seen off Cormorant, and Iron Constitution's late bid failed by a length and a half. The Belmont was a doddle, leading every step of the way to beat his regular pursuer Run Dusty Run by four lengths. He had not dominated the series with the power and panache of a Secretariat, but he came through the Triple Crown an unbeaten horse, which none of his predecessors had done.

The plan now was to give Seattle Slew a rest until the autumn, but when Hollywood Park dangled the carrot of an additional $100,000 in prize money for him to compete in the Grade 1 Swaps Stakes, the temptation was irresistible. Seattle Slew ran and finished fourth behind J.O. Tobin, beaten 16 lengths. He did not run again that season, and was said to have picked up a throat infection. His owners were certainly choked. Before the year was out his trainer had been fired and replaced by Doug Peterson, a young man who had never held a trainer's licence.

Seattle Slew was out of competition for 11 months, during which time he contracted and shook off a virus and was half-sold in a deal which would

*Seattle Slew, who has imparted both his racing brilliance and conformation problems to his stock.*

take him to Spendthrift Farm at a valuation of $12 million. He won a seven-furlong allowance race at Belmont Park in May and another at Saratoga in August, both by wide margins, before his first serious assignment of the season in the Paterson Handicap at The Meadowlands on 5 September. He set the pace and looked likely to win easily, but tired in the straight and was overhauled by Dr Patches, who was receiving 14lb. Jockey Jean Cruguet (who had ridden him in all his races) blamed trainer Peterson for having under-prepared the colt, and the trainer retaliated by insisting on a change of rider. Angel Cordero had the mount for the remainder of Seattle Slew's career.

The Grade 1 Marlboro Cup featured the first clash in history between two Triple Crown winners.

Seattle Slew led throughout, Affirmed chased throughout, and the margin was three lengths. In the Woodward he was again allowed his own way and had four lengths to spare over Exceller. The Jockey Club Gold Cup was a very different kind of race. Affirmed was back in contention, this time with a pacemaker in Life's Hope to help him, and Exceller tried again, with extra distance to aid his cause. Before the first turn Affirmed's saddle slipped. Out of Steve Cauthen's control, he charged off to battle with Seattle Slew and Life's Hope for the lead, and for six furlongs they went head-and-head at a sprinter's pace. Then Life's Hope faded, and in due time Affirmed did too, leaving Seattle Slew clear. Exceller, coming from way back, picked up ground steadily, and as Seattle Slew's stride shortened, the pair joined issue. The race seemed to be Exceller's for the taking, but Seattle Slew, with a battle on his hands for the first time in his life, fought back valiantly and was only a nose behind at the wire. If he had anything left to prove, it was perhaps that he could come back and win after a punishing Grade 1 race over 12 furlongs. He did that in the Grade 3 Stuyvesant Handicap, then called it a day.

By now breeders in America were not going to care if Seattle Slew's pedigree said he was by nothing out of nothing. In fact it had improved considerably, as the unknown quantity Bold Reasoning had proved himself a remarkably good sire, apart from his most famous son. He had died early, getting only three crops, but a ratio of 16 per cent stakes winners to foals was impressive, even from a small sample. Before too long the bottom half of Seattle Slew's pedigree would read better, too, as his dam, to a mating with Northern Dancer, produced 2000 Guineas winner Lomond. The test was going to be whether Seattle Slew got sound-looking stock and, if not, whether they would be able to run.

Seattle Slew has not sired show-ring specimens, but he has got his share of passably good-looking progeny. More typically they are big, plain and angular, ewe-necked and without the best of joints. Plenty clearly suffer from soundness problems, as their sire's ratio of runners to foals is well below the average for North American stallions. It is not unlikely that many have been materially damaged by trainers who have tried to exploit them too soon; they have very open knees as youngsters and need time, as Seattle Slew did himself, at two years. His ratio of winners to runners is also not good, the same factor probably applying again, but the quality of the winners has been remarkable. Those who can run really *can* run, and they go on running. They are effective at two, three and four, they are tough and they are triers.

Seattle Slew's fee for his first four seasons at Spendthrift was $150,000, but when his runners appeared, thrived and continued to thrive there were several sharp upward revisions. In 1982 he was North America's leading freshman sire, thanks to the brilliant and ill-fated Landaluce, so in 1983 he covered at $225,000. After Slew o' Gold's impressive three-year-old campaign and the promise shown by the juvenile Swale, he was up to $500,000, and after his amazing year in 1984, when Slew o' Gold and Swale starred and a host of others played effective supporting roles, his fee rocketed to $750,000. Also in 1984 the market for his yearlings (the last conceived at $150,000) went crazy, with an average of more than $1.3 million for

## SEATTLE SLEW (bay, 1974)

| | | | |
|---|---|---|---|
| Bold Reasoning (b/br 1968) | Boldnesian | Bold Ruler | Nasrullah |
| | | | Miss Disco |
| | | Alanesian | Polynesian |
| | | | Alablue |
| | Reason to Earn | Hail to Reason | Turn-to |
| | | | Nothirdchance |
| | | Sailing Home | Wait a Bit |
| | | | Marching Home |
| My Charmer (b 1969) | Poker | Round Table | Princequillo |
| | | | Knight's Daughter |
| | | Glamour | Nasrullah |
| | | | Striking |
| | Fair Charmer | Jet Action | Jet Pilot |
| | | | Busher |
| | | Myrtle Charm | Alsab |
| | | | Crepe Myrtle |

### Racing record

| Year | Starts | Wins | 2nd | 3rd | 4th | $ |
|---|---|---|---|---|---|---|
| 1976 | 3 | 3 | - | - | - | 94,350 |
| 1977 | 7 | 6 | - | - | 1 | 641,370 |
| 1978 | 7 | 5 | 2 | - | - | 473,006 |
| | 17 | 14 | 2 | - | 1 | 1,208,726 |

### Principal wins

| | |
|---|---|
| 1976 | Champagne Stakes-Gr1 |
| 1977 | Flamingo Stakes-Gr1 |
| | Wood Memorial Stakes-Gr1 |
| | Kentucky Derby-Gr1 |
| | Preakness Stakes-Gr1 |
| | Belmont Stakes-Gr1 |
| 1978 | Marlboro Cup Handicap-Gr1 |
| | Woodward Stakes-Gr1 |
| | Stuyvesant Handicap-Gr3 |

17 sold, including $6.5 million for a colt who came to England and proved worthless.

That colt, a brother to Adored called Amjaad, was one of a number who failed to live up to expectations in Europe, with the inevitable result that demand for Seattle Slews on this side of the Atlantic waned. It did not, however, fall off completely, and a more discriminating attitude, with buyers concentrating on types who promised to be physically suited to European conditions, has already begun to pay off. Chances are that Europe will see more and better Seattle Slews before long. After the stallion's move to Three Chimneys Farm in 1986, his fee was reduced four years in a row, and in 1990 he stood at the more reasonable level of $200,000.

## Principal progeny

### 1980

b f ADORED (ex Desiree, by Raise a Native)
    1984    Santa Margarita Invitational Handicap-Gr1
              Hawthorne Handicap-Gr2
              Milady Handicap-Gr2
              Delaware Handicap-Gr1
    1985    Santa Maria Handicap-Gr2
              Hawthorne Handicap-Gr2
              Milady Handicap-Gr2
b/br f LANDALUCE (ex Strip Poker, by Bold Bidder)
    1982    Hollywood Lassie Stakes-Gr2
              Del Mar Debutante Stakes-Gr2
              Anoakia Stakes-Gr3
              Oak Leaf Stakes-Gr1
b c SLEW O' GOLD (ex Alluvial, by Buckpasser)
    1983    Wood Memorial Stakes [Div.2]-Gr1
              Peter Pan Stakes-Gr2
              Woodward Stakes-Gr1
              Jockey Club Gold Cup Stakes-Gr1
    1984    Whitney Handicap-Gr1
              Woodward Stakes-Gr1
              Marlboro Cup Handicap-Gr1
              Jockey Club Gold Cup Stakes-Gr1
b c SLEWPY (ex Rare Bouquet, by Prince John)
    1982    Young America Stakes-Gr1
    1983    Paterson Handicap-Gr2
              Meadowlands Cup Handicap-Gr1

### 1981

b c AL MUNDHIR (ex Huggle Duggle, by Never Bend)
    1985    Grosser Preis der Stadt Gelsenkirchen-Gr3
b/br f LE SLEW (ex Le Moulin, by Hawaii)
    1986    Vagrancy Handicap-Gr3
b c SEATTLE SONG (ex Incantation, by Prince Blessed)
    1983    Prix de la Salamandre-Gr1
    1984    Washington D.C. International Stakes-Gr1
b/br c SWALE (ex Tuerta, by Forli)
    1983    Saratoga Special Stakes-Gr2
              Futurity Stakes-Gr1
              Breeders' Futurity-Gr2
              Young America Stakes-Gr1
    1984    Hutcheson Stakes-Gr3
              Florida Derby-Gr1
              Kentucky Derby-Gr1
              Belmont Stakes-Gr1
b/br c TSUNAMI SLEW (ex Barbs Compact, by Barbizon)
    1984    Will Rogers Handicap-Gr3
              Del Mar Derby-Gr2
    1985    American Handicap-Gr2
              Eddie Read Handicap-Gr2
              Carleton F. Burke Handicap-Gr1

### 1982

b f ORIENTAL (ex Eastern Classic, by Damascus)
    1986    Queen's Handicap-Gr3
b/br f SAVANNAH SLEW (ex Pilferer, by No Robbery)
    1985    Linda Vista Handicap-Gr3
              La Brea Stakes-Gr3
b c SLEW THE DRAGON (ex Gueniviere, by Prince John)
    1985    Hollywood Derby [Div.2]-Gr1
b f SO SHE SLEEPS (ex Shy Dawn, by Grey Dawn)
    1986    Columbiana Handicap-Gr3

### 1983

b f LIFE AT THE TOP (ex See You At the Top, by Riva Ridge)
    1986    Las Virgenes Stakes-Gr3
              Mother Goose Stakes-Gr1
              Rare Perfume Stakes-Gr3
              Ladies Handicap-Gr1
              Long Look Handicap-Gr2
    1987    Rampart Handicap-Gr3
b/br c VERNON CASTLE (ex Rullian's Princess, by Prince John)
    1986    California Derby-Gr2
              La Jolla Mile Stakes-Gr3
              Del Mar Derby Handicap-Gr2

### 1984

br c CAPOTE (ex Too Bald, by Bald Eagle)
    1986    Norfolk Stakes-Gr1
              Breeders' Cup Juvenile Stakes-Gr1
b/br c SLEW CITY SLEW (ex Weber City Miss, by Berkley Prince)
    1988    Salvator Mile Handicap-Gr3
    1989    Gulfstream Park Handicap-Gr1
              Oaklawn Handicap-Gr1

### 1985

b f BITOOH (ex It's in the Air, by Mr Prospector)
    1987    Criterium de Maisons-Laffitte-Gr2
b/br f GLOWING HONOR (ex Glowing Tribute, by Graustark)
    1988    Diana Handicap-Gr2
              Leixable Stakes-Gr3
    1989    Diana Handicap-Gr2
b f MAGIC OF LIFE (ex Larida, by Northern Dancer)
    1987    Mill Reef Stakes-Gr2
    1988    Coronation Stakes-Gr1

### 1986

b/br c FAST PLAY (ex Con Game, by Buckpasser)
    1988    Breeders' Futurity-Gr2
              Remsen Stakes-Gr1
b c HOUSTON (ex Smart Angle, by Quadrangle)
    1989    Bay Shore Stakes-Gr2
              Derby Trial Stakes-Gr3
              King's Bishop Stakes-Gr3
b f SEATTLE METEOR (ex Northern Meteor, by Northern Dancer)
    1988    Astoria Stakes-Gr3
              Spinaway Stakes-Gr1
b c SLEW THE KNIGHT (ex Gueniviere, by Prince John)
    1989    Saranac Stakes [Div.2]-Gr2
              Hill Prince Stakes-Gr3

### 1987

b c DIGRESSION (ex Double Axle, by The Axe)
    1989    Royal Lodge Stakes-Gr2
b f HAIL ATLANTIS (ex Flippers, by Coastal)
    1990    Santa Anita Oaks-Gr1
b f SEASIDE ATTRACTION (ex Kamar, by Key to the Mint)
    1990    Kentucky Oaks-Gr1
b c SEPTIEME CIEL (ex Maximova, by Green Dancer)
    1989    Prix Thomas Bryon-Gr3
              Criterium de Maisons-Laffitte-Gr2
b/br c YONDER (ex Far, by Forli)
    1989    Remsen Stakes-Gr2
    1990    Jersey Derby-Gr2

# Secretariat

SECRETARIAT timed his run perfectly in America's 'Horse of the Century' Stakes. He came along when there were still people around who remembered Man o' War; he won them over to his side, and he so convinced the younger generation of his supremacy that there was never a fear of his being deposed by the year 2000. There have been good horses since, and there will be more before the new century dawns, but there will still be folk who remember Secretariat.

What made Secretariat unique was that he represented a breakthrough in the history of the breed. Horsemen had long been aware of what the ideal racehorse should look like, how he should be made in every department of his physique. They had the blueprint, but they just could not construct him, not in over 200 years of trying. When his breeder, Penny Chenery, first saw Secretariat as a foal, she spoke for the thousands, living and dead, who had dreamed this impossible dream in the single word: 'Wow'. When the greatest American racing writer of the century, Charlie Hatton (who remembered Man o' War) first saw Secretariat at the racetrack, he put it more poetically: 'Trying to fault his conformation is like dreaming of dry rain.'

It was one thing to stand as a revelation in terms of the perfect Thoroughbred specimen, but there was more to being a racehorse. Secretariat was the complete package. He had the constitution. He had the temperament. Better yet, he proved that the blueprint, when constructed in flesh and blood, did produce the perfect racing machine. He had super-equine powers. He could do things no member of his species had ever been able to do.

None of the ideals that Secretariat expressed could have been foreseen, but there were nevertheless high hopes when his dam, Somethingroyal, visited Bold Ruler. Never mind that she had run only once and not earned a cent; she had already proved her worth as a broodmare by producing three stakes winners, one of them an outstanding performer in Sir Gaylord, who had become the sire of Sir Ivor and Habitat. The mare's second-best foal had been Syrian Sea, winner of the valuable Selima Stakes at two and third in the filly classic, the Coaching Club American Oaks, at three.

Syrian Sea was herself by Bold Ruler, and when Somethingroyal returned to him in 1969 he was en route to his seventh consecutive North American sires' title, a sequence without parallel this century. Secretariat had every right to be good.

The big red chesnut went into training with Lucien Laurin and had his first start on 4 July 1972. There were no celebrations. A rival clouted him early in the race, nearly bringing him down, and though he finished strongly there were three ahead of him at the wire. In eight more races that season, nothing finished in front of him. His second race, like the first, was at Aqueduct, and he won by six lengths. He moved to Saratoga and won a little allowance race by a length and a half. Then he beat a good colt, Linda's Chief, by three lengths in the Sanford Stakes, and followed up with a five-length victory over Flight to Glory in the Hopeful Stakes, with Stop the Music third. Stop the Music kept chasing Secretariat. At Belmont Park Secretariat beat him by a length and three-quarters in the Futurity and by two lengths in the Champagne Stakes. Unfortunately the Stewards reversed the order of finish in the latter race, as Secretariat had bumped his rival before beating him decisively. No matter, when they resumed hostilities in the Laurel Futurity, the margin between them was widened to eight lengths. Stop the Music did not bother to try again, and Secretariat wound up his year with an easy win over his stable companion Angle Light in the Garden State Stakes.

Secretariat was not just the season's dominant juvenile; he was 'Horse of the Year' as well, an accolade rarely bestowed on a two-year-old. His fame had already spread across the nation, and almost the only man in America who knew nothing about him was Christopher Chenery, nominally, at least, his breeder. He had been incapacitated for nearly five years before his death on 3 January 1973, an event which meant that Secretariat must be sold. By the end of February the colt had been syndicated at a valuation of $6.08 million, and it was one of the last genuine syndications on record, with only four shares being retained by the Chenery estate. The deal ensured that Secretariat would spend his stud career at Claiborne, but first he had to prove his worth as a three-year-old.

The colt's first three races of 1973 were at Aqueduct, and the first two went well. He won the Bay Shore Stakes over seven furlongs by four and a half lengths and the mile Gotham Stakes by three lengths. Then he tried nine furlongs for the first time in the Wood Memorial Stakes. The plan was to come from behind, and he did, but he ran wide into the straight and simply failed to fire when Ron Turcotte pressed the accelerator. The winner was his stable's supposed second string Angle Light, who beat Sham by a head, with Secretariat four lengths away third. The writing seemed to be on the wall for those shareholders who had bought into him for $190,000. The prophets of doom spoke up. Bold Ruler's stock were not stayers, and he never had got a winner of any of the Triple Crown races. In seven weeks' time, Secretariat would ensure that he had a complete set.

In the Kentucky Derby Secretariat did what no horse had done before. It was not just that he broke Northern Dancer's track record, but the way that he did it. Effectively he ran his field into the ground from the back. Turcotte settled him in last place and the colt just built up momentum, relentlessly piling on pressure. He covered his first quarter-mile in 25.2 seconds, his second in 24.2, his third in 23.6, his fourth in 23.4 and his fifth in 23.0. Sham was the last one he blew by, at the turn for home, and he was beaten by two and a half lengths. Sham was again his nearest pursuer in the Preakness Stakes, defeated by the same margin, though Secretariat had his measure much earlier on that occasion. He was deprived of a track record because the Pimlico tele-timing equipment was faulty.

Secretariat's Belmont Stakes performance was his finest, maybe the finest ever given by a Thoroughbred. This time he ran his rivals into the ground from the front, accomplished that by half-way, and turned the second half into an exhibition. He ran, and he kept running, underlining, with every 25-foot stride, the fact that here was the ultimate racing machine, performing to a peak unsurpassed and unsurpassable in any era. At the finish he was 31 lengths in front of runner-up Twice a Prince. The track record was broken. The first Triple Crown in 25 years had been won. He was still running, and while Turcotte vainly tried to halt him, he was clocked in world-record time for a mile and five furlongs.

It really did not matter what Secretariat did after that, but what he did not do was rest on his laurels. Three weeks later he won the Arlington Invitational Stakes by nine lengths. In August he contrived to get beaten by a moderate gelding called Onion in the Whitney Stakes at Saratoga, but he put matters right at Belmont in the following month, when he gave Onion 8lb and beat him out of sight in the Marlboro Cup. That day Secretariat was opposed by Riva Ridge, the previous year's Kentucky Derby and Preakness winner, and he was his runner-up, three and a half lengths adrift. Two weeks later came another reverse, when Prove Out beat him in the Woodward Stakes, but again the champion returned in triumph. Trying grass for the first time, he romped home by five lengths from Tentam in the Man o' War Stakes; the second time he enjoyed it even more, trouncing Big Spruce by six and a half lengths in the Canadian International Championship.

In 1973 Secretariat was not just 'Horse of the Year'. One sports magazine bent the rules to name him 'Man of the Year', while the New York Turf Writers gave him their award as the 'man who did most for racing in the year'. Those honours seemed to be touched with irony when Secretariat failed his first fertility tests, but that scare passed when the horse got down to the real business. He put 34 of 36 mares in foal in his first season and 43 of 44 in his second. The magic of Secretariat's name was inevitably soon converted to commercial success. One of the first mares offered in foal to him was Artists Proof, who realised $385,000. Among his first foals to be offered was a colt sold for a record $250,000 and a filly for $200,000. One of the first yearlings was Canadian Bound, whose price of $1.5 million more than doubled the previous world record. Everyone waited for the sensations to occur at the races.

The wait for the first winner lasted until 13 September 1977, when Feuille d'Erable took a maiden at Woodbine. The first stakes winner came a month later when Dactylographer (the product of the aforementioned Artists Proof) won Doncaster's Group 1 Futurity. Clearly the first crop was not very good, but there was better in the second, such as General Assembly, Terlingua and Canadian champion Medaille d'Or helping him to the title of America's leading sire of two-year-olds. It seemed that things were about to look up, but it did not happen then, and in fact it never happened.

It would be a harsh critic who called the sire of 'Horse of the Year' Lady's Secret and wide-margin Belmont Stakes winner Risen Star a failure, yet much, much more had been expected than the token offering of an occasional very good runner. He did not supply champions on a regular basis, and he was not even able to provide a reasonable quota of above-average performers; his ratio of 8 per cent stakes winners to foals does not qualify him for even

*Secretariat, who in terms of physique and racing performance, was arguably the perfect racehorse.*

the modest designation of 'a good sire'. There is no getting away from the fact that he has proved extremely disappointing in his second career.

There are all manner of reasons why good – even great – racehorses fail to excel at stud, but it is not always easy to identify them. It would seem ridiculous to suggest that he lacked opportunity, yet it is possible that the mares he had were not those most suitable for him. Because he was precocious and had tremendous speed, he was perceived by many breeders as basically a speed horse, in the Bold Ruler mould. That is one thing he never was. He was a one-off, who did not express his pedigree background. He expressed himself, but in crude terms he was basically a stayer, a resolute galloper, and a machine at that. His action was more that of a greyhound than of a racehorse. How do you mate a creature so different from the rest of his race? Perhaps we should have suspected that he would get only the odd good one, thrown up by chance rather than by design. His sons to date have not proved good sires, but he has many excellent broodmares among his daughters. It may well be that he is not even a great contributor to their success; they were all good, well-bred mares with the potential to produce good winners however they were mated.

Secretariat did represent a breakthrough. In physique and performance he set new standards in the development of the Thoroughbred, but it was not within his powers to take it a stage further. For all that he seemed on that glorious day at Belmont in June 1973, he was only mortal. He was put down at Claiborne on 4 October 1989, having developed laminitis in all four feet.

| **SECRETARIAT** | | | (chesnut, 1970) |
|---|---|---|---|
| Bold Ruler (b 1954) | Nasrullah | Nearco | Pharos Nogara |
| | | Mumtaz Begum | Blenheim Mumtaz Mahal |
| | Miss Disco | Discovery | Display Ariadne |
| | | Outdone | Pompey Sweep Out |
| Somethingroyal (b 1952) | Princequillo | Prince Rose | Rose Prince Indolence |
| | | Cosquilla | Papyrus Quick Thought |
| | Imperatrice | Caruso | Polymelian Sweet Music |
| | | Cinquepace | Brown Bud Assignation |

## Racing record

| Year | Starts | Wins | 2nd | 3rd | 4th | $ |
|------|--------|------|-----|-----|-----|---|
| 1972 | 9 | 7 | 1 | - | 1 | 456,404 |
| 1973 | 12 | 9 | 2 | 1 | - | 860,404 |
| | — | — | — | — | — | ——— |
| | 21 | 16 | 3 | 1 | 1 | 1,316,808 |

## Principal wins

| | |
|---|---|
| 1972 | Sanford Stakes |
| | Hopeful Stakes |
| | Futurity Stakes |
| | Laurel Futurity |
| | Garden State Stakes |
| 1973 | Bay Shore Stakes-Gr3 |
| | Gotham Stakes-Gr2 |
| | Kentucky Derby Stakes-Gr1 |
| | Preakness Stakes-Gr1 |
| | Belmont Stakes-Gr1 |
| | Arlington Invitational Stakes |
| | Marlboro Cup Invitational Handicap |
| | Man o' War Stakes-Gr1 |
| | Canadian International Championship Stakes-Gr2 |

## Principal progeny

### 1975
b c DACTYLOGRAPHER (ex Artists Proof, by Ribot)
　　1977　Futurity Stakes-Gr1

### 1976
ch c GENERAL ASSEMBLY (ex Exclusive Dancer, by Native Dancer)
　　1978　Saratoga Special Stakes-Gr2
　　　　　Hopeful Stakes-Gr1
　　1979　Gotham Stakes-Gr2
　　　　　Travers Stakes-Gr1
　　　　　Vosburgh Stakes-Gr2
ch f TERLINGUA (ex Crimson Saint, by Crimson Satan)
　　1978　Hollywood Lassie Stakes-Gr2
　　　　　Hollywood Juvenile Championship Stakes-Gr2
　　　　　Del Mar Debutante Stakes-Gr2
　　1979　Santa Ynez Stakes-Gr3
ch c SIFOUNAS (ex Trevisana, by Aristophanes)
　　1980　Premio Ellington-Gr2

### 1977
b f CINEGITA (ex Wanika, by Sadair)
　　1980　Railbird Stakes-Gr3
b/br c GLOBE (ex Hippodamia, by Hail to Reason)
　　1982　Grey Lag Handicap-Gr3
　　　　　Excelsior Handicap-Gr2

### 1978
b f WHO'S TO ANSWER (ex Orissa, by First Landing)
　　1982　Bed o' Roses Handicap-Gr3

### 1979
b c D'ACCORD (ex Fanfreluche, by Northern Dancer)
　　1981　Breeders' Futurity-Gr2

### 1980
b f WEEKEND SURPRISE (ex Lassie Dear, by Buckpasser)
　　1982　Schuylerville Stakes-Gr3
　　　　　Golden Rod Stakes-Gr3

### 1982
ch f FIESTA LADY (ex Faneuil Girl, by Bolinas Boy)
　　1984　Del Mar Debutante Stakes [Div.1]-Gr2
　　　　　Matron Stakes-Gr1
ch c IMAGE OF GREATNESS (ex By the Hand, by Intentionally)
　　1985　San Felipe Handicap-Gr1
gr f LADY'S SECRET (ex Great Lady M., by Icecapade)
　　1985　Test Stakes-Gr2
　　　　　Ballerina Stakes-Gr2
　　　　　Maskette Stakes-Gr1
　　　　　Ruffian Handicap-Gr1
　　　　　Beldame Stakes-Gr1
　　1986　El Encino Stakes-Gr3
　　　　　La Canada Stakes-Gr1
　　　　　Santa Margarita Invitational Handicap-Gr1
　　　　　Shuvee Handicap-Gr1
　　　　　Molly Pitcher Handicap-Gr2
　　　　　Whitney Handicap-Gr1
　　　　　Maskette Stakes-Gr1
　　　　　Ruffian Handicap-Gr1
　　　　　Beldame Stakes-Gr1
　　　　　Breeders' Cup Distaff Stakes-Gr1
ch c PANCHO VILLA (ex Crimson Saint, by Crimson Satan)
　　1985　Bay Shore Stakes-Gr2
　　　　　Silver Screen Handicap-Gr2
　　　　　National Sprint Championship Handicap-Gr3

### 1984
ch c CLEVER SECRET (ex Small Loaf, by Pia Star)
　　1987　Lamplighter Handicap-Gr2
　　1988　Aqueduct Handicap-Gr3

### 1985
ch f ATHYKA (ex Princesse Kathy, by Luthier)
　　1988　Prix Chloe-Gr3
　　　　　Prix de l'Opera-Gr2
　　1989　Prix Corrida-Gr3
　　　　　La Coupe-Gr3
　　　　　Prix de l'Opera-Gr2
ch f BLUEBOOK (ex Pushy, by Sharpen Up)
　　1987　Princess Margaret Stakes-Gr3
　　1988　Fred Darling Stakes-Gr3
　　　　　Prix de Seine-et-Oise-Gr3
b c RISEN STAR (ex Ribbon, by His Majesty)
　　1988　Louisiana Derby-Gr3
　　　　　Lexington Stakes-Gr2
　　　　　Preakness Stakes-Gr1
　　　　　Belmont Stakes-Gr1
ch f SUMMER SECRETARY (ex Golden Summer, by Key to the Mint)
　　1989　Beaugay Handicap-Gr3

# Secreto

IT never was obligatory for the good Northern Dancers to be good-looking, but Secreto did seem to abuse the privilege somewhat. When he was sold at Keeneland, the joke was that some mug had given $340,000 for him and the guy who had bid $330,000 was holding a celebration party. All the usual fanciers of the sire's stock had turned him down. He was not up to Maktoum standards, and as for the Ballydoyle team, well, they reckoned they already had far better Northern Dancers in the home-bred Sadler's Wells and the one with the parrot mouth, El Gran Senor. Luigi Miglietti, the Venezuelan 'mug' who had bought the colt, did not care what anyone else thought . . . or perhaps he did. He had toyed with the idea of sending the colt to Ben Hanbury in Newmarket, but on second thoughts he sent him to David O'Brien, where he could be trained almost in Ballydoyle's back garden.

Miglietti was quite big in the horse business, with studs in Venezuela, Argentina and Kentucky. He was a good deal bigger in the transportation business, owning the biggest bus company in Caracas, and his purchase of Secreto did seem to indicate that he was probably a better judge of things which ran on wheels. The back end of a bus was attractive compared with the front end of this colt; he was a vehicle who came with a guarantee of low mileage.

As it turned out, Miglietti got a total of only four and a quarter miles out of Secreto. Nevertheless, when two Northern Dancer models from the same Maryland factory were tested over a mile and a half at Epsom, the sleek, high-performance limousine tuned by Vincent O'Brien ran out of fuel just before the finish, while the poorly designed runabout patched up by David O'Brien kept going. After that it did not really matter if the vehicle was no longer in running order. Miglietti could sell a half-share for $20 million, and there would be other uses for him.

Secreto's trainer did a marvellous job with him. The colt ran only once as a two-year-old, over seven furlongs in a race of no importance at Phoenix Park, and he quickened nicely to beat a German-bred maiden called Antikitos. In the following spring he became a Pattern winner in the Group 3 Tetrarch Stakes, again showing good acceleration and just being pushed out to beat Without Reserve, a previous

Group 3 winner who was trying to give him 7lb. He was beginning to acquire quite a reputation - to the extent that he started 6/4 favourite for the Irish 2000 Guineas next time out. He again acquitted himself well, being beaten only a neck and half a length by Sadler's Wells and Procida; the mile probably suited him less than it suited them, but they were better racehorses anyway.

The Derby was the obvious target for Secreto in some respects. He was likely to be better over the longer distance, and if he was ever going to make a real name for himself, there could be no better occasion. On the other hand, Epsom was unlikely to prove the ideal course for one with his foreleg construction. There was also the little matter of Secreto's one-time paddock companion at Windfields to consider. David O'Brien was only too well aware that his father rated El Gran Senor as potentially the best horse he had ever trained, and he knew there was talk of a $60 million syndication over that colt, to be confirmed after the formality of his Derby victory. Still, there was every reason to believe that El Gran Senor would not be so good at 12 furlongs as he obviously was at eight, and it promised to be the other way around with Secreto. Once the decision

*Secreto, who covered 100 mares in one season.*

had been taken, Vincent O'Brien was convinced that his son had the one real threat to El Gran Senor.

Secreto handled Epsom rather well. For all his physical faults he was a good-actioned horse, and he came down the hill as well as anything - apart from the favourite, who lobbed along ominously on his inside. He came into the straight about seventh, could not quicken as El Gran Senor quickened, but kept going under pressure. It was soon apparent that the two Northern Dancer colts were going to fill first and second places, and the order was not in doubt. While Pat Eddery sat motionless on El Gran Senor, Christy Roche was committing something akin to grievous bodily harm on Secreto. The next development would surely be that Eddery would let out an inch of rein, and ask his mount to go. Then Roche could realize the futility of his violence, put away his stick, and remain content with the thought that second place in the Derby was not at all bad. It worked out differently. When Eddery made the call, El Gran Senor was out - all out. Roche took the message, rightly reckoned that first place was still available, and stepped up the tempo of his assault on Secreto. It was a furious finale. Eddery abandoned finesse in favour of all-out action, but El Gran Senor had given everything he had before the whip was drawn, and he could not quicken again. Roche just kept raining blows on Secreto and did not care how unedifying it looked. His mount's momentum was irresistible now. He was going to win the Derby.

The verdict was only a short head, and it did not exactly make Secreto the undisputed champion of his crop. Whatever title he might have been assumed to have won, he was not to be lured out of his box to defend it, not in the Irish Derby, nor in the 'King George', nor in the Benson & Hedges Gold Cup, nor in the Arc de Triomphe, nor in the Washington DC International, nor yet in the Breeders' Cup Turf Stakes. All, at some time or other, were supposed to be objectives, but he sent his apologies on every occasion. He had reached the end of his mileage at Epsom, and it was to the credit of all concerned that such a basically unsound individual had contrived to triumph in the supreme test of a three-year-old's talents.

The valuation of $40 million put on Secreto in the deal which took him to Calumet Farm in Kentucky was a little bit hard to believe, and it did not seem to square with the fact that nominations for his first season changed hands for 'only' $80,000. Of course, that latter figure would make more sense if he were to be more than usually actively employed, and that has turned out to be the case. In 1987, his third season (when he covered at $100,000), he saw

## SECRETO                                          (bay, 1981)

| | | | |
|---|---|---|---|
| **Northern Dancer** (b 1961) | Nearctic | Nearco | Pharos / Nogara |
| | | Lady Angela | Hyperion / Sister Sarah |
| | Natalma | Native Dancer | Polynesian / Geisha |
| | | Almahmoud | Mahmoud / Arbitrator |
| **Betty's Secret** (ch 1977) | Secretariat | Bold Ruler | Nasrullah / Mumtaz Begum |
| | | Somethingroyal | Princequillo / Imperatrice |
| | Betty Loraine | Prince John | Princequillo / Not Afraid |
| | | Gay Hostess | Royal Charger / Your Hostess |

### Racing record

| Year | Starts | Wins | 2nd | 3rd | 4th | £ |
|---|---|---|---|---|---|---|
| 1983 | 1 | 1 | - | - | - | 1,190 |
| 1984 | 3 | 2 | - | 1 | - | 243,714 |
| | 4 | 3 | - | 1 | - | 244,904 |

### Principal wins

1984    Tetrarch Stakes-Gr3
        Derby Stakes-Gr1

### Principal progeny
**1986**
b f MISS SECRETO (ex My First Fling, by Olden Times)
        1988    Premio Dormello-Gr3 [dead-heat]
        1989    Premio Regina Elena-Gr2
                Premio Lydia Tesio-Gr2

more action than any other horse in North America, serving exactly 100 mares. He got 69 foals in that crop, and at a median price of $67,000 the 40 who went to auction as yearlings did not fare too well.

Many of Secreto's progeny have come to Europe, but with the notable exception of his first crop daughter Miss Secreto, their record to date has been dismal. A lot of them are good-looking specimens, without their sire's obvious faults, but they seem unable to run very fast, an even more serious defect. Calumet appeared to have set a lot of store by Secreto, but at the moment the horse is not repaying that trust. It will be a pity if the farm's revitalization, exemplified through Alydar, should now be checked by a stallion calculated to do more harm than good.

# Shadeed

IT might seem logical that there should be no difference in the price of two horses, a well-bred one and an indifferently bred one, who have an identical defect of conformation likely to inhibit their usefulness on the racecourse. It stands to reason that if they are going to be equally unsound, they should be equally worthless. Logic can be many-sided, however, and the market takes a different view. The poorly bred horse was probably never going to be any good anyway; his defect will simply make it more certain that he proves useless. The really well-bred horse is different. He will have a lot of good things going for him to be weighed against his fault, and if his parents have progeny which have raced, there may be evidence to suggest that this fellow will have the character, the courage and the constitution to overcome it. He might yet be able to express his inherent ability, and as the demands of modern racing are not severe, in terms of how often a horse must race, he might well represent an acceptable risk. The question then is, what is a reasonable price to pay for a horse who just might be every bit as good as his breeding suggests?

In nine cases out of ten, the market is wrong to pursue that line of reasoning, and the proof is to be found in the vast numbers of six- and seven-figure yearlings who descend into poor company on the racecourse or never aspire to racing at all. One of the exceptions was Shadeed. He came up for sale at Keeneland on a day when the market reached sublime heights of insanity, quite surpassing the comparatively mild madness of the day before. On 19 July 1983 ten yearlings brought more than $1 million and one fetched more than $10 million; few of them seemed half as well-bred as Shadeed, who was knocked down for the pittance of $800,000. He was a fine big colt, in many ways typical of the best of Nijinsky's stock, and he came from a family with abundant market appeal. His price was probably slashed in half by the fact that his forelegs did not conform to specifications. With short pasterns set on that straight, he had the potential to cause himself damage every time he galloped and he probably would not stand training for very long.

Shadeed did not have a long career, but how many high-class horses do these days? He stayed sound enough to register a classic win and one performance at weight-for-age that made him every bit as good as his pedigree entitled him to be. If anything, it was his highly strung temperament, rather than his conformation, which caused concern to his trainer, Michael Stoute.

Shadeed could hardly have picked a tougher maiden for his debut at Newmarket in October, but nobody knew that at the time and because of his sparkling work at home he was the only one anyone wanted to back. If any disappointment was felt at his third place that day (he might have been second but for traffic problems), it did not seem so bad when the winner, Kala Dancer, came out two weeks later to beat Law Society and Local Suitor in the Group 1 Dewhurst Stakes. Shadeed himself reappeared on the day after the Dewhurst, and the fact that he was re-opposed by Al Riyadh, the other colt who had beaten him before, did not deter the punters, who again made him a hot favourite. He duly won the Houghton Stakes, and he won impressively enough to become many people's idea of the 1985 Guineas and Derby winner.

A Guineas win became more a certainty than a probability after Shadeed's brilliant display in the Craven Stakes on his return to action in April. He seemed to have plenty in hand as he drew clear for a six-length win over Damister. In the following week he lost his intended classic jockey when Walter Swinburn picked up a suspension for a misdemeanour at Epsom, but that did not hurt Shadeed's prospects; Lester Piggott, already booked for Sheikh Mohammed's Bairn, was released from his engagement so that he could partner the favourite for Sheikh Maktoum, and the odds became even shorter. The Guineas did not come easily, though. Shadeed became heated during the preliminaries, and Stoute told Piggott to take him out of the parade and straight to the start, a move which caused the displeasure of the Stewards, but probably had a calming influence on the colt. Even so, when Shadeed came to the front this time he was not able to open a wide advantage, as he had in the Craven, and Piggott had to drive him hard to secure his 29th - and last - classic victory, by a head from the colt he had originally been scheduled to ride.

*Shadeed wins the Queen Elizabeth II Stakes impressively from Teleprompter and Zaizafon.*

Shadeed's pedigree gave him a reasonable chance of staying the Derby distance, but his style of running withdrew that licence. He objected to Swinburn's insistence that he should conserve his effort, and by the turn into the straight he was a spent force. It is likely that he also did not appreciate the switchback course, but it scarcely mattered; he beat only one home. Some were inclined to think that the colt's temperament might have got the better of him permanently, and when news came that he was sick, that he was being taken out of training, and that he was going off to recuperate on one of the Maktoum family studs, the not unnatural thought occurred that he might have gone for good.

In fact, he came back in magnificent form. Almost four months after his disastrous run at Epsom, Shadeed returned in the Queen Elizabeth II Stakes and broke the Ascot course record in much the best performance of the season at a mile, leading from half-way and quickening decisively two furlongs out. His stride shortened perceptibly in the last hundred yards, but by then he had out-galloped a classy field, and Teleprompter was still two and a half lengths behind him at the line. It was a great feat of training by Stoute after the colt's recent troubles. On that form Shadeed seemed to hold a first-rate chance in the Breeders' Cup Mile, but he could finish no nearer than fourth to Cozzene and had the Aqueduct Stewards to thank for his third prize; Palace Music, who beat him by a couple of noses, was relegated to ninth place for an offence against two other runners. Nevertheless, Shadeed had given an excellent account of himself, running with greater distinction than Rousillon and Never So Bold, and he could retire with honour.

Sheikh Maktoum retained full ownership of Shadeed for his stud career in Kentucky. The horse spent his first season on Bob Clay's Three Chimneys Farm at Midway, pending completion of facilities on Maktoum's own Gainsborough Farm at Versailles,

## SHADEED                                                      (bay, 1982)

| | | | Nearco |
| | | Nearctic | Lady Angela |
| | Northern Dancer | | Native Dancer |
| Nijinsky | | Natalma | Almahmoud |
| (b 1967) | | | Bull Lea |
| | | Bull Page | Our Page |
| | Flaming Page | | Menow |
| | | Flaring Top | Flaming Top |
| | | | Sunglow |
| | | Sword Dancer | Highland Fling |
| | Damascus | | My Babu |
| Continual | | Kerala | Blade of Time |
| (b/br 1976) | | | Aristophanes |
| | | Forli | Trevisa |
| | Continuation | | Double Jay |
| | | Continue | Courtesy |

### Racing record

| Year | Starts | Wins | 2nd | 3rd | 4th | £ |
|---|---|---|---|---|---|---|
| 1984 | 2 | 1 | - | 1 | - | 11,081 |
| 1985 | 5 | 3 | - | 1 | - | 227,849 |
| | 7 | 4 | - | 2 | - | 238,930 |

### Principal wins
1985    Craven Stakes-Gr3
        2000 Guineas Stakes-Gr1
        Queen Elizabeth II Stakes-Gr2

where he has covered since 1987. His fee has remained unchanged at $50,000 in his first five years and he has been mated with numerous top-class mares, many of them inevitably supplied by members of the Maktoum family. His auction yearlings have proved acceptable, their prices helped by the fact that there have been relatively few of them, but there have been some with their sire's forelegs and the market will be looking for proof that they can run before it gets over-excited about him.

# Shahrastani

IN the long run it turned out to be Shahrastani, not Dancing Brave, who had the bad luck in the 1986 Derby. Shahrastani was – make no mistake – a very good horse, and he did everything right that day, as on several other days. Unfortunately, there was more than a strong suspicion that he might not have won if everything had gone right for his runner-up, and when subsequent events clearly did reverse the order of merit, his reputation suffered more than it should have done. If he had finished second he could have worn his 'Good enough to have won most Derbys' badge, and everyone would have acknowledged it as fair comment, pointed to all his other fine efforts and given him the credit that was his due. Instead of that he is dismissed as 'the horse who should not have won the Derby'. Period. It was reckoned at the time that Walter Swinburn had ridden the perfect Derby race. On reflection, it might have been in the best interests of his mount if he had taken a pull and waved Dancing Brave on.

Shahrastani was not as good as Dancing Brave. That was not conclusively established at Epsom, nor even at Ascot in the King George VI & Queen Elizabeth Stakes when Shahrastani was clearly out of sorts, but it was proved at Longchamp. Shahrastani was inferior to Dancing Brave because he did not have the lightning acceleration that Dancing Brave had. Nevertheless, if the pair had met not three times but ten times, as Affirmed and Alydar did, there would have been occasions when the Epsom, rather than the Longchamp, result would have been confirmed. It is conceivable that if Shahrastani had turned up for the Breeders' Cup when Dancing Brave had his off-day, it would have happened there.

While Shahrastani, in common with every other horse of his generation, did not have Dancing Brave's quickening powers, he was anything but deficient in that department. His acceleration was the first quality he revealed on his debut at Newbury in September 1985, and it was what caused many to mark him down as a colt with a future. In a competitive group of 18 on the straight mile, he had to be switched to find daylight and found it just too late. He finished like a train, and had the race been a mile and 20 yards, he would have won instead of losing by a head.

The 2000 Guineas was never on Shahrastani's agenda, and Michael Stoute started his Derby preparation in the Group 3 Classic Trial at Sandown. It was a good start, too, as he swept past Bonhomie without urging from Walter Swinburn and displayed a fine turn of speed when asked. In the Group 2 Dante Stakes at York he was not so impressive. The opposition really did not amount to much, so Shahrastani was made odds-on to brush it aside, but once he had taken the lead at the quarter-mile marker, he just ran on and completed a workmanlike job. Still, he was a very inexperienced horse, and – like Secreto two years earlier – he would have only three races behind him when he went to Epsom.

Shahrastani had a very different Derby experience from that suffered by Secreto. Swinburn gave him the classic ride, lying handy, keeping a good position, coming fourth into the straight, kicking for home and driving clear. Shahrastani was the model mount, too. He did everything on demand with fluent efficiency, handled the turns and the gradients beautifully, quickened and stayed. He actually won unchallenged, as Dancing Brave came so late and the post so soon for him that there was never a struggle between them.

The ten who started against Shahrastani in the Irish Derby seemed unlikely to trouble him, the principal interest in the race being to assess the style of his victory. That was impeccable, best exemplified by the facts that he more than trebled his Epsom margin over Mashkour while also giving a sounder beating to Bakharoff than that colt had suffered from Bering in the Prix du Jockey-Club. Greville Starkey, having been castigated over his riding of Dancing Brave at Epsom, rode a much worse race at The Curragh on Bakharoff and escaped criticism only because he was not expected to win. Shahrastani reaped all the benefit of Bakharoff's pacemaker, lobbing along behind him then bursting clear to win by eight lengths. Bakharoff, a horse without a turn of foot, was kept at the back and could only run on through beaten horses to claim a distant third place.

The so-called 'grudge match' at Ascot, where Pat Eddery replaced Starkey on Dancing Brave, never really materialized. Shahrastani actually started favourite, though he obviously was not on best terms with himself, sweating up and fretting in the preliminaries and showing reluctance to enter his stall. For some reason he just did not want to run that day, and quite early in the straight Swinburn acceded to his plainly stated wish to be an onlooker rather than a participant.

It seemed like the end for Shahrastani, especially as his stud future had already been settled. The deal which would take him to Three Chimneys Farm was said to value him at £16 million, with the Aga Khan retaining 25 per cent, and what occurred at Ascot was scarcely calculated to extend the list of would-be shareholders. Many took it for granted that he would now slink away, hanging his head in shame, his tail between his legs. Far from it. Michael Stoute repeated the feat of horse-mastership he had displayed with Shadeed, restoring Shahrastani to vibrant health and pristine enthusiasm sufficient to run something close to the race of his life in the Arc de Triomphe. It was an exceptionally strong field, and on firm ground they ran the race to suit Dancing Brave, constantly stepping up the tempo from half-way and ensuring that victory went to the one who could use his speed last. Shahrastani was there in the firing line a furlong and a half out, but he was a spent force when Dancing Brave came by. Even so, he lasted well to be fourth, within half a length or so of Bering and an inch or two of Triptych.

Shahrastani could go out with his head held high after that. As a son of Nijinsky, who had had the Kentucky Derby winner in Ferdinand from the same crop, he was entitled to some respect, and if the Americans were not too familiar with the bottom half of his pedigree they were unlikely to hold that against him. In fact it was pretty good, and there was a recent American connection, which would do no harm. His dam had been only a useful mile handicapper in England, but she was a half-sister to the Grand Prix de Saint-Cloud winner Shakapour and to Sharannpour, who had won the Grade 1

## SHAHRASTANI (chestnut, 1983)

| | | | Nearco |
|---|---|---|---|
| Nijinsky (b 1967) | Northern Dancer | Nearctic | Lady Angela |
| | | Natalma | Native Dancer |
| | | | Almahmoud |
| | Flaming Page | Bull Page | Bull Lea |
| | | | Our Page |
| | | Flaring Top | Menow |
| | | | Flaming Top |
| Shademah (ch 1978) | Thatch | Forli | Aristophanes |
| | | | Trevisa |
| | | Thong | Nantallah |
| | | | Rough Shod |
| | Shamim | Le Haar | Vieux Manoir |
| | | | Mince Pie |
| | | Diamond Drop | Charlottesville |
| | | | Martine |

### Racing record

| Year | Starts | Wins | 2nd | 3rd | 4th | £ |
|---|---|---|---|---|---|---|
| 1985 | 1 | - | 1 | - | - | 1,820 |
| 1986 | 6 | 4 | - | - | 2 | 648,541 |
| | 7 | 4 | 1 | - | 2 | 650,361 |

### Principal wins

1986   Classic Trial Stakes-Gr3
Dante Stakes-Gr2
Derby Stakes-Gr1
Irish Derby-Gr1

Bowling Green Handicap at Belmont in 1985. Shahrastani covered at $100,000 in his first season but was reduced to $40,000 after a couple of years. A lot of his stock take after him, being plain and lengthy staying types, not the eye-catching sort in a sale-ring but well enough made to develop into successful athletes.

*Shahrastani draws well clear of Bonhomie and Bakharoff to win the Irish Derby.*

# Shardari

THE Aga Khan tends to be as hasty as most other owners in packing his classic winners off to stud. All three of his Derby winners (Shergar, Shahrastani and Kahyasi) became stallions at four, as did a host of other celebrities from Blushing Groom to Doyoun. On the other hand, he has always adopted a more adventurous policy with his late-developing colts, and he has managed to establish several as viable stallion prospects by keeping them in training for a third season and running them in the best company. He has been boldness itself in that respect, often much to his own benefit, and greatly to the benefit of the sport; on occasions, his older horses have provided the keenest competition for the new crop of three-year-olds, and thereby the best gauge of its merits.

Shardari had three seasons in training, but only two in racing; his owner-breeder did not bother to register a name for him until he was past the age at which his dam had finished winning. Sharmada had been a precocious two-year-old – a winner twice over five furlongs and runner-up in the Group 3 Prix d'Arenberg – before an accident called a halt to her career. She went to stud as a three-year-old and was covered by her owner's second-season stallion Top Ville, himself a dual Group 3 winner at two, but a much more finished racehorse at three, when he took the Prix du Jockey-Club. It was a mating which offered reasonable hopes of a product which would run early and fast; the result was something extremely backward, never to run at less than ten furlongs.

Michael Stoute finally got Shardari to the racecourse in June 1985, and for once he had a newcomer whose merit he had not realized. In a mile-and-a-quarter maiden at Sandown the colt started friendless at 14/1 and strolled home alone, ten lengths clear of the second, 20 lengths clear of the fourth. Two weeks later, this time at long odds-on, he broke the course record at Folkestone when winning by 12 lengths. In August he stepped up to a mile and a half, and more exalted company, for the Alycidon Stakes at Goodwood. Here he had the useful Newbury winner Royal Coach to beat, and he duly beat him by ten lengths, but he could not cope with his owner's other contender, the four-year-old Shernazar, who showed the better pace in the final furlong.

There went the unbeaten certificate, but never mind. This was obviously a good colt, and he deserved a tilt at some of the best of his crop. In the Group 2 Great Voltigeur Stakes at York Shardari took on Damister, third in both the Derby and the Irish Derby. What is more, he beat him rather cleverly by a neck, only to lose the race in the Stewards' room for a trifling infraction of the rules which did not affect the order of finish. The best policy was evidently to steer well clear of other horses, so Walter Swinburn did that on Shardari in his last two races of the season; the colt finished six lengths clear in the Cumberland Lodge Stakes and 15 lengths clear in the St Simon Stakes. That Group 3 double advertised Shardari as the most improved staying three-year-old of the season, little, if anything, below classic standard.

Shardari's four-year-old campaign began with an embarrassing defeat on soft ground at Chester, where 33/1 shot Brunico came by him in the final furlong. When he again ran below par in the Coronation Cup (fourth to Saint Estephe and apparently unhappy about the gradients), it seemed as though his extra season in training might not have been such a good idea, but he did nothing wrong thereafter.

He romped home by three lengths in the Group 2 Princess of Wales's Stakes at Newmarket, beating Baby Turk and Petoski, then resisted Dancing Brave nobly in the 'King George'. The star three-year-old spent most of his season running away from his rivals, but he found it tough enough to edge ahead of Shardari and could not extend his lead to as much as a length. Triptych was four lengths behind him in third place.

Shardari was overdue a Group 1 win. His connections boldly opted to go for the York International Stakes, whose distance (ten and a half furlongs) seemed likely to suit several of his rivals rather better than it would suit him. Still, his performance against the champion three-year-old at Ascot had a powerful deterrent effect on other leaders of that generation, who did not offer a challenge. As expected, Triptych found the distance much to her liking, but Shardari kept going too strongly for her, winning by three-quarters of a length.

Shardari finished out of the frame for the first time in his life at Longchamp, beaten a neck into fifth place by Shahrastani in Dancing Brave's Arc de Triomphe. It was another thoroughly game effort, though, and he was easily the best of the senior colts on view.

Surprisingly, he was asked to turn out again only a fortnight later – and on the other side of the Atlantic, in the Grade 1 Canadian International Championship at Woodbine. If he had finished last he could have been excused, in view of his strenuous recent effort in France, but in fact he was beaten only three-quarters of a length by the three-year-old American colt Southjet.

The Aga Khan took Shardari home to Ballymany and installed him there for the 1987 season at a fee of IR15,000gns. Inevitably, the horse was strongly supported by his owner, and chances are that both will be all the better for it. As was predictable, his stock are not attractive sales youngsters. They are the slow-maturing type and they will need the same kind of patience that Shardari's breeder exercised over him.

The modest prices for the first dozen auction yearlings – only four made more than 20,000gns – may do him no long-term harm. He promises to be essentially a private breeders' horse, and it is to be hoped that many will afford him appropriate chances, in view of his 'different' pedigree background. It must be short odds, though, that the Aga will obtain the best results.

## SHARDARI                                    (bay, 1982)

| | | | |
|---|---|---|---|
| Top Ville (b 1976) | High Top | Derring-Do | Darius / Sipsey Bridge |
| | | Camenae | Vimy / Madrilene |
| | Sega Ville | Charlottesville | Prince Chevalier / Noorani |
| | | La Sega | Tantieme / La Danse |
| Sharmada (gr 1978) | Zeddaan | Grey Sovereign | Nasrullah / Kong |
| | | Vareta | Vilmorin / Veronique |
| | Shireen | Prince Taj | Prince Bio / Malindi |
| | | Clair Obscur | Honeyway / Gourabe |

### Racing record

| Year | Starts | Wins | 2nd | 3r | 4th | £ |
|---|---|---|---|---|---|---|
| 1984 | 0 | | | | | |
| 1985 | 6 | 4 | 2 | - | - | 49,667 |
| 1986 | 7 | 2 | 3 | - | 1 | 313,308 |
| | — | — | — | — | — | |
| | 13 | 6 | 5 | - | 1 | 362,975 |

### Principal wins

| | | |
|---|---|---|
| 1985 | Cumberland Lodge Stakes-Gr3 | |
| | St Simon Stakes-Gr3 | |
| 1986 | Princess of Wales's Stakes-Gr2 | |
| | York International Stakes-Gr1 | |

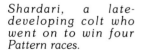

*Shardari, a late-developing colt who went on to win four Pattern races.*

# Shareef Dancer

IN the space of ten minutes at the 1981 Keeneland July Sales Sheikh Mohammed created a sensation by bidding $6.7 million for two Northern Dancer colts submitted from Windfields Farm. He missed the first one because Robert Sangster, Stavros Niarchos and others outbid him at a world record price of $3.5 million, and as it turned out he was lucky because that colt, called Ballydoyle, was not very good. The second one he did get, a small bay son of the Kentucky Oaks winner Sweet Alliance, for $3.3 million, but in due course he was to lose him as well. As had happened on previous occasions, and would happen again with Green Desert and numerous other Mohammed acquisitions, the buyer became obliged to transfer ownership in his purchase to his eldest brother, Sheikh Maktoum Al-Maktoum. Such arrangements are family matters, normally of no concern to anyone else. However, in this instance there were repercussions which did concern, and involve, other people, and with hindsight it seems a pity that a transfer occurred.

The colt was Shareef Dancer, whose arrival in Michael Stoute's yard made him newsworthy enough, as the most highly-priced horse ever to be trained in England. Every time he ran he was news; on one very special occasion when he ran he was wonderful news. Then he began a new career as a non-runner, and he was bad news for the Maktoum family, for racing and for himself. Indifference to public relations, always a Maktoum failing, exacerbated the situation. A mountain of misunderstanding, which persisted for years, was founded on a basic communication problem. As for Shareef Dancer, the policy adhered to with him progressed from the unexplained to the inexplicable. His problem was, and still is, one of credibility.

Shareef Dancer made his debut in the Park Lodge Maiden Stakes at Newmarket in August 1982. He won it, but he was not very impressive, for which most were inclined to forgive him; he was raw, he was not fully fit, and anyway, he still beat 17 others. Anybody who really wanted to criticize him for his two-year-old form might more realistically point to his defeat on his only subsequent outing at Doncaster. He ran fourth there in a field of 25, looking decidedly one-paced, half an hour before Gorytus, by his brilliant display in the Group 2 Champagne Stakes, showed what a really top-class juvenile could do.

At three Shareef Dancer reappeared on the Sandown card which featured the Group 3 Classic Trial Stakes, but his target was the much less significant Esher Cup Handicap, and he could not even win that. He came to the front a quarter of a mile out, then put his head in the air and showed no fight when So True came at him, and past him. It was later learned that Shareef Dancer had been suffering from a throat infection, which might well have excused that performance, but he clearly needed to win a worthwhile race to gain any kind of reputation. He did. He went to Royal Ascot and he won the Group 2 King Edward VII Stakes in pleasing style, progressing from fifth to first quite quickly in the straight, then running on well to hold the late effort of Russian Roubles by a length. His form was still nothing like classic calibre, but his trainer had always liked him, he was an improving sort, and a run in the Irish Derby would do him no harm, even if it did come only nine days after his Ascot race.

In order to win the Irish Derby, Shareef Dancer had to beat the winners of both the Derby (Teenoso) and the Prix du Jockey-Club (Caerleon). Amazingly, he beat them pointless. He pulled hard behind a strong pace, and he was still pulling hard a quarter of a mile from home when Walter Swinburn decided to let him go. He had the race won in a matter of strides, quickening clear and beating Caerleon by rather more than the official margin of three lengths. The runner-up had been switched to escape a trap on the rails, which must have cost him some ground, while Teenoso (who finished two lengths behind him in third place) seemed to be unhappy on the firm ground. Even so, it was a remarkable performance, surely the best of the season by a three-year-old over a middle distance.

The arrival of a new star on the scene is, of course, an event of great significance for the public, and English racegoers naturally became very excited over the prospect of seeing this much-improved colt demonstrate his formidable powers at home. The date set for that was 16 August, in the Benson & Hedges Gold Cup, and the promise of Shareef Dancer's appearance inevitably meant that many

*Shareef Dancer is an emphatic winner of the Irish Derby with Caerleon in his wake.*

journeyed to York especially to see him. They were dismayed to find that he had opted out, deterred by morning rain which had changed the ground from 'good to firm' to 'good to soft'. The going was by no means bad, nothing else was withdrawn, and the public felt cheated. Not long afterwards the colt was withdrawn overnight from Kempton's September Stakes, supposedly on the grounds of an unfavourable weather forecast. At least nobody travelled for that race, but it seemed a pathetic excuse all the same; nobody believed the next announcement, to the effect that he would run in the 'Arc', and, sure enough, he was not among the declarations.

There were inevitably all sorts of rumours, several of them hinting at an unsoundness, another that he had turned savage. The one with the ring of truth about it was that there were fears for Sheikh Maktoum's health. That story had it that the owner

had become terribly fond of Shareef Dancer and was making himself ill over the prospect of the horse coming to some mishap or even getting defeated. If that was the case, it would have been far better if he had remained the property of Sheikh Mohammed. Still, whatever the truth was, nobody was telling, and that was the saddest fact of all.

It also emerged, during all the confusion and frustration, that there were moves afoot to syndicate Shareef Dancer for a world record sum of $40 million. Indeed, it was soon announced that such a syndication had taken place. Exactly how that could have been effected, nobody could imagine. What constituted a 'syndicate' in such circumstances? Very few Americans would want to stump up $1 million for a share in a prospective stallion to stand in the States, and it was scarcely conceivable that a queue would be forming there to buy shares in a horse to stand in England – a horse who was yet another pony-sized son of Northern Dancer, really no better bred than a dozen others, and whose reputation (which he was not being allowed to lay on the line) rested on a single top-class performance. Yet that was the story. There undoubtedly were concerted efforts to procure American involvement in the syndication, and when Shareef Dancer's fee for 1985 was announced, it was even quoted in dollars. At $150,000 (around £100,000) he was placed on a par with Habitat and Mill Reef, the most successful sires in Europe.

Whatever was happening, or was going to happen, in America, England was not ready for this. Shareef Dancer was bound to be named champion three-year-old, because nothing could surpass what he had done on that remarkable afternoon at The Curragh; but the refusal to let him be tested again made him, if not a bogus champion, a craven one. The syndication deal seemed to run counter to the Maktoum family's image as protector and benefactor of the British breeding industry, and it was hard to see how it could do anybody any good. The one logical deduction that could be drawn from the whole sorry mess was that Shareef Dancer had been set on immediate course for failure as a sire.

In his first four years at Dalham Hall the horse covered at £100,000 and initially he did get his quota from American farms. He certainly had a lot of very good mares, about a third from the Maktoum family in the first season and higher percentages since then. Considering the chances he has had, the racecourse results to date have been extremely disappointing. Trainers have complained about soundness problems in his stock, and in both 1988 and 1989 the market for his yearlings was poor. His fee was reduced to £25,000 for his fifth season and to £20,000 in 1990.

Shareef Dancer may yet come up with better performers, but he has suffered severely from the way he was campaigned as a racehorse and the way he was marketed at the outset of his stallion career. It is a long haul back to credibility after such setbacks, and his situation is all the more disappointing for the knowledge that those setbacks need never have occurred.

## SHAREEF DANCER (bay, 1980)

| | | | |
|---|---|---|---|
| Northern Dancer (b 1961) | Nearctic | Nearco | Pharos / Nogara |
| | | Lady Angela | Hyperion / Sister Sarah |
| | Natalma | Native Dancer | Polynesian / Geisha |
| | | Almahmoud | Mahmoud / Arbitrator |
| Sweet Alliance (b 1974) | Sir Ivor | Sir Gaylord | Turn-to / Somethingroyal |
| | | Attica | Mr Trouble / Athenia |
| | Mrs Peterkin | Tom Fool | Menow / Gaga |
| | | Legendra | Challenger / Lady Legend |

## Racing record

| Year | Starts | Wins | 2nd | 3rd | 4th | £ |
|---|---|---|---|---|---|---|
| 1982 | 2 | 1 | - | - | 1 | 3,402 |
| 1983 | 3 | 2 | 1 | - | - | 140,929 |
| | 5 | 3 | 1 | - | 1 | 144,331 |

## Principal wins

1983    King Edward VII Stakes-Gr2
          Irish Derby-Gr1

## Principal progeny

**1985**
b c NEDIYM (ex Nilmeen, by Right Royal)
      1990    Rolling Green Handicap-Gr3

**1986**
b f COLORADO DANCER (ex Fall Aspen, by Pretense)
      1989    Prix Minerve-Gr3
                Prix de Pomone-Gr2
b c SHARNFOLD (ex Clarina, by Klairon)
      1989    Prix Berteux-Gr3

**1987**
b c ROCK HOPPER (ex Cormorant Wood, by Home Guard)
      1990    Derby Trial Stakes-Gr3

# Sharpen Up

ANYBODY who was a minute late returning from the tote window on the occasion of Atan's debut at Aqueduct in July 1963 missed his entire racing career. In the space of 58.4 seconds he won easily and broke down irreparably. As it happened, it was quite the fashionable thing for a two-year-old son of Native Dancer to do in New York that month; Raise a Native was not seen in public again after his Aqueduct win in the Great American Stakes. There was a difference, though. Raise a Native had won all of his four races, the last two in stakes company, he had set two track records and equalled a third. He was a horse in such high repute that he had a syndicate who could not wait to throw good money into him and better mares at him. Atan's one win in a five-furlong maiden could never be the same.

Raise a Native went to stand in Kentucky, and Atan to stand in obscurity – until he was found, bought for the proverbial song and taken to Ireland by Tim Rogers. He stood there at Grangewilliam Stud for two seasons and in that time attracted 93 mares, his attraction to all bar one breeder being that his fee was only 100gns. The exception was Mimi van Cutsem, who sent him her mare Rocchetta – not a winner, but a sister to champion staying filly Outcrop – because her parents, Jimmy and Alice Mills, had stood him in America. In 1969 Atan was exported to Japan, leaving behind an extremely good-looking colt-foal out of Rocchetta and little else that would ever amount to much.

By the time he went into training with his owner-breeder's husband, Bernard van Cutsem, Sharpen Up could almost have been designated an area of outstanding natural beauty, and it was quite something that he should create that impression when the world's most highly-priced yearling, the immaculately-made Crowned Prince, was decorating a box in the same stable block at Newmarket's Stanley House Stables. The pair of them could run, too. Crowned Prince became champion two-year-old, and Sharpen Up was rated only 7lb below him. At stud things were different. Sharpen Up, son of the despised maiden winner Atan, earned renown on two continents. Crowned Prince, son of the celebrated casualty Raise a Native, was banished as a failure to Japan.

Sharpen Up was unbeaten as a two-year-old. He began as well as his sire with an easy five-furlong maiden win at Nottingham, and better still, survived the experience intact. Then he won comfortably at Doncaster over six furlongs, conceding weight to eight of nine modest rivals. He had higher-class competition to contend with in Ascot's Hyperion Stakes, but he made them look ordinary, leading throughout and quickening to run away from them in the sixth furlong. At Newcastle, in the Group 3 Seaton Delaval Stakes, he allowed Workboy to lead him for more than half the journey, then passed him and spurted clear in another impressive display of acceleration. Then came the real test, in the Group 1 Middle Park Stakes, and it seemed that his limitations were exposed. This time the finishing burst was not there when Willie Carson asked for it, and he was tiring perceptibly at the finish, where he held on by just a head from Philip of Spain.

If that race had been 50 yards longer, Sharpen Up would have lost. As it turned out, his career was over after only three more races, and he lost all of them. In his first start as a three-year-old he was tried for the first time at seven furlongs in the Group 3 Greenham Stakes at Newbury. He ran well, and chased Martinmas gamely over the last quarter-mile, but never really looked like catching him. After a three-month absence, Sharpen Up came back to sprinting in the Group 2 July Cup, and he was a bit keyed up for the occasion, sweating profusely in the parade ring. Nevertheless he ran a fine race, getting the measure of Shoolerville inside the last furlong and only just failing to hold the renewed challenge of early leader Parsimony. There was more than a suspicion after that run that another attempt at seven furlongs might be justified, but instead he reverted to five for the Group 2 Nunthorpe Stakes at York. It was a mistake; he ran fast for two furlongs, then faded to finish last of seven.

That was a disappointing way to go out, the more so as it meant that he had nothing to show for a second season in which he had performed almost as well as he had as an unbeaten youngster. He was retired to Newmarket's Side Hill Stud (which was partly owned by his trainer) and syndicated in shares of £3750, giving him a total valuation of £150,000.

*Sharpen Up, who has in general failed to pass on his impressive physique to his progeny.*

With his nominations priced at around £1000, Sharpen Up could not expect a glut of high-class mares; he would have to earn his right to them by getting plenty of winners. It did not happen immediately, and in the first season sires' list of 1976 he could do no better than tenth, but as Mill Reef was only eighth and Brigadier Gerard eighteenth, he could hardly be condemned. The second batch of two-year-olds won more races and showed more class; it began to look as though he might make a useful contribution as a middle-market sire of precocious horses, perhaps on a level with Mummy's Pet. The third crop caused further reassessment.

In a sense, Kris made Sharpen Up. Lord Howard de Walden's champion unquestionably focused attention on his sire, and his brilliance was largely responsible for Sharpen Up's transfer to Kentucky, where further glory awaited. Even so, there was plenty more of consequence on the racecourse and 'in the pipeline' before the deal was done with Gainesway Farm in 1980. Sharpo was a fine sprinter, in spite of a pair of bad hocks, and Pushy was a good precocious filly, retired to stud after two Pattern wins at two. Still, the deal was one which could not be refused by shareholders who had bought in at the outset for under £4000, and there was no prospect of its terms being matched in England on the strength of his results to that point. Sharpen Up was gone and well established in Kentucky before we came to appreciate Kris's young brother Diesis and the magnificent Pebbles, the leading representatives of the last two crops conceived here.

Sharpen Up had 15 stakes-winners, mostly of a minor character, from his first two Gainesway crops, and a real celebrity in his third. That was Trempolino, who won an Arc de Triomphe in similar style to Dancing Brave, while breaking his record time for the race. Sharpen Up began at $50,000 in America and rose to $75,000 before reverting to the original amount for 1989, his last season. He got only two mares in foal that year, and had experienced fertility problems during the previous two seasons.

As Sharpen Up was always an impressive physical specimen – he turns his toes out slightly, but is otherwise hard to fault – it is remarkable that he has failed to do anything for the beauty of the breed. Many of his stock, including some of the very best, have been plain, lean and angular creatures, deficient in bone and substance. He has been commonly blamed for transmitting bad hocks, but it was sheer coincidence that both Sharpo and Kris exhibited them, as legacies from their dams. Sharpen Up's principal gifts to the breed have been class and speed. While most of his stock are sprinters and milers, he did get, in Pebbles, Trempolino and Sanglamore, a trio who could turn on sprinting pace at the end of a mile and a half. Trempolino has now taken over from his sire at Gainesway, while Kris in England, and Diesis in Kentucky, are already thoroughly established top-class sires.

## Racing record

| Year | Starts | Wins | 2nd | 3rd | 4th | £ |
|------|--------|------|-----|-----|-----|------|
| 1971 | 5 | 5 | - | - | - | 17,808 |
| 1972 | 3 | - | 2 | - | - | 2,080 |
|  | 8 | 5 | 2 | - | - | 19,888 |

## Principal wins

1971    Seaton Delaval Stakes-Gr3
        Middle Park Stakes-Gr1

## Principal progeny

**1974**
ch c DUBLIN TAXI (ex Floral Palm, by Floribunda)
    1977    Premio Umbria-Gr3
    1978    Premio Melton-Gr3

**1975**
ch f SMARTEN UP (ex L'Anguissola, by Soderini)
    1978    Temple Stakes-Gr3 [dead-heat]

**1976**
ch c KRIS (ex Doubly Sure, by Reliance)
    1978    Horris Hill Stakes-Gr3
    1979    Greenham Stakes-Gr3
            St James's Palace Stakes-Gr2
            Sussex Stakes-Gr1
            Waterford Crystal Mile-Gr2
            Queen Elizabeth II Stakes-Gr2
            Challenge Stakes-Gr3
    1980    Lockinge Stakes-Gr2

**1977**
b f EPSIBA (ex Kaolin, by Kalydon)
    1981    Prix d'Astarte-Gr3
ch c SHARPO (ex Moiety Bird, by Falcon)
    1980    Temple Stakes-Gr3
            York Sprint Championship Stakes-Gr3
    1981    Prix de Saint-Georges-Gr3
            York Sprint Championship Stakes-Gr3
    1982    July Cup-Gr1
            York Sprint Championship Stakes-Gr2
            Prix de l'Abbaye de Longchamp-Gr1
ch f SOVEREIGN ROSE (ex Sovereign Flower, by Sovereign Path)
    1980    Diadem Stakes-Gr3

**1978**
ch f PUSHY (ex Mrs Moss, by Reform)
    1980    Queen Mary Stakes-Gr2
            Cornwallis Stakes-Gr3
b c SHARP END (ex Death Ray, by Tamerlane)
    1984    Badener Meile-Gr3

**1980**
ch c DIESIS (ex Doubly Sure, by Reliance)
    1982    Middle Park Stakes-Gr1
            Dewhurst Stakes-Gr1

**1981**
ch f PEBBLES (ex La Dolce, by Connaught)
    1984    Nell Gwyn Stakes-Gr3
            1000 Guineas Stakes-Gr1

# SHARPEN UP                                        (chesnut, 1969)

| | | Polynesian | Unbreakable / Black Polly |
|---|---|---|---|
| Atan (ch 1961) | Native Dancer | | |
| | | Geisha | Discovery / Miyako |
| | Mixed Marriage | Tudor Minstrel | Owen Tudor / Sansonnet |
| | | Persian Maid | Tehran / Aroma |
| Rocchetta (ch 1961) | Rockefella | Hyperion | Gainsborough / Selene |
| | | Rockfel | Felstead / Rockliffe |
| | Chambiges | Majano | Deiri / Madgi Moto |
| | | Chanterelle | Gris Perle / Shah Bibi |

1985    Trusthouse Forte Mile-Gr2
        Eclipse Stakes-Gr1
        Champion Stakes-Gr1
        Breeders' Cup Turf Stakes-Gr1
b f PRICKLE (ex Jungle Queen, by Twilight Alley)
    1983    Lowther Stakes-Gr2
ch f SCYTHE (ex Wolverene, by Relko)
    1986    Yerba Buena Handicap-Gr3

**1982**
ch f ONLY (ex Cambretta, by Roberto)
    1985    Gilltown Stud Stakes-Gr3
ch f SHARP ASCENT (ex Rivermande, by Riverman)
    1985    Honeymoon Handicap-Gr3

**1984**
gr c NESHAD (ex Nasseem, by Zeddaan)
    1987    Oettingen Rennen-Gr3
ch c TREMPOLINO (ex Trephine, by Viceregal)
    1987    Prix Niel-Gr2
            Prix de l'Arc de Triomphe-Gr1

**1985**
ch c EXACTLY SHARP (ex Exactly So, by Caro)
    1988    Grosser Preis der Steigenberger Hotels-Gr3
            Prix Lupin-Gr1
ch c HARP ISLET (ex Formentera, by Ribot)
    1989    Jaipur Stakes-Gr3
b c IN EXTREMIS (ex Vintage, by Foolish Pleasure)
    1988    Prix de Guiche-Gr3
            Prix du Rond Point-Gr3
b f SVANZEGA (ex Dancing Light, by Dancer's Image)
    1988    Premio Baggio-Gr3

**1986**
ch f DREAM DEAL (ex Likely Exchange, by Terrible Tiger)
    1989    Monmouth Oaks-Gr1

**1987**
ch c SANGLAMORE (ex Ballinderry, by Irish River)
    1990    Dante Stakes-Gr2
            Prix du Jockey-Club-Gr1

# Shernazar

THE sale of a yearling brother or half-brother to a champion colt is often quite an occasion. In 99.5 per cent of cases it is the biggest occasion in the youngster's life. It is natural to want to believe that what has occurred once can occur again, and there are examples – like dual classic winners Ribocco and Ribero – to indicate that it is not impossible. There are, though, all too few such examples, and it is not hard to understand why. Only a handful of stallions in history have achieved a ratio of 20 per cent stakes winners to foals; none has ever turned out champions at anything like that rate. Most mares do not produce as many as ten foals in their lifetime; to expect one to deliver 20 per cent champions is expecting too much. It does happen, but it is never something to bet on.

In May 1981, a month before her second produce, Shergar, won the Derby, the Aga Khan's mare Sharmeen gave birth to her fourth foal, a colt called Shernazar. To nobody's surprise, he proved to be a lesser racehorse than his half-brother. He did not win a Derby, but he did beat a Derby winner.

Sharmeen was not a particularly notable athlete herself. She won only one race, a modest maiden at Evry over ten and a half furlongs, and when she tried to better herself there were always others more gifted, exposing her limitations. Even so, she had more breeding than most mares, arguably even more than most in her owner's celebrated stud. There were Derby winners dotted all over her pedigree, and if that seemed like overloading the stamina, her bottom line was mostly speed, going back to the great Mumtaz Mahal.

Sharmeen was entitled to be a broodmare of some consequence, but she was not expected to produce two colts of the calibre of Shergar and Shernazar. The entire philosophy of the Aga Khan's breeding operation is built on numbers. He mates 200-odd mares a year because he hopes that from somewhere among that vast collection he might get two or three colts of outstanding ability. It almost makes a nonsense of the whole idea when, in the space of four years, one mare is responsible for two of the required celebrities. How much more

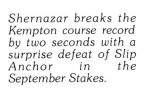

*Shernazar breaks the Kempton course record by two seconds with a surprise defeat of Slip Anchor in the September Stakes.*

remarkable, then, that the mare who should produce him a second colt worthy of a stallion's career should be the one whose first was the greatest horse her owner bred (or ever will breed) and is now missing, presumed dead.

Busted was 17 years old when Sharmeen came to him. A lot of prominent breeders had already given up on him by then, working on the common but untenable notion that he was 'past his prime'. It is true that the records of most stallions deteriorate at 15 or thereabouts, but the usual reason for that is the neglect of breeders; they will produce the effect if they provide the cause. A stallion does not have a 'prime', as such. His potential to sire a good horse is the same at four as at 24; his genetic make-up alters not one iota. Busted kept proving the point for those who did not neglect him, and two years after Shernazar he sired Mtoto, probably the best son he ever got - and another who beat a Derby winner.

In keeping with his pedigree, Shernazar was a late-maturing colt, and Michael Stoute gave him only one outing as a two-year-old. He ran creditably, finishing a length second to Test of Time in a minor event over seven furlongs at Sandown. He was second again on his first run at three, unfortunate to come up against a colt like Commanche Run in a maiden at Doncaster. Commanche Run soon got better, and so did Shernazar, losing his maiden allowance in a field of 20 at Newbury. That race was over 13 furlongs, and next time at Yarmouth he moved up to 14, winning with much more authority than before.

There was no proof yet that Shernazar was a high-class performer, but it came within a month. Stoute pitched him into Group 3 company for the Gordon Stakes at Goodwood, just hoping he would run respectably, and he came back an excellent second, beaten five lengths by Commanche Run, but with Pattern winners strung out eight lengths and more behind him. Tougher assignments followed, and in both he was found wanting for pace, first in the Great Voltigeur and then in the St Leger. At York he tried to slip his field on the turn, but was collared by a cantering Rainbow Quest at the furlong pole. At Doncaster, where he came from behind, he joined the leaders three furlongs out, but the necessary change of gear proved elusive, and though he stuck to his task well, he finished only fifth, about two lengths behind the winner, his old enemy Commanche Run.

A foot injury caused a delayed start to Shernazar's third season, and it was probably a blessing in disguise. He began by producing a useful turn of speed to surprise his younger stable-companion

*Shernazar, half-brother to Shergar, beats Spicy Story in the Geoffrey Freer Stakes.*

Shardari in the Alycidon Stakes at Goodwood, then at last became a Pattern winner with a smooth victory over Spicy Story in the Group 2 Geoffrey Freer Stakes at Goodwood. That excellent effort meant that he started second favourite for the Group 3 September Stakes, preferred to the 1984 Oaks winner Circus Plume and to the current season's Derby fourth, Supreme Leader. However, he was not supposed to trouble the latest Derby winner, Slip Anchor, who was making his first appearance since his runaway classic triumph. The fact that he beat Slip Anchor was less remarkable than the way that he accomplished it. As expected, the Epsom hero tried to repeat the tactics he had employed there, setting a severe gallop. Shernazar was at first disconcerted, but by half-way he had begun to enjoy it and at the turn for home he was only a length in arrears. Walter Swinburn visibly gained in confidence when he realized that he had more horse left under him than Steve Cauthen, calmly waited until inside the last furlong, then asked Shernazar to quicken. His mount swiftly gained a half-length advantage and passed the post in a time which beat the course record by nearly two seconds.

Shernazar now had to be taken seriously in any company, and he was the best-fancied of the three English-trained challengers for the Arc de Triomphe. Unfortunately, he became involved in some scrimmaging as he began to make his move towards the leaders, was almost brought down, and understandably gave up the chase. In the Breeders' Cup Turf he offered no excuses, and he scarcely needed any for a creditable sixth place in an extremely strong field. Pebbles won it in record time, and Shernazar made some late ground to finish under six lengths behind her.

A powerfully built, rather plain individual with straight hindlegs, Shernazar is no 'ringer' for his lamented half-brother, and though he had a similar low action at the gallop, it was nothing like so pronounced or so effective as that which Shergar deployed. He went to Ballymany Stud at IR15,000gns, something less than a quarter of the fee charged for Shergar's services in his solitary season, and he has been quite widely used by leading private breeders. As was to be expected, his commercial yearlings have not found a lot of favour, and his first two-year-olds were slow to come to hand. The real test will come with his three-year-olds, and he made a good start with 1990 Derby Italiano winner Houmayoun among the first batch.

## SHERNAZAR (bay, 1981)

| | | | |
|---|---|---|---|
| Busted (b 1963) | Crepello | Donatello | Blenheim / Delleana |
| | | Crepuscule | Mieuxce / Red Sunset |
| | Sans le Sou | Vimy | Wild Risk / Mimi |
| | | Martial Loan | Court Martial / Loan |
| Sharmeen (b 1972) | Val de Loir | Vieux Manoir | Brantome / Vieille Maison |
| | | Vali | Sunny Boy / Her Slipper |
| | Nasreen | Charlottesville | Prince Chevalier / Noorani |
| | | Ginetta | Tulyar / Diableretta |

### Racing record

| Year | Starts | Wins | 2nd | 3rd | 4th | £ |
|---|---|---|---|---|---|---|
| 1983 | 1 | - | 1 | - | - | 599 |
| 1984 | 6 | 2 | 2 | - | 1 | 13,884 |
| 1985 | 5 | 3 | - | - | - | 53,337 |
| | 12 | 5 | 3 | - | 1 | 67,820 |

### Principal wins

1985 Geoffrey Freer Stakes-Gr2
September Stakes-Gr3

### Principal progeny
**1987**
b c HOUMAYOUN (ex Halwah, by The Minstrel)
1990 Derby Italiano-Gr1

# Shirley Heights

MILL REEF had an excellent book of 39 mares for his second season at the National Stud in 1974. There were classic winners, dams of classic winners and any number who were closely related to classic winners. If, for any reason, there had been a need to reduce the stallion's quota to 30, there can be doubt that one of those rejected would have been Hardiemma; she might just have been the one to go if the reduction were only to 38.

Hardiemma's excuse for visiting Mill Reef was that she was owned by a shareholder (Lord Halifax) who had nothing better to send. Normally it is marvellous for a young syndicated horse to receive the best mares of those who have an interest in him; in fact, in most cases that is precisely what is needed in order to give the stallion a reasonable shot at making the grade. It was a shame about Hardiemma, though. Her owner had bought her as a four-year-old, in foal for the first time, at the 1973 Newmarket December Sales, and 12,000gns seemed plenty for a mare of her modest ability – winner of a five-runner maiden at Lanark over seven furlongs and of a handicap at Ayr over 11 furlongs. She had no family to speak of – not close up, anyway – and half of the reason for her price must have been that her sire, Hardicanute, got the Prix du Jockey-Club winner Hard to Beat in the same crop. Hardicanute, unfortunately, had got nothing else of note. He had been a good two-year-old, and an unbeaten one, but he did not appear at three, when he would have needed to tangle with Sea-Bird. His main claim to fame seemed to be that he had been bred by Richard Greene, the man who played Robin Hood on television. One way and another, it had to be said that Hardiemma did not seem to be a very suitable mate for a great Derby and Arc de Triomphe winner, one of the best horses of modern times.

Hardiemma's 1974 mating with Mill Reef resulted in Shirley Heights. It is possible that he was not absolutely the best of that crop by his sire, because the Prix du Jockey-Club winner Acamas was also very good, but Shirley Heights did win the Derby and the Irish Derby, and in the years to come it would be Hardiemma's son, rather than any of those out of the hoity-toity mares, who would be renowned as the best Mill Reef horse at stud – and up to 1990 the

only one of any real importance. Unfortunately, those developments came all too late for Lord Halifax and his heir, Lord Irwin. When Shirley Heights was a yearling they sent Hardiemma back to Mill Reef, then decided that perhaps, after all, the mare had been getting ideas above her station. They sent her to the December Sales and she fetched 15,000gns, which at that time was Mill Reef's covering fee. The foal she was carrying was a filly who herself came up for sale as a yearling just after Shirley Heights had won his classics. She realized 250,000gns, equalling the European record, but never won a race.

Shirley Heights went into training at Arundel with John Dunlop, and he had quite an active first campaign. He turned out as early as 10 June for a debut at York over six furlongs, but started slowly, did not begin to get going until well past half-way, and was never in contention; he finished fifth of six. He knew better next time at Doncaster, keeping in touch and running on well, but Cunard was always going too strongly for him and beat him by five lengths. The colt's maiden victory came at the Newmarket July meeting in the competitive Limekilns Stakes over seven furlongs, when a tremendous late burst saw him home in a finish of short heads with debutants Sexton Blake and Be Better. Shirley Heights met Sexton Blake again in the Group 3 Seaton Delaval Stakes at Newcastle and was beaten both by him and by Labienus, proving unable to quicken after having been ridden up with the pace. He came from way back in the Solario Stakes, run on soft going at Sandown, but having reached a challenging position he then could not get to grips with Bolak, who beat him by two lengths.

On firm ground at Ascot, with a mile instead of seven furlongs as the distance, Shirley Heights was able to turn the tables on Bolak in the Group 2 Royal Lodge Stakes. Ridden for the first time by Greville Starkey, he came late on the scene and was travelling much the fastest at the finish, winning by three-quarters of a length from Bolak, with Hawaiian Sound and Julio Mariner next best. The official handicapper respected that form, placing Shirley Heights only 6lb below the season's leading juvenile, Try My Best.

Shirley Heights was comprehensively beaten in his

*Shirley Heights (rails) gets up in the final stride to beat Hawaiian Sound in the Derby.*

first race at three, but did nothing wrong thereafter. His defeat came on soft ground in the Group 3 Sandown Classic Trial, where Whitstead ran right away from him over the last quarter-mile to win by ten lengths. At Newmarket, on good going, he had a tremendous tussle with an up-and-coming colt called Ile de Bourbon over the last two of the ten furlongs in the Heathorn Stakes. There was only a short head in it at the finish, but it was his nose in front, and he was conceding Ile de Bourbon 10lb. Even so, he was allowed to start at 10/1 for the Group 3 Dante Stakes at York, where the favourite was the nine-day-wonder horse Leonardo da Vinci, a son of Brigadier Gerard. Shirley Heights won with remarkable ease from old rivals Julio Mariner and Sexton Blake, while Leonardo da Vinci took his first steps back to oblivion in fifth place.

On that form Shirley Heights had to be considered a live contender for one of the most open Derbys for years, and he was sent off as joint second favourite in a field of 25. He had to come from a long way back, and there were one or two problems en route, but the strong, even pace set by Bill Shoemaker on Hawaiian Sound had most of his rivals going backwards in the straight and ensured that only a true stayer would get home. Starkey was the best mounted in that regard, and when he made the crucial decision to switch to the rail inside the final furlong, the only question was whether the post would come too soon. Under strong driving, Shirley Heights got there in the last stride. The Irish Derby was a similar race, but even tougher to win. The Epsom winner was off the bridle a long way from home and Starkey had to work hard to keep in touch while Hawaiian Sound again blazed the trail. This time the poor Derby runner-up had two bearing down on him at the furlong marker, and as the post neared he had to give best to both of them. Shirley Heights got home by a head from Exdirectory, who beat Hawaiian Sound by a neck. It was a gruelling contest for all three.

John Dunlop's plan now was to prepare Shirley

Heights for the St Leger, with a preliminary outing in the Great Voltigeur Stakes at York. Unfortunately, the colt damaged a tendon at exercise in August and he was not seen in action again. He was syndicated at a valuation of £1.6 million to stand at the Queen's Sandringham Stud in Norfolk, with the Royal Studs figuring as the most substantial shareholders, and he began his new career without causing too much excitement in the industry. It was good to have him around, of course, but he was bound to suffer by comparison with his sire. He was essentially a stayer, he did not have Mill Reef's sharp acceleration, and the bottom half of his pedigree left an awful lot to be desired. He was also nothing like Mill Reef to look at, only half an inch taller at 16 hands but with none of the quality which distinguished the National Stud's champion. Nevertheless he had won two Derbys, he was certain to suit owner-breeders wanting to produce classic-type horses, and he would undoubtedly get stayers. He would do, until a better Mill Reef came along.

It may be that Reference Point was that better Mill Reef, but he was a long time coming, and meanwhile Shirley Heights has easily outshone all the other sons of his sire at stud – those who had more of Mill Reef's pace and quality, and those who had

more fashionable female pedigrees. Shirley Heights is the real horseman's stallion, a man of a horse with good size, strength and scope. What is more, he gets his stock like that and gives them his gameness, honesty and stamina, too. Better still, he gives them, on occasions, a touch of class that had not really been expected of him.

It was a remarkable feat to have sired, in consecutive crops, two colts of better class than himself in Darshaan and Slip Anchor, one the winner of a Prix du Jockey-Club, the other successful in the Derby. In the wake of those results Shirley Heights' fee rocketed from £15,000 to £60,000 and on to £100,000 before coming back to more realistic levels. As predicted, he is chiefly an owner-breeder's horse and he has not been widely represented at the sales, but those yearlings who have been offered have generally made money, except, inevitably, for those conceived for the six-figure sum. If he is to be faulted, it might be said that he has the common failing among horses who are predominantly sires of stayers – quite a lot of his stock tend to stay in the same place too long. Nevertheless, he belongs on a short list of English-based stallions with the capability to sire classic-calibre horses at distances beyond a mile.

## Racing record

| Year | Starts | Wins | 2nd | 3rd | 4th | £ |
|---|---|---|---|---|---|---|
| 1977 | 6 | 2 | 2 | 1 | - | 14,897 |
| 1978 | 5 | 4 | 1 | - | - | 191,728 |
| | 11 | 6 | 3 | 1 | - | 206,625 |

## Principal wins

1977   Royal Lodge Stakes-Gr2
1978   Dante Stakes-Gr3
        Derby Stakes-Gr1
        Irish Derby-Gr1

## Principal progeny
**1980**
b f ACCLIMATISE (ex Habituee, by Habitat)
    1982   Fillies' Mile-Gr3
    1983   Nassau Stakes-Gr2
b f HIGH HAWK (ex Sunbittern, by Sea Hawk)
    1983   Ribblesdale Stakes-Gr2
        Park Hill Stakes-Gr2
        Prix de Royallieu-Gr3
        Premio Roma-Gr1

**1981**
b c DARSHAAN (ex Delsy, by Abdos)
    1983   Criterium de Saint-Cloud-Gr2
    1984   Prix Greffulhe-Gr2
        Prix Hocquart-Gr2
        Prix du Jockey-Club-Gr1

## SHIRLEY HEIGHTS                    (bay, 1975)

| | | | |
|---|---|---|---|
| Mill Reef (b 1968) | Never Bend | Nasrullah | Nearco / Mumtaz Begum |
| | | Lalun | Djeddah / Be Faithful |
| | Milan Mill | Princequillo | Prince Rose / Cosquilla |
| | | Virginia Water | Count Fleet / Red Ray |
| Hardiemma (b 1969) | Hardicanute | Hard Ridden | Hard Sauce / Toute Belle |
| | | Harvest Maid | Umidwar / Hay Fell |
| | Grand Cross | Grandmaster | Atout Maitre / Honorarium |
| | | Blue Cross | Blue Peter / King's Cross |

b c ELEGANT AIR (ex Elegant Tern, by Sea-Bird)
    1983   Horris Hill Stakes-Gr3
    1985   Westbury Stakes-Gr3
        Rogers Gold Cup-Gr2
b c HEAD FOR HEIGHTS (ex Vivante, by Bold Lad)
    1984   King Edward VII Stakes-Gr2
        Princess of Wales's Stakes-Gr2

b f OUT OF SHOT (ex Shooting Season, by Silly Season)
  1984 Lingfield Oaks Trial Stakes-Gr3
b f SATINETTE (ex Silk Stocking, by Pardao)
  1983 May Hill Stakes-Gr3

**1982**

b c IADES (ex Isabella Moretti, by Sir Gaylord)
  1985 Prix du Lys-Gr3
  1986 Prix Dollar-Gr2
  1987 Louisiana Downs Handicap-Gr3
b c SLIP ANCHOR (ex Sayonara, by Birkhahn)
  1985 Lingfield Derby Trial Stakes-Gr3
     Derby Stakes-Gr1

**1983**

b c VERD-ANTIQUE (ex Vejana, by Braccio Da Montone)
  1987 Yorkshire Cup-Gr2

**1984**

gr f INFAMY (ex Seriema, by Petingo)
  1987 Sun Chariot Stakes-Gr2
  1988 Gordon Richards Stakes-Gr3
     Canadian International Championship Stakes-Gr1

b c SHADY HEIGHTS (ex Vaguely, by Bold Lad)
  1988 Rogers Gold Cup-Gr2
     Bayerisches Zuchtrennen-Gr2
     York International Stakes-Gr1
br c TABAYAAN (ex Tedusa, by Busted)
  1987 Prix Berteux-Gr3
     Prix de l'Esperance-Gr2
     La Coupe de Maisons-Laffitte-Gr3

**1985**

b f HI LASS (ex Good Lass, by Reform)
  1989 Prix Gladiateur-Gr3
b f LIGHT THE LIGHTS (ex Lighted Glory, by Nijinsky)
  1988 Prix de Pomone-Gr2
b f SAILOR'S MATE (ex Sea Venture, by Diatome)
  1988 Meld Stakes-Gr3

**1986**

b c HIGH ESTATE (ex Regal Beauty, by Princely Native)
  1988 Coventry Stakes-Gr3
     Vintage Stakes-Gr3
     Solario Stakes-Gr3
     Royal Lodge Stakes-Gr2

# Silver Hawk

ONE of the saddest results of recent developments in the pattern of ownership in Britain is that the vast majority of the better horses are now concentrated into a tiny minority of unnaturally flourishing stables. The likes of Henry Cecil, Michael Stoute, Luca Cumani, Dick Hern and Guy Harwood are obviously very good trainers, but they are not that much better than a host of talented smaller trainers who, until a few years ago, had a chance of competing with them. The little man has been robbed of his dreams, while the favoured fellow at the top really has nothing to congratulate himself about beyond having made the most of what were, at best, his exceptional opportunities, at worst, his unfair advantages.

The media's inevitable tendency to concentrate on the big trainers and their strings only exacerbates matters. Countless second-rate horses, who would not be deemed worthy of notice in a smaller yard, become hyped, while the first-rate horse in an unfashionable stable is overlooked, seemingly powerless to attract attention to himself. One in the latter category was Silver Hawk, who was trained by a man whom few people knew and who, quite possibly, was not the greatest trainer in Newmarket. The horse was penalized on account of his trainer, and only now, after changing countries and careers, is he acquiring the recognition he always deserved.

Bred by Robin Scully of Clovelly Farms in Lexington, Silver Hawk was sold as a yearling for $77,000 at the Fasig-Tipton Kentucky July Sales to Ibrahim Moubarak, an associate of the noted Lebanese owner and breeder Mahmoud Fustok. The colt belonged to the fifth crop by Derby winner Roberto and was out of the excellent racemare Gris Vitesse, heroine of the 1969 Prix Jacques le Marois, a top-class mile event at Deauville; her family had been prominent in France over many generations. He had enough breeding, even if he was a somewhat plain yearling.

In due course Silver Hawk became one of the team of 16 horses – nearly all two-year-olds – collected for his first season at Eve Lodge Stables in Newmarket by Michael Albina, an Egyptian-born trainer who had some 800 wins to his credit in his native country, Jordan and Lebanon; his patrons were all from the Middle East, with Moubarak and Fustok prominent among them. Silver Hawk did not appear until August, but began well, easily outpacing a hot favourite in Balanchine for a maiden race at Yarmouth. Next time out at Sandown he ran up against a smart newcomer in Sandhurst Prince, and he failed by four lengths to give him 6lb, while beating the rest by five lengths and more. Then came an outstanding display in the Solario Stakes at Kempton. Always in touch, he assumed a narrow lead with a quarter of a mile to run and fairly flew when Brian Taylor asked him to quicken nearing the furlong pole. He was soon clear and won with ease by five lengths from Montekin, with Coventry Stakes winner Red Sunset third and future Dewhurst Stakes winner Wind and Wuthering only fourth. In his last race of the season Silver Hawk started favourite for the Group 2 Royal Lodge Stakes at Ascot, but his appearance in the paddock suggested that he had gone 'over the top', and his performance in the race confirmed it. He could never get in a blow at all-the-way winner Norwick, but he did get up close home to snatch second place from Lobkowiez.

In four efforts as a three-year-old Silver Hawk gave three excellent performances, and his one dull effort brought him second place in a classic, yet nobody seemed to notice. The one prestige win of his career came in the Group 3 Craven Stakes at Newmarket, where he showed sharp acceleration to go clear in the Dip and had only to be pushed out by Tony Murray up the hill. On the strength of that run he was made favourite for the 2000 Guineas, but the number one draw proved a definite hindrance. He led virtually all the way on the stands side, but the group in the middle always held sway and the best he could contrive was fifth. If he was unlucky at Newmarket, Silver Hawk was unluckier still in the Derby. Twice his progress was checked, once at the top of the hill and again nearing Tattenham Corner, but he stayed on stoutly under pressure to be third, a length behind Touching Wood (another son of Roberto) and four lengths behind Golden Fleece. In the Irish Derby he seemed to represent the only threat to Prix du Jockey-Club victor Assert, but he sweated up in the parade and looked distinctly out of sorts; he at no stage menaced the wide-margin winner and was clearly not in his Epsom form, though he did preserve a comfortable second place.

Unfortunately, Silver Hawk was not seen again. He cracked a cannon bone on the Newmarket gallops in July and had to be retired. He had beaten many of the best of his crop, at a mile and a mile and a half, and his merit received some acknowledgement with sixth place in the Free Handicap. However, he had nothing better than a single Group 3 win to show for his efforts, and there was no mad rush to find him a stud base in England. He went instead to Brereton Jones's Airdrie Stud in Kentucky, standing initially as the property of Fustok's Buckram Oak Farm and from 1984 in the joint ownership of Fustok and Jones. It was not until 1989 that a syndicate was formed for the horse, and at that point Fustok retained six shares.

In his first three seasons Silver Hawk covered at $12,500, but before his first runners appeared he was dropped to $5000 and he remained at that figure until 1989. There was not a lot to get excited about in the first crop, but in the second came Silver Lane, whose win in the Prix de la Grotte and third place in the Irish Oaks managed to jog one or two European memories about her sire. Just as important, there were three American stakes winners among the foals of 1985, in addition to a champion in Panama, for whatever that was worth. The move to syndicate Silver Hawk came in the wake of the

Grade 1 Norfolk Stakes victory by Hawkster (a full brother to Silver Lane), and the consequent rise in fee to $10,000 seemed justified.

There was much better to come. Hawkster proceeded to become one of America's leading grass-course performers in 1989, taking his earnings through the $1 million barrier, and two others from the same crop also excelled at the highest level. Dansil won the Arkansas Derby and took creditable fourth places in both the Kentucky Derby and the Preakness Stakes; Lady in Silver surpassed him, becoming a French classic winner in the Prix de Diane before notching a fine second place in the Arlington Million. Early in 1990 came the first Graded Stakes winner from one of those conceived at $5000, Silver Ending in the El Camino Real and Arkansas Derbys.

Silver Hawk has already done a remarkable job, but in some respects it may now become harder. His fee for 1990 was advanced to $40,000, which was no doubt justifiable on the basis of his results and the desire to attract better-class mares, but he will need to sustain his excellent start with the cheaply produced crops still in the pipeline. Few enough of those will have pedigrees fashionable enough for the summer sales, and they will just have to keep winning in order to attract the better mares. In his favour is the fact that he does have the right kind of pedigree

*Silver Hawk, placed in two Derbys before injury forced his retirement to stud.*

## Racing record

| Year | Starts | Wins | 2nd | 3rd | 4th | £ |
|------|--------|------|-----|-----|-----|---|
| 1981 | 4 | 2 | 2 | - | - | 21,388 |
| 1982 | 4 | 1 | 1 | 1 | - | 69,157 |
| | — | — | — | — | — | — |
| | 8 | 3 | 3 | 1 | - | 90,545 |

## Principal win

1982   Craven Stakes-Gr3

## Principal progeny

### 1985
b f SILVER LANE (ex Strait Lane, by Chieftain)
   1988   Prix de la Grotte-Gr3

### 1986
b c DANSIL (ex Upper Dancer, by Upper Nile)
   1989   Arkansas Derby-Gr2
b/br c HAWKSTER (ex Strait Lane, by Chieftain)
   1988   Norfolk Stakes-Gr1
   1989   Del Mar Derby-Gr2
         Secretariat Stakes-Gr1
         Oak Tree Invitational Stakes-Gr1
ch f LADY IN SILVER (ex Lorn Lady, by Lorenzaccio)
   1989   Prix de Diane-Gr1

# SILVER HAWK                                      (bay, 1979)

| | | | Royal Charger |
|---|---|---|---|
| | | Turn-to | Source Sucree |
| | Hail to Reason | | Blue Swords |
| Roberto | | Nothirdchance | Galla Colors |
| (b 1969) | | | Nasrullah |
| | | Nashua | Segula |
| | Bramalea | | Bull Lea |
| | | Rarelea | Bleebok |
| | | | Pharos |
| | | Nearco | Nogara |
| | Amerigo | | Precipitation |
| Gris Vitesse | | Sanlinea | Sun Helmet |
| (gr 1966) | | | Birikil |
| | | Mat de Cocagne | Fascine |
| | Matchiche | | Coaraze |
| | | Chimere Fabuleuse | Nine |

### 1987
b c SILVER ENDING (ex Copperhead, by Hawaii)
   1990   El Camino Real Derby-Gr3
         Arkansas Derby-Gr2

to persuade breeders that he is a suitable subject for upgrading.

The horse everyone ignored on the racecourse may yet attract world-wide attention. It is interesting to contrast his stud record with those of the horses from fashionable stables who finished in front of, and alongside, him in the Derby. The winner, Golden Fleece, covered at IR100,000gns, died young and was a failure. The second, Touching Wood, was a failure in England and was sent to New Zealand. The fourth, Persepolis, was a failure in France and was sent to Italy.

# Sir Ivor

CHARLES Engelhard was the man who set the trend at the dawn of the new era for racing and breeding, but the key equine role in the internationalization process was taken by a horse owned by his compatriot Raymond Guest. Ribocco and Ribero had been bred and bought in America, of course, but they were both by Ribot, and to many people that made them half-European. Sir Ivor was different. He was wholly a product of the American system, and a wonderful advertisement for it. His performance at Epsom made Europe appreciate what America could do; his performance at Laurel made Americans realize the full commercial implications of what they had achieved.

Sir Ivor was bred at Mill Ridge Farm, outside Lexington, by Alice Headley Bell (now Chandler). He came from the second full crop of Sir Gaylord, a horse who had bowed a tendon when supposedly days away from winning the 1962 Kentucky Derby, and he was out of Attica, a mare with decent form whose own dam was a three-quarter sister to Menow, a racehorse and sire of some consequence in the States. He was well enough bred for the Keeneland July catalogue, and attractive enough to fetch the then sizeable sum of $42,000. It took an exceptional yearling to make as much as $50,000 in 1966, and only 30 did; among them was Maui Chief, an $88,000 half-brother to Kentucky Derby winner Kauai King, bought by Vincent O'Brien at Saratoga on behalf of Charlie Engelhard.

Maui Chief's only win was to come in a two-mile amateur riders' event at Mallow as a four-year-old, but he and Sir Ivor set out on their racing careers together, as competitors for the Tyros Stakes at The Curragh, an hour after Ribocco's Irish Derby triumph. Maui Chief was eleventh and Sir Ivor only sixth, while Raymond Guest's Irish-bred Ballygoran took second place as best of the O'Brien stable entry. Sir Ivor just needed the experience that day. With a 5lb advantage at the weights he turned the tables on the Tyros winner, Mistigo, in the Probationers Stakes, only by a neck yet with plenty in hand. Even so, excuses were made for the third, Candy Cane, and he started favourite to beat Sir Ivor in the National Stakes, which promised to be Ireland's best race of the year for juveniles. It proved to be just that, and

the Candy Cane bubble was burst as Sir Ivor quickened impressively away over the last furlong. In those days it was not the done thing for foreigners to challenge for the top French two-year-old prize, the Grand Critérium, but Sir Ivor did, and became its first foreign winner with an easy three-length victory over Pola Bella.

The next novel move for Sir Ivor was a winter holiday in Pisa, where O'Brien believed that the relative warmth would benefit him. Meanwhile, intense speculation was under way on the new season's racing, with a Guineas clash between Sir Ivor and England's top mile hope, Petingo, as the immediate focal point. Sir Ivor tuned up in the Ascot 2000 Guineas Trial, and won it handily from Dalry; Petingo won the Craven Stakes by a wide margin. Lester Piggott could have ridden either at Newmarket, but he plumped unhesitatingly for Sir Ivor. On the day the result was never in doubt, with Piggott nonchalantly letting Petingo go clear before making his move. When Sir Ivor accelerated, the classic was over, won more impressively than any Guineas in the last 20 years. Of course, that did not mean that Sir Ivor would be able to reproduce that burst at the end of a mile and a half. That remained to be seen – and was, gloriously. Two furlongs out in the Derby he was going very well, but he was not going to win if Connaught, out in front, kept up his momentum. Sir Ivor continued to gain ground, and he was on the leader's heels at the furlong pole, but Connaught would surely have to capitulate for the order to be amended. Suddenly, there was a different race, not because Connaught yielded but because Sir Ivor produced the most devastating change of pace ever seen in the closing stages of a 12-furlong classic. He was two lengths clear in a matter of strides, and Piggott was virtually standing up in the irons at the finish.

For the next month the racing world was convinced that Sir Ivor was unbeatable; during the four months after that he was beaten four times. In the Irish Derby, with Liam Ward aboard, he came to challenge Ribero but simply could not quicken and finished two lengths adrift. A week later he appeared in the Eclipse Stakes at Sandown and was only third, beaten three-quarters of a length by the near-dead-heaters Royal Palace and Taj Dewan after Piggott had given him a lot to do in the straight. The firm ground at Sandown was certainly no help to his cause, and firm ground at Ballydoyle now interfered with Sir Ivor's preparation for the Arc de Triomphe. He was still short of work when he returned to action in the Prix Henry Delamarre, and he failed by half a length to catch Prince Sao, who was receiving 9lb. Again he seemed unable to produce his old acceleration, but it was by no means lost for good.

Sir Ivor ran a marvellous race in the 'Arc', though not marvellous enough to win in 1968, one of the race's vintage years. Vaguely Noble beat him by three lengths, having got first run and burst clear; Sir Ivor chased him hard, quickening as of old, but while he left the rest far behind he could not gain ground on an exceptional mile-and-a-half horse at the height of his powers. Only 13 days later Sir Ivor was back in action at Newmarket, as odds-on favourite for the Champion Stakes. He gained his first win since the Derby with astonishing ease, coming late, accelerating on demand, easing up at the finish.

There was more to come from Sir Ivor, and in the context of what was to come in racing it was as important as anything he ever did. At that time the Washington DC International at Laurel was the only significant meeting-point for horses from opposite ends of the Atlantic. No Epsom Derby winner had run in America since the ill-omened venture by Papyrus in 1923, and enormous interest was generated by Sir Ivor's appearance. The fact that he won, and the way that he won, produced the kind of publicity that anyone who wanted to advance the cause of international racing and breeding could never have bought. Piggott rode in his most supremely confident style, secure in the knowledge that he had the fastest horse in the race, but for a long way it was a moot point whether the colt would have an opportunity to display his speed. There was only a furlong left to run when Sir Ivor found release from his box on the rail, darted through and settled the issue. It was a sensational outcome to a wonderful occasion, and it received the full treatment from the press. Piggott's ride provoked most comment, but the more thoughtful writers reflected that international racing had come of age.

International breeding made immediate progress, too. Sir Ivor could have been at home in Kentucky in a couple of hours from Laurel, but Raymond Guest, a former US ambassador to Dublin, had made a commitment to Ireland. His colt would stand at Ballygoran Stud, available to European breeders for

*Sir Ivor, who made his name at stud as a sire of fillies.*

two seasons at a fee of £4000. The price was high by current standards in Ireland, but the chance to use a horse of his quality made him seem a bargain – a big, handsome individual with a fine pedigree, a classic winner at eight and 12 furlongs, as tough as he was brilliant. He would surely succeed at stud, and it was to be hoped that breeders in England and Ireland would make the most of the opportunity.

The results of those two seasons were good, perhaps most notable in terms of racecourse performance for the Derby runner-up Cavo Doro, a colt bred – and ridden on the day – by Lester Piggott. Later a much more significant development was the emergence of the second-crop colt Sir Tristram as the most important sire in the southern hemisphere. He continues to rewrite the record books from his base in New Zealand and, oddly, remains the only son of Sir Ivor to have excelled at stud anywhere in the world. Nevertheless, there was some disappointment over the fact that there was no Group 1 winner among the 54 foals conceived in Ireland, and it seemed ironic that the first crop conceived at Claiborne should include an Arc de

Triomphe heroine in Ivanjica, the daughter of a French-bred mare.

Sir Ivor sired one filly, Optimistic Gal, of exceptional merit in American racing conditions, and had one colt, Bates Motel, who raced there with considerable distinction. Otherwise he has relied on his European runners to earn him renown at stud, and he has achieved that primarily through his daughters. There was the odd good colt, but few seemed to live up to early promise, whereas the fillies had talent in abundance and tended to keep expressing it.

Sir Ivor started out at stud as the most highly priced stallion on record in Ireland. By the time of the great market boom several there had reached greater heights than he ever attained at Claiborne, largely because he acquired the reputation of being a 'filly sire'; his yearling colts could never make prospective stallion prices. From the mid 80s Sir Ivor's record deteriorated, along with the quality in his book of mares. Never higher than $75,000, his services were available for only $10,000 when he covered at the age of 25 in 1990.

## Racing record

| Year | Starts | Wins | 2nd | 3rd | 4th | £ |
|---|---|---|---|---|---|---|
| 1967 | 4 | 3 | - | - | - | 35,822 |
| 1968 | 9 | 5 | 3 | 1 | - | 152,904 |
| | 13 | 8 | 3 | 1 | - | 188,726 |

## Principal wins

| | |
|---|---|
| 1967 | National Stakes |
| | Grand Criterium |
| 1968 | Ascot 2000 Guineas Trial Stakes |
| | 2000 Guineas Stakes |
| | Derby Stakes |
| | Champion Stakes |
| | Washington D.C. International Stakes |

## Principal progeny

**1970**
b c CAVO DORO (ex Limuru, by Alcide)
    1973    Ballymoss Stakes-Gr3
                Royal Whip Stakes-Gr3
ch f ISTIEA (ex Ambergris, by Sicambre)
    1973    Lancashire Oaks-Gr3
b f PASSIOVA (ex Passionata, by Sicambre)
    1973    Prix Cleopatre-Gr3
b f REINE DE NAPLES (ex Caroline M., by War Relic)
    1973    Prix Vanteaux-Gr3

**1971**
b c HONOURED GUEST (ex Nagaika, by Goyama)
    1974    Dante Stakes-Gr3
b f LADY REBECCA (ex Pocahontas, by Roman)
    1974    Prix Vanteaux-Gr3

## SIR IVOR

(bay, 1965)

| | | | |
|---|---|---|---|
| Sir Gaylord (b 1959) | Turn-to | Royal Charger | Nearco / Sun Princess |
| | | Source Sucree | Admiral Drake / Lavendula |
| | Somethingroyal | Princequillo | Prince Rose / Cosquilla |
| | | Imperatrice | Caruso / Cinquepace |
| Attica (ch 1953) | Mr Trouble | Mahmoud | Blenheim / Mah Mahal |
| | | Motto | Sir Gallahad / Maxima |
| | Athenia | Pharamond | Phalaris / Selene |
| | | Salaminia | Man o' War / Alcibiades |

b f NORTHERN PRINCESS (ex Caramel, by Crepello)
    1974    Ribblesdale Stakes-Gr2
b c SIR PENFRO (ex Running Blue, by Blue Peter)
    1974    Gallinule Stakes-Gr2
                Desmond Stakes-Gr3

**1972**
gr f FASCINATING GIRL (ex Windy Miss, by Windy City)
    1976    Santa Margarita Invitational Handicap-Gr1

b f IVANJICA (ex Astuce, by Vieux Manoir)
 1975 Poule d'Essai des Pouliches-Gr1
    Prix de la Nonette-Gr3
    Prix Vermeille-Gr1
 1976 Prix du Prince d'Orange-Gr3
    Prix de l'Arc de Triomphe-Gr1
b/br f LAND GIRL (ex Arrangement, by Intentionally)
 1974 Demoiselle Stakes-Gr3
 1975 Gazelle Handicap-Gr2
ch f MISS TOSHIBA (ex Royal Warrant, by Hill Prince)
 1975 Pretty Polly Stakes-Gr2
 1976 Wilshire Handicap-Gr3
    Vanity Handicap-Gr3
ch f REALTY (ex Reveille, by Star Kingdom)
 1975 Prix du Gros Chene-Gr3
    Prix de Seine-et-Oise-Gr3
    Prix du Petit Couvert-Gr3

### 1973

ch f I'VE A BEE (ex Honey Portion, by Major Portion)
 1976 Mulcahy Stakes-Gr3
b f IVORY WAND (ex Natashka, by Dedicate)
 1976 Test Stakes-Gr3
b c MALINOWSKI (ex Best in Show, by Traffic Judge)
 1976 Craven Stakes-Gr3
b/br f OPTIMISTIC GAL (ex Hopes Ahead, by Traffic Judge)
 1975 Adirondack Stakes-Gr3
    Matron Stakes-Gr1
    Frizette Stakes-Gr1
    Alcibiades Stakes-Gr3
    Selima Stakes-Gr1
 1976 Ashland Stakes-Gr3
    Kentucky Oaks-Gr2
    Alabama Stakes-Gr1
    Delaware Handicap-Gr1
    Spinster Stakes-Gr1
b/br f ROSE OF STANBUL (ex Ribald, by Ribot)
 1976 Prix Chloe Gr3
b c SIR WIMBORNE (ex Cap and Bells, by Tom Fool)
 1975 National Stakes-Gr2
    Royal Lodge Stakes-Gr2

### 1974

b g BLUE BARON (ex Blue Lass, by Blue Prince)
 1978 Brighton Beach Handicap-Gr3
b f CLOONLARA (ex Fish-Bar, by Baldric)
 1976 Phoenix Stakes-Gr2
b c ERCOLANO (ex Green Valley, by Val de Loir)
 1977 Prix du Lys-Gr3
b/br c GOLDEN RESERVE (ex Golden Circlet, by Round Table)
 1979 Tidal Handicap-Gr2
gr f LADY CAPULET (ex Cap and Bells, by Tom Fool)
 1977 Irish 1000 Guineas-Gr1
b f SWEET ALLIANCE (ex Mrs Peterkin, by Tom Fool)
 1977 Jersey Belle Handicap-Gr3
    Kentucky Oaks-Gr2

### 1975

b f EQUANIMITY (ex Constant Nymph, by Never Bend)
 1978 Fantasy Stakes-Gr1
gr f TURKISH TREASURE (ex Turban, by Bagdad)
 1977 Cherry Hinton Stakes-Gr3
    Park Stakes-Gr3

### 1976

ch f GODETIA (ex Native Glitter, by Native Dancer)
 1979 Athasi Stakes-Gr3
    Irish 1000 Guineas-Gr1
    Pretty Polly Stakes-Gr2
    Irish Oaks-Gr1

### 1977

b f CALANDRA (ex Intrepid Lady, by Bold Ruler)
 1980 Pretty Polly Stakes-Gr2
b f MONROE (ex Best in Show, by Traffic Judge)
 1980 Ballyogan Stakes-Gr3
b c SUPER ASSET (ex Sunday Purchase, by T.V. Lark)
 1979 Horris Hill Stakes-Gr3

### 1978

ch f DRAMA (ex Drury Nell, by Bold Lad)
 1981 Greenlands Stakes-Gr3
ch c GIELGUD (ex Best in Show, by Traffic Judge)
 1980 Champagne Stakes-Gr2

### 1979

b c BATES MOTEL (ex Sunday Purchase, by T.V. Lark)
 1983 San Antonio Handicap-Gr1
    Santa Anita Handicap-Gr1
    San Diego Handicap-Gr3
    Monmouth Handicap-Gr1
ch f DREAMING AWAY (ex Northern Gem, by Northern Dancer)
 1982 Grosser Preis der International Harvester-Gr3

### 1980

b f AIR DISTINGUE (ex Euryanthe, by Nijinsky)
 1982 Prix d'Aumale-Gr3
b c TOP COMPETITOR (ex Shinnecock, by Tom Fool)
 1984 Sierra Nevada Handicap [Div.2]-Gr3

### 1982

b c ST HILARION (ex Fabulous Native, by Le Fabuleux)
 1985 Gran Premio d'Italia-Gr1
    Gran Premio del Jockey Club-Gr1

### 1983

b f IVOR'S IMAGE (ex Embryo, by Busted)
 1985 Premio Dormello-Gr2
 1986 Oaks d'Italia-Gr1
    E.P. Taylor Stakes-Gr2
 1987 Yerba Buena Handicap-Gr3

### 1984

ch f SOMETHING TRUE (ex Agretta, by Graustark)
 1988 Grand Prix d'Evry-Gr2

# Slip Anchor

IF he had been an owner or breeder of racehorses, Robert Louis Stevenson would not have asserted that it was better to travel hopefully than to arrive. He might, though, have remarked that anyone who did not travel hopefully would be unlikely to arrive at all. It is an optimist's game, and once you allow yourself to be disheartened by the inevitable disappointments along the way, you might as well give up. Most especially, you should never compare your own misfortunes with the luck of others who attain your goals with the minimum of effort. That can be soul-destroying. If Lord Howard de Walden had stopped to think about the fact that Luigi Miglietti had won the 1984 Derby with the first horse he had ever run in Europe, and then wondered why he had been bothering to try to win a classic for the last 37 years, he would have sold up there and then. Instead he soldiered on, and in 1985 proved that in racing everything comes to him who waits – so long as he keeps pouring in the millions and lives long enough.

The travelling hopefully for 38 years was good, but the arrival, with a Derby winner in Slip Anchor and a champion sire in Kris in the same season, was assuredly better. Kris had brought Lord Howard nearest to that classic goal in 1979, when he chose the 2000 Guineas to be one of only two races he would lose in a 16-race career; he was beaten half a length by Tap on Wood. In all those years of striving to produce a Derby winner, he had had only one realistic contender, and that one – the enigmatic Oncidium in 1964 – had declined to do his best on the day.

Any premature fancy that Slip Anchor might be the one to change the pattern was discouraged by Lester Piggott's terse comment: 'He's no good,' after he had ridden him into fourth place on his debut in a Newmarket maiden in October 1984. Still, jockeys had erred before, and it seemed a bit soon to be contemplating shooting or selling the colt. Instead, the owner let Henry Cecil send him to Nottingham 12 days later, and there, with Paul Eddery up, Slip Anchor won in excellent style by four lengths. He might be all right after all.

Slip Anchor began his second season with a respectable third place in decent company over nine furlongs at Newmarket; he was unable to produce

any finishing speed when Paul Eddery requested it, but he was not beaten far, and he was conceding 7lb to both of those who beat him. Two weeks later he met one of his conquerors again, and this time the order was decisively reversed. Slip Anchor made all the running over Newmarket's straight ten furlongs, enjoying himself in front and winning by four lengths from Flying Saucer. As the field for the Lingfield Derby Trial promised to be weak, Cecil decided that here might be an opportunity to make Slip Anchor a Group 3 winner. He was right, but more than a little surprised when the colt not only made all, but ran

*Slip Anchor represents a complete outcross.*

*Slip Anchor cruises to a ten-length victory in the Lingfield Derby Trial.*

clean away from his seven rivals. His margin was ten lengths over Lord Grundy.

It was only now that Cecil began to think of Slip Anchor in terms of a potential Derby winner. The colt still had not beaten a horse of any consequence on the racecourse, but he was obviously on the upgrade – and admirably suited to the front-running tactics which Steve Cauthen employed so well. Slip Anchor suddenly began to work like a good horse, too, and Cecil made no secret of his growing confidence. It was a remarkable Derby. Shergar had at least kept company with his rivals until Tattenham Corner, and Troy had even allowed half of his to think they had beaten him early in the straight. Slip Anchor would not give his opponents the time of day. When the stalls opened he just ran off into the distance and stayed there, while they made their own race without him. Cauthen made the appropriate use of his partner's powerful galloping action and great length of stride, and the outcome was more like a cross-country run than a classic. Slip Anchor was showered and changed before the others got home.

It was the first time in 59 years that a Derby winner had led every inch of the way, and the margin between first and third – 13 lengths – had never been exceeded in the history of the race. Slip Anchor, it seemed, was a horse and a half. So much for appearances; he never won again. Unfortunately, he jarred a near-fore joint at exercise and had to miss

the King George VI & Queen Elizabeth Stakes. That was won by Petoski, who had finished more than 43 lengths behind him at Epsom. He came back in the September Stakes at Kempton and set a Derby-style cracking gallop, only to find himself playing mouse to Shernazar's cat in the final furlong. The four-year-old pounced to beat him by half a length. The time was a course record, and Slip Anchor was meeting the winner on worse than weight-for-age terms, but it was disappointing for all that. In the Champion Stakes he was made to take a dose of the humiliation he had served up to others at Epsom. Having burst from his stall, he pounded away with the intention of running his rivals into the ground, and he was still galloping strongly, giving it all he had, when Pebbles came up to him, still cantering. She tormented him by staying there for a few seconds, perhaps to ask if he could not go any faster, then scampered away to win by three lengths. Still, it was much to Slip Anchor's credit that after looking in serious danger of finishing only fourth, he battled on up the hill to claim second place.

For all his great galloping qualities, Slip Anchor obviously had a problem with lack of finishing speed. He was more than a front-runner now, he was a free-runner, impetuous and not disposed to be restrained. In an effort to change the colt's ways, Lord Howard gave 52,000gns for Rakaposhi King to act as his lead horse and pacemaker for his four-year-old campaign. The ploy was not a success. Slip Anchor did not like the idea of being led in his gallops, preferring to run away from Rakaposhi King. The efforts to persuade him not to do what came naturally upset him, and on his reappearance for the Group 2 Jockey Club Stakes he was no longer the calm and collected colt of his early three-year-old days. He sweated up before the start, and in the race he refused to settle, making himself virtually a sitting target for a late challenger. Greville Starkey, on Phardante, assessed the situation perfectly, and delivered the *coup de grâce* close home.

Lord Howard soon acknowledged that Slip Anchor's form was beyond recall and consoled himself with a few good performances from Rakaposhi King. Relieved of his impossible pacemaking duties, that colt proved better than ever, winning twice and gaining places in Pattern races. Slip Anchor, meanwhile, rested and prepared for the start of his new career at his owner's Plantation Stud near Newmarket, where he covered his first mares at a fee of £30,000 in 1987. He was well supported by both private and commercial breeders, and his first crop of auction yearlings, offered in 1989, was well received.

It will be fascinating to see whether Slip Anchor can make the grade as a stallion. He is a taller edition of his sire Shirley Heights, very like him about the head, and with a wholly German background in the first few generations of his dam's pedigree, he represents a complete outcross for most British mares. His fee was reduced to £25,000 in 1989 and to £20,000 in 1990.

## SLIP ANCHOR (bay, 1982)

| | | | |
|---|---|---|---|
| **Shirley Heights** (b 1975) | Mill Reef | Never Bend | Nasrullah / Lalun |
| | | Milan Mill | Princequillo / Virginia Water |
| | Hardiemma | Hardicanute | Hard Ridden / Harvest Maid |
| | | Grand Cross | Grandmaster / Blue Cross |
| **Sayonara** (b 1965) | Birkhahn | Alchimist | Herold / Aversion |
| | | Bramouse | Cappiello / Peregrine |
| | Suleika | Ticino | Athanasius / Terra |
| | | Schwarzblaurot | Magnat / Schwarzgold |

### Racing record

| Year | Starts | Wins | 2nd | 3rd | 4th | £ |
|---|---|---|---|---|---|---|
| 1984 | 2 | 1 | - | - | 1 | 3,472 |
| 1985 | 6 | 3 | 2 | 1 | - | 283,496 |
| 1986 | 1 | - | 1 | - | - | 9,754 |
| | 9 | 4 | 3 | 1 | 1 | 296,722 |

### Principal wins

1985  Lingfield Derby Trial Stakes-Gr3
Derby Stakes-Gr1

# Storm Bird

THERE was a scene in a Marx Brothers film of around 1930 when Chico and Harpo, as musicians, offered their services to Groucho for a function he was to stage. Asked to name their terms, Chico replied: 'For playing, we charge five dollars an hour, and for not playing we charge ten dollars an hour.' Was that funny, or just plain silly? Whatever it was, it did not date. In 1981 there was a revival of the theme, starring Storm Bird. In January, fit and well and hot favourite for both the 2000 Guineas and the Derby, he was worth $15 million. In July, having not turned out for either classic – or any other race that year – and obviously not exactly in the pink of condition, he was worth $30 million.

Storm Bird's name will always be closely identified with the 1980s madness in the Thoroughbred business. He seemed to be the living definition of hype, in both breeding and betting environments. He was the most publicized horse of his crop, generating more media space in his inactivity than Shergar could contrive by being the best horse in the world. He was the victim of a vandal's attack. For his bewildered public he was an object, at various times, of wonder, pity, amazement, ridicule and disgust. Yet this ill-used creature managed to escape from racing with a measure of his dignity intact, acknowledged as one more sinned against than sinning, and he has earned genuine credibility and respect in his second career.

Storm Bird was a $1 million Robert Sangster purchase at Keeneland in July 1979. A Windfields Farm product, by Northern Dancer out of Canadian Oaks winner South Ocean, he had numerous pedigree links with both Nijinsky and The Minstrel but looked like neither of those Derby winners. He was not imposing, and nor was he flashy; he was a tall, rangy, good-looking colt, and he promised to be an athlete. As a two-year-old, he certainly was.

Following in Nijinsky's hoofprints, Storm Bird made his debut in the Erne Maiden Plate, over six furlongs at The Curragh, in July 1980. There were 19 runners, and 18 of them were ignored, both by the punters and by their favourite. Thoroughly businesslike, Storm Bird trotted up by six lengths. A month later Vincent O'Brien reckoned he was ready for Group 3 competition and was proved just right. In the Anglesey Stakes the colt showed his inexperience, idling once he had taken the lead, but jockey Tommy Murphy kept him going well enough to resist the challenge of Prince Echo, who was trying to concede him 7lb. He was sharper next time out in the Group 2 National Stakes, his first effort at seven furlongs, trouncing Master Thatch and Silver Creek by four lengths and the same.

In his first race away from The Curragh, the Group 3 Larkspur Stakes at Leopardstown, Storm Bird gave his best display in Ireland. He was required to give weight to all his rivals, most significantly 7lb to a good colt in Band Practice, winner of his maiden by ten lengths and beaten a head in the Group 1 Phoenix Stakes. With Steve Cauthen in the saddle, Storm Bird made Band Practice look ordinary, showing tremendous acceleration to go clear early in the straight and winning by four lengths.

It was time for a stiffer test, in the race where Nijinsky and The Minstrel had both confirmed their class. The field for the Dewhurst Stakes included the winners of the best seven-furlong races run to date in England (the Solario Stakes) and France (the Prix de la Salamandre), so there seemed little doubt that the race would decide the European championship. Pat Eddery took the mount on Storm Bird and took him at once into the lead, chased by England's chief hope, To-Agori-Mou. There were still four possible winners with a furlong and a half to run, then, suddenly, only two. Storm Bird and To-Agori-Mou quickened simultaneously, leaving the French-trained Miswaki and Royal Ascot winner Kirtling apparently running on the spot. A battle royal developed, with Storm Bird always just in command, and at the post he led by half a length, with Miswaki eight lengths adrift. Storm Bird had beaten better horses than Nijinsky and The Minstrel had beaten in their Dewhursts, and within minutes the new champion was named favourite for both the 2000 Guineas and the Derby. The time was ripe for hype.

The New Year began with news of a bizarre episode at Ballydoyle. The wonder horse had had his mane and tail hacked by an intruder, who turned out to be a young man with a grudge against Vincent O'Brien. When the case came to court it was mentioned in evidence that Storm Bird (who had suffered no permanent physical damage) was insured

*Storm Bird wins the Dewhurst Stakes at Newmarket from To-Agori-Mou and Miswaki (left).*

for $15 million, nearly double the valuation placed on The Minstrel less than four years earlier, after he had won two Derbys. Storm Bird was obviously a classic certainty, and the punters felt encouraged to pile more money on the favourite.

The colt should have resumed his racing career on 4 April in the Gladness Stakes at The Curragh. On the eve of this eagerly awaited event it was announced that he was lame in his off-hind and could not take part. When he recovered he was taken for a racecourse gallop at Naas, and he worked badly. Two weeks before the 2000 Guineas O'Brien reported that Storm Bird had coughed at exercise; it seemed that he had succumbed to a virus, and he would therefore have to miss Newmarket. He went on to miss the Irish 2000 Guineas, the Derby, the Irish Derby, and every tentative engagement that was mentioned. By Royal Ascot the presumably still-ailing Storm Bird had been dubbed 'the invisible horse' by a wag in the training profession. The one-time champion had become a figure of fun, the $15 million valuation part of the joke.

By the end of July he who laughed last, and loudest, appeared to be Robert Sangster. On his trip to Keeneland he had not only bought Storm Bird's yearling brother for $3.5 million, but he had also sold three-quarters of the infamous non-runner for $22.5 million! Storm Bird had doubled his price in six months by remaining in his box, while Shergar,

who had been busily proving himself the best horse in a decade, was syndicated for little more than half of his price. The visions conjured up by this evidence that not racing was more profitable than racing were frightening.

In August came word that Storm Bird would definitely be trained for the Arc de Triomphe. Subsequent 'information' that he had worked brilliantly with Kings Lake prompted a surge of support in the ante-post market on that race, with his odds tumbling from 16/1 to 6/1 in two days. There seemed to be no end to the madness surrounding the colt. Eventually he had to run, and he was sent for the Prix du Prince d'Orange at Longchamp on 20 September. After he had finished a pathetic seventh of nine, it was announced that the 'Arc' bid was off, and that his racing career was over. Effectively, it had been over for nearly a year.

From start to finish, 1981 had been a fiasco for Storm Bird, but he was always going to get a chance to live it down. His new owners could not afford to give him anything less than the best possible support, and after all, it was only his genes which counted now. Full marks to the horse. He came up trumps with no fewer than seven Pattern or Graded winners among his first crop of 31 foals, including a Grade 1 two-year-old scorer in Storm Cat, and Magical Wonder, who collected the Group 1 Prix Jean Prat in France at three. In his second crop there was the

## Racing record

| Year | Starts | Wins | 2nd | 3rd | 4th | £ |
|------|--------|------|-----|-----|-----|------|
| 1980 | 5 | 5 | - | - | - | 72,594 |
| 1981 | 1 | - | - | - | - | 0 |
| | 6 | 5 | - | - | - | 72,594 |

## Principal wins

1980    Anglesey Stakes-Gr3
         National Stakes-Gr2
         Larkspur Stakes-Gr3
         Dewhurst Stakes-Gr1

## Principal progeny

**1983**

b f ACUSHLA (ex Intrepid Lady, by Bold Ruler)
    1986    Phoenix Sprint Stakes-Gr3
    1987    Phoenix Sprint Stakes-Gr3
b c CONQUERING HERO (ex Wave in Glory, by Hoist the Flag)
    1988    San Gabriel Handicap-Gr3
gr f GIVE A TOAST (ex Salud, by Raise a Cup)
    1987    Beaugay Handicap-Gr3
ch c MAGICAL WONDER (ex Flama Ardiente, by Crimson Satan)
    1986    Prix de la Jonchere-Gr3
         Prix Jean Prat-Gr1
         Prix du Rond Point-Gr3
b c SPLENDID MOMENT (ex Racquette, by Ballymore)
    1985    Prix des Chenes-Gr3
b/br c STORM CAT (ex Terlingua, by Secretariat)
    1985    Young America Stakes-Gr1
b f STORM STAR (ex Cinegita, by Secretariat)
    1985    Cherry Hinton Stakes-Gr3

**1984**

b c BLUEBIRD (ex Ivory Dawn, by Sir Ivor)
    1987    Ballyogan Stakes-Gr3
         King's Stand Stakes-Gr1
b c DAVID'S BIRD (ex Splendid Girl, by Golden Eagle)
    1986    Pilgrim Stakes-Gr3
gr f INDIAN SKIMMER (ex Nobiliare, by Vaguely Noble)
    1987    Musidora Stakes-Gr3
         Prix Saint-Alary-Gr1
         Prix de Diane-Gr1
    1988    Phoenix Champion Stakes-Gr1
         Sun Chariot Stakes-Gr2
         Champion Stakes-Gr1

## STORM BIRD                          (bay, 1978)

| | | | |
|---|---|---|---|
| Northern Dancer (b 1961) | Nearctic | Nearco | Pharos / Nogara |
| | | Lady Angela | Hyperion / Sister Sarah |
| | Natalma | Native Dancer | Polynesian / Geisha |
| | | Almahmoud | Mahmoud / Arbitrator |
| South Ocean (b 1967) | New Providence | Bull Page | Bull Lea / Our Page |
| | | Fair Colleen | Precipitic / Fairvale |
| | Shining Sun | Chop Chop | Flares / Sceptical |
| | | Solar Display | Sun Again / Dark Display |

    1989    Trusthouse Forte Mile-Gr2
         Prix d'Ispahan-Gr1
ch f SPUR WING (ex Equal Change, by Arts and Letters)
    1988    Carousel Handicap-Gr3

**1985**

b f LONELY BIRD (ex Reinvestment, by Key to the Mint)
    1988    Premio Regina Elena-Gr2
ch c PRINCE OF BIRDS (ex Special Key, by Key to the Mint)
    1988    Tetrarch Stakes-Gr3
         Irish 2000 Guineas-Gr1
b f SAVANNAH'S HONOR (ex Honor to Her, by Sir Ivor)
    1987    Prix du Calvados-Gr3

**1987**

b c SUMMER SQUALL (ex Weekend Surprise, by Secretariat)
    1989    Saratoga Special Stakes-Gr2
         Hopeful Stakes-Gr1
    1990    Jim Bean Stakes-Gr2
         Blue Grass Stakes-Gr2

exceptional racemare Indian Skimmer, a winner five times at Group 1 level in Europe, twice among her own sex, three times at weight-for-age in open company.

Storm Bird did not long sustain his opening fee of $175,000, and has been reduced by stages to $50,000 (with no guarantee of a foal) in 1990. Some of his stock have had wind problems, which has caused a certain lack of confidence about him in the market-place, but there is no doubting his capacity to get high-class performers. He gets his share of precocious runners, and in the main they are sprinters or milers in their maturity. If he cannot quite rank among the very best of Northern Dancer's stallion sons, he is top of the second division, still with chances of gaining promotion.

# Sure Blade

MOST of Sheikh Mohammed's great successes as an owner have been achieved with yearling purchases bred and raised in America. His favourite English stallion, outside his own, is Kris, an understandable preference as it was that horse's first-crop daughter Oh So Sharp who won a filly Triple Crown in his colours in 1985. In the case of Sure Blade, whom he acquired five days after Oh So Sharp had completed an undefeated first season, the Sheikh had the best of both worlds.

Sure Blade's sire and dam were both Yorkshire-based at the time of his conception, but within eight months the pregnant Double Lock left Ribblesdale Stud for Newmarket, there to be sold for 105,000gns to Bill duPont's Pillar Stud. Off she went to Kentucky, and in the following April she delivered Sure Blade, a colt with a largely British background and, inevitably, rather less commercial appeal in the States than where he had originated. Accordingly, after spending his first 18 months in the Blue Grass, the colt who had crossed the Atlantic inside his dam took the return trip on his own four legs, with an appointment booked in the Highflyer Sales. He chose the right day to appear, as 2 October 1984

produced all-time record business for a Newmarket auction; three yearlings made over a million, the average for the session was 189,772gns, and Sure Blade, decidedly above average, fetched 270,000gns.

The youngster was bought on the Sheikh's behalf by Lambourn trainer Barry Hills, a man with a partiality for Kris's stock himself. The dam had been trained by Jeremy Hindley and had proved a useful performer over a mile and a quarter, winning the Sandleford Priory Stakes at Newbury as a three-year-old after an idle first season. Sure Blade did not take after her. He wasted no time making his presence felt as a juvenile, and at three the one poor race he ran was in his only attempt at his dam's favourite distance.

Sure Blade proved precocious enough to make his debut at the end of May, when he turned out for a maiden at Newmarket against ten others. The race had a supposedly unbeatable favourite in Green Desert, carrying the colours of Sheikh Maktoum, but Sure Blade was the sharper, quickening well to beat that rival by two and a half lengths. At Royal Ascot, in the Group 3 Coventry Stakes, his change of pace again proved decisive. He responded immediately

*Sure Blade on his way to post before winning the Queen Elizabeth II Stakes at Ascot.*

when jockey Brent Thomson asked for his effort, swiftly had matters under control, and won with authority by a length and a half from Moorgate Man. After those wins at five and six furlongs, Sure Blade moved up to seven for the Group 2 Champagne Stakes at Doncaster, where he met two worthy foes in Faustus and Truely Nureyev. This time there were no volunteers to set the pace, so Thomson took on the task himself; he judged things well, waiting in front then kicking for home at the two-furlong pole and driving the colt out for a game victory over Faustus by half a length. Sure Blade's last outing at two came in the Dewhurst, and if he had won it he would have been named champion two-year-old. It was not to be. After chasing the leaders he arrived on the scene in time to win, but Huntingdale always just had his measure, and right on the line Bakharoff pipped him for second place. That pair, in reverse order, were the only pair to head him in the Free Handicap.

Sure Blade ventured north for his Guineas prep race. The target was the Thirsk Classic Trial, over a mile, and though he did not much care for the softish ground he won easily, courtesy of negligible opposition. It was a different story at Newmarket, where Dancing Brave dominated a slowly run '2000'; Thomson found the cupboard bare when he looked for acceleration, and the colt eventually had to settle for fifth place. However, Sure Blade's two best performances were yet to come, and they both came at Ascot, in consecutive races but three months apart. In the Group 2 St James's Palace Stakes he had his third encounter with Green Desert, who started favourite and tried to make all the running. Sure Blade tracked him, challenged him early in the straight, and lasted the mile while the other's stamina gave out.

The rich programme of summer mile events now beckoned, but Sure Blade was unable to answer the call. A mysterious muscle injury caused him to lose his action behind, and by the time he came right there was little time for Hills to prepare him for the Group 2 Queen Elizabeth II Stakes. Nevertheless, a trusting public made the colt a hot favourite, and they were proved right. Teleprompter was a tough customer at the best of times, and he provided a severe test for Sure Blade in his first effort against older horses. For a long time in the straight it looked as though the six-year-old would maintain his advantage, but with Thomson driving hard, Sure Blade kept gaining ground and finally snatched the race away from him in the last few strides.

The widely held view that Sure Blade would stay ten furlongs went on trial in the Champion Stakes,

## SURE BLADE (bay, 1983)

| | | | |
|---|---|---|---|
| Kris (ch 1976) | Sharpen Up | Atan | Native Dancer / Mixed Marriage |
| | | Rocchetta | Rockefella / Chambiges |
| | Doubly Sure | Reliance | Tantieme / Relance |
| | | Soft Angels | Crepello / Sweet Angel |
| Double Lock (b 1975) | Home Guard | Forli | Aristophanes / Trevisa |
| | | Stay at Home | Bold Ruler / Alanesian |
| | St Padina | St Paddy | Aureole / Edie Kelly |
| | | Rose of Medina | Never Say Die / Minaret |

### Racing record

| Year | Starts | Wins | 2nd | 3rd | 4th | £ |
|---|---|---|---|---|---|---|
| 1985 | 4 | 3 | - | 1 | - | 73,602 |
| 1986 | 5 | 3 | - | - | - | 66,565 |
| | 9 | 6 | - | 1 | - | 140,167 |

### Principal wins

| 1985 | Coventry Stakes-Gr3 |
|---|---|
| | Champagne Stakes-Gr2 |
| 1986 | St James's Palace Stakes-Gr2 |
| | Queen Elizabeth II Stakes-Gr2 |

but a verdict of not proven was all that could be returned. Uncharacteristically, he pulled hard, and his failure to settle meant that he had run his race by the time Triptych and others turned on their speed. He came back a disappointing eighth of 11.

Sure Blade was retired to Kildangan Stud in County Kildare, where he was advertised to cover at what seemed the remarkably high fee of IR£30,000. Most people were inclined to accept that he was probably of Group 1 calibre, but the fact that he missed the summer schedule of weight-for-age mile races meant that a certain amount had to be taken on trust. There was no reason to believe that he was anything but sound after the Champion Stakes, and the more adventurous policy of letting him race at Group 1 level in 1987 would surely have benefited him. Nevertheless, he has been well supported at stud, and he has been represented by yearlings and foals who have both done him credit and brought his breeders profit in the sale ring.

# Teenoso

IT always used to be said that part of the prize for victory in the Derby was immortality. In recent years the winner has been lucky to avoid the kiss of death. The 1979 winner, Troy, was dead within four years of his great triumph, while Shergar (1981) and Golden Fleece (1982) survived theirs by less than two. This was a rather sorry chapter in the history of the world's greatest race, further exemplified by the fact that the 1980 winner, Henbit, was later condemned to what most self-respecting Derby heroes would have regarded as a fate worse than death, namely employment in the ranks of jumping stallions.

There may yet be a sequel. Poor Teenoso, Lester Piggott's ninth and last Derby winner in 1983, was dismissed by the market as a certain stud failure before he had left Geoff Wragg's Newmarket stable to take up duties at Highclere. He could not attract as many as 40 mares in his first season, not 30 in his second, and by his fourth the figure was down to 20. His career seemed to be in ruins before he had had a runner to represent him. Part of his problem stemmed from follies committed when he was still in training, part possibly preceded even his birth.

Ralph ('Budgie') Moller was an owner-breeder over a long period, based at his White Lodge Stud near Newmarket, but not so much one of the old school that he failed to see which way the wind was blowing in the bloodstock business of the early

1970s. In fact, he was one of the first British breeders to keep mares in the USA, and from one of them he bred Silky, the first winner sired by Nijinsky. He had mares based in Kentucky right up to his death early in 1980, and one of the last matings he arranged there matched Furioso, his 1974 Oaks runner-up, with Youth, who then stood at Gainesway Farm. There were not too many people who believed in Youth, a big, long-backed horse, very powerful behind the saddle, with an enormous raking stride; he was a very good racehorse, top-class in both France and America, but he did not seem the type to get suitable runners for the States, and his pedigree was somewhat outlandish for Europe. For all that, Budgie Moller believed in him, and as a result his brother - who took over the White Lodge interests - became the owner of Teenoso.

The colt went into training with Harry Wragg and as a two-year-old he had three runs, doing best in the last, when fourth in a mile maiden at Newmarket. In the following year, when Wragg's son took over the stable, he maintained his progress, reaching unimagined heights. After a second place in a minor race at Haydock Park he finally broke his maiden at Newmarket, appreciating his first opportunity to go a mile and a half and winning by eight lengths. He then won the Lingfield Derby Trial by three lengths and, suddenly, with the confirmation that Piggott would take the ride, he was favourite for the Derby. He had

*Teenoso is too tough for Sadler's Wells, Tolomeo and the rest of a high-class field in Ascot's King George VI and Queen Elizabeth Stakes.*

the classic won quite early in the straight, opening a gap and then running on resolutely to beat Carlingford Castle by three lengths. It was an amazing transformation – maiden to Derby winner inside two months. When two more races brought two defeats, third to Shareef Dancer in the Irish Derby and to Seymour Hicks in the Great Voltigeur Stakes, it seemed that he had not only reached the limit of his progress but was now on the way downhill. On the other hand, he did come back lame from York, so there was an excuse for his performance there.

Teenoso made a slightly disappointing start at four, only third in the John Porter Stakes at Newbury, and was not impressive when he won the Ormonde Stakes at Chester, but on his remaining two appearances he showed himself in an altogether different light – in fact, in the best form of his career. He won a fast-run race for the Grand Prix de Saint-Cloud, galloping home in tremendous style on firm ground he was supposed to dislike. Better still, he beat an intensely competitive field for the King George VI & Queen Elizabeth Stakes. First or second all the way, he had a string of other classic winners coming at him in the straight, but he just kept up his relentless gallop and, one by one, they were forced to concede, the last of them being Sadler's Wells. It was an outstanding display, again on firm going, positive proof that Teenoso was one of the best mile-and-a-half horses of the last decade. Sadly, he did not run again; he was withdrawn from the 'Arc', for which he had been ante post favourite, two days before the race.

Although he was a favourite with backers, Teenoso had already proved less popular with breeders – or rather, he could not find favour on the terms proposed by Eric Moller. The owner had offered the colt for syndication at £300,000 a share after the 'King George', and he found nobody willing to agree that £12 million was a reasonable valuation. That would have entailed his standing at a fee of around £75,000 or £80,000, a fierce amount for one of his breeding, and it just was not on. Moller accordingly went back to the market and said he would stand the horse himself, offering a choice of fees – £25,000, or £40,000 with a live foal concession. Many breeders felt that the real choice was to take him or leave him, and they were quite content to leave him. The horse might well suit private breeders who wanted a horse with no two-year-old form and no winning form at under 12 furlongs, but Moller would find that such people were thin on the ground. As for commercial breeders, the price made him a 'no-go area'.

## TEENOSO                                    (bay, 1980)

| | | | |
|---|---|---|---|
| **Youth** (b 1973) | Ack Ack | Battle Joined | Armageddon / Ethel Walker |
| | | Fast Turn | Turn-to / Cherokee Rose |
| | Gazala | Dark Star | Royal Gem / Isolde |
| | | Belle Angevine | L'Amiral / Bella |
| **Furioso** (b 1971) | Ballymoss | Mossborough | Nearco / All Moonshine |
| | | Indian Call | Singapore / Flittemere |
| | Violetta | Pinza | Chanteur / Pasqua |
| | | Urshalim | Nasrullah / Horama |

### Racing record

| Year | Starts | Wins | 2nd | 3rd | 4th | £ |
|------|--------|------|-----|-----|-----|---|
| 1982 | 3 | - | - | - | 1 | 262 |
| 1983 | 6 | 3 | 1 | 2 | - | 209,150 |
| 1984 | 4 | 3 | - | 1 | - | 242,589 |
| | 13 | 6 | 1 | 3 | 1 | 452,001 |

### Principal wins

| | |
|---|---|
| 1983 | Lingfield Derby Trial Stakes-Gr3 |
| | Derby Stakes-Gr1 |
| 1984 | Ormonde Stakes-Gr3 |
| | Grand Prix de Saint-Cloud-Gr1 |
| | King George VI & Queen Elizabeth Stakes-Gr1 |

Teenoso went to Lord Carnarvon's Highclere Stud while numerous individuals attempted to make Moller see reason, but he was a difficult man. By the time he permitted a significant reduction in the horse's fee, most people in the industry had written him off as a lost cause. The charge came down to £10,000 in 1988, when Teenoso's first eight runners appeared, winning three races between them. Moller died that year and in 1989 rather more than 30 mares were attracted at a further reduced fee of £6000. When White Lodge Stud and all its bloodstock were acquired by Sheikh Mohammed, it was announced that Teenoso would stand in 1990 at only £3000. By the end of February bookings were running at around 40. He will need good results soon to avoid following Henbit into the ranks of N.H. sires.

# Thatching

THE Thoroughbred racehorse is the best documented of all animal species, the human race not excepted. There are accurate breeding and performance records of the entire breed since its creation around 300 years ago – a vast bank of information which, you might think, ought to yield an immense amount of knowledge on what breeders should do to enable them to breed better racehorses. It would surely be impossible to spend a day in the British Museum Library and come out as ignorant as you went in, so there must be wisdom available from racing's equivalent store of data. Unfortunately, that analogy is not as apt as it might seem. Imagine how much you would learn in a day at the British Museum Library if you were unable to read.

All the breeding and performance records amount to nothing unless we have the key to understanding them. That lies in the science of genetics, and without a thorough knowledge of how heredity works in the Thoroughbred, we are illiterate, as clueless about how to interpret the records as our forefathers were when James Weatherby began setting them out in the first edition of the *General Stud Book* in 1791. Genetics is still a young science, and geneticists have yet to apply themselves to a proper study of the racehorse, so until they do breeders will rely on their traditional tools of observation, experience and intuition when devising their matings - unless, as often occurs, all those aids are dispensed with for the sake of commercial expediency.

In addition, until genetics provides proofs, theories will abound, and breeders who put theories into practice need never feel foolish. There is nobody who can say what is right and what is wrong. When they obtain the result they sought, they can never be certain that it happened because of their theory; but who is to say that it did not work when the creature stands proudly in the winner's enclosure?

Vincent O'Brien, a successful breeder as well as an exceptional trainer, had a theory. He owned a mare called Abella, a good winner of three races who descended in the female line from Dalmary, a notable broodmare herself and the dam of daughters who had excelled at stud. Dalmary had become the ancestress of numerous outstanding performers on both sides of the Atlantic, and among them was

Thatch, an outstanding sprinter and miler whom O'Brien had trained to win the St James's Palace Stakes, the July Cup and the Sussex Stakes in 1973. In the following year, O'Brien hit upon the idea of mating Abella with Thatch, the theory being that a 'double dose' of Dalmary's influence might well produce a superior racehorse. Whether or not the theory was right, he got his superior racehorse. The result was Thatching, one of the two best sprinters of his crop. For good measure, the product of an identical mating in the following year was Golden Thatch, also a high-class sprinter.

Thatching's rise to stardom came late and suddenly. He broke a bone in a hind foot as a two-year-old and was not seen on a racecourse until October 1978, when he made up for lost time with three races in 24 days. O'Brien took him to Newmarket for his debut in a minor race over a mile, and the colt finished second, beaten three lengths. Back in Ireland he ran twice at Leopardstown, second again (at 7/2 on) in a maiden over seven furlongs, but successful a week later against modest opponents over nine furlongs.

That first-season form really did not amount to much, but O'Brien was keenly aware that Thatching had talent. He took him back to Newmarket in the following spring and ran him in the Group 3 Earl of Sefton Stakes, although the colt's owner, Robert Sangster, had the obvious favourite for the race in Hawaiian Sound. Victory went to the first colours, while Thatching was clearly a spent force at the end of seven furlongs. The trainer decided to switch him back to sprints, and gave him his first trial in the Group 3 Duke of York Stakes at York. He started slowly and he did not run straight, but he won decisively all the same, finishing two lengths clear of Persepolis. It was too soon to get over-excited about him. Next time at Sandown he met better rivals and could finish only fourth to Double Form in the Temple Stakes. Once more he veered off a straight line, and blinkers were prescribed.

Thatching's summer performances established him as a sprinter of outstanding merit. At Royal Ascot he was never headed in the Group 3 Cork and Orrery Stakes, bounding away to beat Rose Above by four lengths. At Newmarket he gave a brilliant display in the Group 1 July Cup, leading throughout and winning by five lengths from a top-quality field which included leading sprinters from France (Sigy) and America (Topsider). Such was Thatching's dominance that day that O'Brien resolved to allow him the opportunity to emulate his sire in the Sussex Stakes, but the colt was not up to that. He led them all for six furlongs, and that was his limit; Kris won it, and he finished last.

Having run out of his distance, Thatching now ran out of luck. His last two races were over five furlongs and he lost them both, the first after he had finished first, the second before he had started. There was never a doubt about the identity of the best horse in the Group 2 York Sprint Championship. Thatching showed much the best pace and was being pulled up as he passed the post with two and a half lengths to spare over Ahonoora. Unfortunately, as at the spring meeting, Thatching had drifted across the course, and this time he caused interference to others as he did so. The Stewards placed him last and suspended the 'careless' Lester Piggott for four days. At the end of a season in which he never ran in Ireland, Thatching made a wasted trip to France. On the notoriously unfair Longchamp sprint course he drew the impossible 12 stall in a field of 13 for the Prix de l'Abbaye; his ninth place was as good as could be expected.

Thatching retired to stand at the Longfield Stud, and though he has moved since on two or three occasions he has always served under the Coolmore banner. His original fee was IR6000gns, and from the start he proved popular with Irish breeders, covering large books yet remaining commercially viable through the ready acceptance of his yearlings. In 1984, by which time he had had nothing of much consequence to race for him, his fee was up to IR15,000gns, presumably based on his good sales record and his large number of minor winners.

The Thatching style has not varied much over the years. A good-looking horse himself, he has tended to get athletic yearlings who appeal to trainers. Because of his large crops he has had plenty of winners, but his ratio of winners to foals has always been low, and for a long time there seemed to be a definite limit to the class he could impart to his offspring. Of his ten European Pattern winners to the end of 1989, only one (Wiganthorpe) won at Group 2 level; all the others were Group 3 horses. In the spring of 1990 Tirol, with his splendid victories in the Newmarket and Curragh 2000 Guineas, proved himself the exception to the rule.

The most remarkable facet of Thatching's career at stud is that he has proved such a great friend to breeders. After seven seasons' representation he was apparently exposed as just an ordinary sire, yet the demand for his eighth crop of yearlings was extraordinary, with prices ranging up to 140,000gns. His fee for 1990, when he stood at Grange Stud in County Cork, was IR12,500gns.

*Thatching, a popular stallion among breeders, being exercised at Longfield Stud.*

## Racing record

| Year | Starts | Wins | 2nd | 3rd | 4th | £ |
|------|--------|------|-----|-----|-----|---|
| 1977 | 0 | | | | | |
| 1978 | 3 | 1 | 2 | - | - | 2,065 |
| 1979 | 8 | 3 | - | - | - | 48,541 |
| | — | — | — | — | — | ———— |
| | 11 | 4 | 2 | - | - | 50,606 |

## Principal wins

1979   Duke of York Stakes-Gr3
         Cork and Orrery Stakes-Gr3
         July Cup-Gr1

## Principal progeny

**1981**

ch f ALABAMA NANA (ex Image Intensifier, by Dancer's Image)
     1985   First Flight Handicap-Gr3
b f ARVEL (ex Twist of Lemon, by Northfields)
     1984   Premio Omenoni-Gr3

**1982**

ch f ABERUSCHKA (ex Veruschka, by Lorenzaccio)
     1986   Palomar Handicap-Gr2
             Dahlia Handicap-Gr3
ch c EXHIBITIONER (ex Miss Pudge, by Green God)
     1985   Greenlands Stakes-Gr3
ch f QUIET THOUGHTS (ex Fleet Serenade, by Lorenzaccio)
     1985   Athasi Stakes-Gr3

**1983**

b f BEAUJOLAISE (ex Benthose, by Dapper Dan)
     1985   Prix Eclipse-Gr3
b c RUSTIC AMBER (ex Forever Amber, by Bold Lad)
     1986   Greenlands Stakes-Gr3

**1984**

b c DARCY'S THATCHER (ex Lancette, by Double Jump)
     1986   Anglesey Stakes-Gr3
b f FITZWILLIAM PLACE (ex Panetona, by Pan)
     1987   Prix de Sandringham-Gr3
             Prix Messidor-Gr3

## THATCHING     (bay, 1975)

| | | | |
|---|---|---|---|
| Thatch (b 1970) | Forli | Aristophanes | Hyperion / Commotion |
| | | Trevisa | Advocate / Veneta |
| | Thong | Nantallah | Nasrullah / Shimmer |
| | | Rough Shod | Gold Bridge / Dalmary |
| Abella (ch 1968) | Abernant | Owen Tudor | Hyperion / Mary Tudor |
| | | Rustom Mahal | Rustom Pasha / Mumtaz Mahal |
| | Darrica | Darius | Dante / Yasna |
| | | Erica Fragrans | Big Game / Jennydang |

     1988   Beverly Hills Handicap-Gr2
     1989   Gamely Handicap-Gr1
ch c MANSOOJ (ex Senta's Girl, by Averof)
     1986   July Stakes-Gr3
ch c WIGANTHORPE (ex Lustrine, by Viceregal)
     1986   Gimcrack Stakes-Gr2

**1986**

b c PUISSANCE (ex Girton, by Balidar)
     1989   Greenlands Stakes-Gr3

**1987**

b f POLAR BIRD (ex Arctic Winter, by Briartic)
     1989   Debutante Stakes-Gr3
br c TIROL (ex Alpine Niece, by Great Nephew)
     1989   Horris Hill Stakes-Gr3
     1990   Craven Stakes-Gr3
             2000 Guineas Stakes-Gr1
             Irish 2000 Guineas-Gr1

# The Minstrel

THERE are probably more good losers in racing than in any other sport, for the excellent reason that everyone involved gets plenty of practice. Even the best and most successful have to lose more often than they win. Nevertheless, there are times when defeats are hard to bear, and in the course of a 14-year association often crowned with triumphs, Vincent O'Brien and Lester Piggott had their share of tribulations, too. They never had a more disastrous weekend than the one in mid-May 1977 when Murphy's Law ruled on The Curragh. Yet out of the darkest despair the pair had ever known together they emerged to strike the richest vein of success they were ever to experience.

It was a two-day fixture, starting on the evening of Friday the 13th, and Piggott was over to ride five three-year-olds for the Ballydoyle stable, among them a prospective Derby mount in Valinsky and that lovely little chesnut, The Minstrel, bidding for what seemed like his last chance of classic glory in the Irish 2000 Guineas. On the Saturday night they sat and reflected despondently on everything that had gone wrong. O'Brien had actually won the Irish 1000 Guineas, but he had won it with a previously unraced filly (Lady Capulet) ridden by Tommy Murphy, while Piggott had finished third on Robert Sangster's other runner, Lady Mere, trained by Barry Hills. The stable had also won the Group 3 Royal Whip, but not with the much-vaunted Valinsky; he had been thoroughly outpointed by 33/1 shot Alleged, the mount of a work-rider. Piggott's other rides for the Ballydoyle had produced an eighth place on Sir Raymond and seconds on Marinsky (at 7/1 on), Loughanreagh and The Minstrel.

What a shame about The Minstrel. The flashy chesnut with four white socks had been such a favourite since Sangster had bought him at Keeneland for $200,000. Everyone at the sale had taken an interest in him, attracted by the fact that he was by Nijinsky's sire out of a daughter of Nijinsky's dam, and they liked him as an individual, too - beautifully put together, and a really athletic-looking little colt. On the other hand, he *was* little, and Nijinsky was large; he was a flashy chesnut, with lots of white about him, whereas Nijinsky was that rich, bright bay most beloved of horsemen. The pair were chalk and cheese, and it seemed inconceivable that they would be runners of comparable merit.

O'Brien soon established that the younger colt had some merit, and he resolved to send him at least some way along the road that Nijinsky had trod. He ran him first in the six-furlong Moy Stakes at The Curragh in September. Remarkably, he sped away from his rivals after half a mile and set a course record time, with margins of five lengths and 12 lengths between him and the third. United with Piggott for the first time in the Group 3 Larkspur Stakes on the same course, The Minstrel won handily by a length from Captain James. Then, as Nijinsky had done before him, The Minstrel journeyed to Newmarket to beat the English in the Dewhurst Stakes, in commanding style by four lengths.

The Minstrel had great speed, of that there was no doubt. He probably was not going to stay, but he ought to be a formidable miler. He began at three at Ascot in a 2000 Guineas Trial Stakes run on atrocious ground. No horse enjoyed those conditions; many could not or would not perform at their best, and some were ruined for life by the experience. The Minstrel showed all his class and courage in a battling win. He went into the 2000 Guineas as an undefeated favourite, but was beaten into third place, a length and the same behind Nebbiolo and Tachypous. As always he tried hard, but on the day he just could not quicken when it mattered. The Irish 2000 Guineas was supposed to provide consolation. Instead, though he beat Nebbiolo and ran his heart out, he failed by a short head to hold Pampapaul. Such gameness deserved better, perhaps, but now his chance of classic fame had gone.

The gloomy Ballydoyle party, at the end of that dreadful Curragh meeting, could only accept that what was done was done. The question was, what next? The Derby was 18 days away. Valinsky was now a no-hoper. Be My Guest was not class enough. Alleged could not be made ready for such a test so soon. Ballydoyle seemed to have nothing to offer to the greatest human asset a horse could have over the Derby course. Piggott had been weighing his options, too, not just from the O'Brien stable, but from everywhere else. He did not wait for the question that Sangster and O'Brien shrank from putting. 'If you run

*The Minstrel, whose toughness and gameness belied his flashy looks.*

The Minstrel, I'll ride him,' he told them, matter-of-fact. It was an option that had seemed not to exist. It took a moment or two to sink in, then assumed the status of a revelation. The party broke up, everyone wreathed in smiles, and racing history changed course.

The Minstrel became a hero in that glorious summer. At Epsom, under a superb ride, he ran the first nine furlongs well within himself. In the tenth his jockey took position and made aim at his target, Hot Grove, and over the last two he charged. The enemy was not going to yield, and the battle had to be won. Every ounce of the colt's courage was required, his last reserves of energy had to be drained. The Minstrel never flinched, and in a display of conspicuous gallantry under fire, the victory was his in the dying strides.

The thought occurred that The Minstrel might emulate Roberto, a Derby winner in similar circumstances, by failing to reproduce his form at The Curragh. In fact he did not need to be so good in the Irish Derby, and he won by a length and a half from Lucky Sovereign, enjoying his easiest race of the season. It was different at Ascot, though. There Piggott used his speed a shade too early, providing the game and tough four-year-old Orange Bay with the opportunity to renew his effort, and The Minstrel was all out to repel him by a short head.

The Minstrel had performed beyond the call of duty, establishing himself as one of the toughest and gamest horses seen in many years. He had done enough, and the time had come to let Alleged show what he could do. His breeder, Eddie Taylor, was eager to have him back at Windfields, and in a deal which valued The Minstrel at $9 million he acquired a half-share. In the following spring he began stud duties, alongside his sire, at a fee of $50,000.

The principal feature of The Minstrel's stud career is the striking difference between the results he has obtained in Europe and those registered in North America. His first Pattern winners here came as soon as they could, in the initial crop of two-year-olds in 1981, but it was 1985 before he was represented by the winner of a Graded race in the States, and that one was a filly repatriated from Europe in a race on grass at The Meadowlands. In fact, until 1990, when Opening Verse improved matters, the sum total of his progeny's Graded wins on dirt in America was one - a race scheduled for the Aqueduct turf course and switched to dirt at the eleventh hour; all the contestants were recognized turf performers.

It is tempting to say that The Minstrel should have spent his stud career in Europe – a move to bring him to England in 1988 failed – but it could not be certain that he would have achieved better results here if he had. He has had access to a deeper pool of quality broodmares in the States, and that may have been crucial to his performance. His overall record is very good, with high-class runners in every crop, ranging from precocious juveniles to classic winners at a mile and a half. What he has lacked is a truly top-class miler and a genuine champion over any distance, and that is what gives him a stud reputation somewhat below those of several other Northern Dancer stallions.

The Minstrel has sired a lot of flashy individuals, but plenty of good hard bays as well. If a number of his fillies have seemed a bit under-sized, they have not under-achieved as a result of it. He has been a notably reliable agent for honesty and determination in the breed. His fee peaked in the mid 80s at $185,000 and he has been available at $50,000 (on 'no-guarantee' terms) since his removal, on the break-up of Windfields, to Overbrook Farm in Kentucky in 1989. He has no son of obvious consequence at stud, and it may well be that he will need his daughters to carry his name into 21st century pedigrees.

## Racing record

| Year | Starts | Wins | 2nd | 3rd | 4th | £ |
|------|--------|------|-----|-----|-----|------|
| 1976 | 3 | 3 | - | - | - | 41,230 |
| 1977 | 6 | 4 | 1 | 1 | - | 291,967 |
| | 9 | 7 | 1 | 1 | - | 333,197 |

## Principal wins

1976    Larkspur Stakes-Gr3
         Dewhurst Stakes-Gr1
1977    Ascot 2000 Guineas Trial Stakes-Gr3
         Derby Stakes-Gr1
         Irish Derby-Gr1
         King George VI & Queen Elizabeth Stakes-Gr1

## Principal progeny

### 1979

b c CHEM (ex Banning, by Crafty Admiral)
     1982    Prix de l'Esperance-Gr3
ch c CRUSADER CASTLE (ex Mille Fleurs, by Jacinto)
     1982    St Leger Italiano-Gr2
ch c LONGLEAT (ex Fair Arrow, by Turn-to)
     1982    Ballyogan Stakes-Gr3
b c PETERHOF (ex Millicent, by Cornish Prince)
     1981    Curragh Stakes-Gr3
         Flying Childers Stakes-Gr2
b c SHARP SINGER (ex Cutty, by Smart)
     1981    Larkspur Stakes-Gr3
     1982    Prix de Guiche-Gr3

### 1980

ch f FIELDS OF SPRING (ex Memory Lane, by Never Bend)
     1983    Herbst Stutenpreis-Gr3
b c L'EMIGRANT (ex Suprina, by Vaguely Noble)
     1982    Prix La Rochette-Gr3
         Criterium de Maisons-Laffitte-Gr2
     1983    Poule d'Essai des Poulains-Gr1
         Prix Lupin-Gr1
b c PLURALISME (ex Cambretta, by Roberto)
     1982    Prix des Chenes-Gr3
     1983    Prix de Guiche-Gr3
     1984    Prix du Chemin de Fer du Nord-Gr3
ch f SHICKLAH (ex Logette, by Forli)
     1982    Zukunfts Rennen-Gr2

## THE MINSTREL       (chesnut, 1974)

| | | | Nearco | Pharos |
|---|---|---|---|---|
| | | Nearctic | | Nogara |
| | Northern Dancer (b 1961) | | Lady Angela | Hyperion |
| | | | | Sister Sarah |
| | | Natalma | Native Dancer | Polynesian |
| | | | | Geisha |
| | | | Almahmoud | Mahmoud |
| | | | | Arbitrator |
| | | | Chop Chop | Flares |
| | | Victoria Park | | Sceptical |
| | Fleur (b 1964) | | Victoriana | Windfields |
| | | | | Iribelle |
| | | | Bull Page | Bull Lea |
| | | Flaming Page | | Our Page |
| | | | Flaring Top | Menow |
| | | | | Flaming Top |

### 1981

b f KANZ (ex Treasure Chest, by Rough'n Tumble)
     1984    Princess Elizabeth Stakes-Gr3

ch f MALAAK (ex Majestic Kahala, by Majestic Prince)
     1984    Cheshire Oaks-Gr3
ch c PALACE MUSIC (ex Come My Prince, by Prince John)
     1984    Prix Daphnis-Gr3
         Champion Stakes-Gr1
     1985    La Coupe de Maisons-Laffitte-Gr3
     1986    John Henry Handicap-Gr1
         Bay Meadows Handicap-Gr2
ch f TREIZIEME (ex Belle Pensee, by Ribot)
     1983    Grand Criterium-Gr1
     1984    Prix de la Grotte-Gr3
         Prix de Psyche-Gr3
ch f VERS LA CAISSE (ex Starushka, by Sham)
     1984    Premio Legnano-Gr2
     1985    Violet Handicap [Div.2]-Gr3

### 1982

ch c WASSL MERBAYEH (ex Avail, by Arturo A.)
     1985    Queen's Vase-Gr3
ch f ZAIZAFON (ex Mofida, by Right Tack)
     1984    Seaton Delaval Stakes-Gr3

**1983**

b c BAKHAROFF (ex Qui Royalty, by Native Royalty)
    1985    Futurity Stakes-Gr1
    1986    Geoffrey Freer Stakes-Gr2
b f HIGH COMPETENCE (ex Starushka, by Sham)
    1986    Premio Legnano-Gr2
b c LASER LANE (ex Kris Kris, by Hoist the Flag)
    1987    Knickerbocker Handicap-Gr3
b c SILVER VOICE (ex Clef d'Argent, by Key to the Mint)
    1987    Manhattan Handicap-Gr1

**1984**

b c BARN FIVE SOUTH (ex Dame Mysterieuse, by Bold Forbes)
    1988    Premio Omenoni-Gr3
gr f MINSTRELLA (ex Flight Dancer, by Misty Flight)
    1986    Phoenix Stakes-Gr1
            Moyglare Stud Stakes-Gr1
            Cheveley Park Stakes-Gr1
b c TERTIARY ZONE (ex Ancient Jewel, by Hail to Reason)
    1987    Lawrence Realization Stakes-Gr2

**1985**

b f MELODIST (ex Native Nurse, by Graustark)
    1988    Oaks d'Italia-Gr1
            Irish Oaks-Gr1 [dead-heat]
ch f MINSTREL'S LASSIE (ex Syriasly, by Damascus)
    1987    Selima Stakes-Gr1
b f SILVER FLING (ex Royal Dilemma, by Buckpasser)
    1988    King George Stakes-Gr3
    1989    Palace House Stakes-Gr3
            Prix de l'Abbaye de Longchamp-Gr1

**1986**

b f MUSICAL BLISS (ex Bori, by Quadrangle)
    1988    Rockfel Stakes-Gr3
    1989    1000 Guineas Stakes-Gr1
ch c OPENING VERSE (ex Obeah, by Cyane)
    1990    Razorback Handicap-Gr2
            Oaklawn Handicap-Gr1

# Top Ville

THERE have been times at Keeneland over the last few years when the profusion of purchases by the Maktoum family has prompted the thought that they would have saved a lot of people a lot of time, trouble and expense by purchasing the entire catalogue beforehand. The idea is generally expressed facetiously, but it is not that outrageous. If it were to happen, it would not be the first time. An auction was scheduled for Longchamp on 3 October 1977, the day after the Prix de l'Arc de Triomphe. Announcements appeared in the press. Catalogues were prepared for mailing to a large international clientele. It promised to be the highlight of the European sales season, upstaging the Newmarket December auction. Then, suddenly, it was off. Somebody had saved a lot of people a lot of time, trouble and expense by buying the entire catalogue.

It was the Aga Khan, clinching one of the shrewdest deals of his life. The cancelled sale was not going to be a regular auction, not an agglomeration of horses from here and there, bred to make money and fattened for market by commercial vendors. This was the dispersal sale of the Haras d'Ouilly, one of the most successful private studs in Europe, and the 39 broodmares, 23 yearlings and 20 foals on offer represented the accumulated wisdom and expertise of 55 years in developing stock which had proved competitive at the highest level in the colours of François Dupré and his widow. Chanteur, Tantieme, Tanerko, Bella Paola, Match, Relko, Reliance, Danseur, Rheffic and a host of other celebrated horses had been raised in the Ouilly paddocks.

In an auction those 82 horses would be dispersed all over the world. The Aga might attend and buy three or six or even a dozen of those he most fancied, and he might strike lucky, but any fraction of the 82 represented only a degree of probability. In the whole group there was certainty. There would be bound to be something to make the 'lock, stock and barrel' purchase worthwhile. Armed with his cash from the Blushing Groom deal, the Aga stepped in. For £1.3 million he had the lot. Among the mares was Val Divine, already carrying Vayrann, the best horse Brigadier Gerard ever got. Among the yearling fillies was Val Divine's daughter, Niece Divine, who became the dam of the Aga's 1987 Prix du Jockey-Club winner, Natroun. Among the yearling colts was Top Ville, who won the Prix du Jockey-Club, became a successful sire, and was sold for £10 million.

Top Ville went into training at Chantilly with François Mathet, who had been associated with the Dupré horses since the days of dual 'Arc' winner Tantieme in the early 50s. He had won a Group 3 race, the Prix de Flore, with the colt's dam Sega Ville, and he had the fondest memories of the grand-dam La Sega, France's champion three-year-old filly of 1962 and Tantieme's most famous daughter. What Mathet did not know about Top Ville's pedigree was that his sire, High Top, in spite of his own good juvenile form and his fine record as a miler, was going to earn renown at stud for middle-distance and staying horses. The trainer soon found that out, though, and Top Ville's career spread the word.

The colt made his debut early in July, taking third place in a hot race for newcomers at Maisons-Laffitte over six furlongs. Both the winner, Pitasia, and the second, Sharpman, outpaced him easily, but he was a respectable third. Later in the month he ran second in a seven-furlong maiden at Chantilly, proving no match for Nadjar but beating 11 others. Mathet had been expecting too much too soon, and he recognized the fact. He gave the colt a few weeks off and brought him back in a mile race at Chantilly against poor maidens. Top Ville disposed of them readily, and soon afterwards began to work like a really promising stayer. In his last two races of the season, he proved that he was one. The Group 3 Prix Saint-Roman featured a highly regarded favourite in Polynikis, but Top Ville showed him no respect, drawing clear in the ninth and last furlong to win by two lengths. Over ten furlongs in the Group 3 Prix de Conde he was even more impressive, pulling away from the battling stable-mates Look Fast and Dear Henry for a four-length victory.

Having won his last three races at two, Top Ville proceeded to win his first three races as a three-year-old. It was a sequence which established him as the dominant middle-distance colt of his crop in the first half of the season. He began in the Group 3 Prix de Guiche with a smooth win over the top-class Bellypha; the margin was only half a length, his superiority greater than that implied. His fourth consecutive Longchamp victory came in the Group 1 Prix Lupin, and he won it by dint of his stamina from Sharpman and Irish River, the latter going down to the only defeat of his career. The time was a course record. In the Prix du Jockey-Club he beat the clock again, but more significantly he beat Le Marmot, who challenged him hard over the last furlong, but was never going to retrieve the ground Top Ville gained in his decisive burst a quarter of a mile from home.

That was the best of Top Ville. Although Le Marmot's challenge failed at Chantilly, he was soon to take over the leadership of the generation. He beat Top Ville decisively in the Group 3 Prix Niel, and when they reconvened at Longchamp for the Arc de Triomphe, Le Marmot ran a blinder to divide Three Troikas and Troy, while an out-of-sorts Top Ville laboured home in seventeenth place.

Top Ville was retired to his owner's Haras de Bonneval in Normandy; the syndication deal valued him at around £3 million, and the Aga Khan retained a substantial shareholding. By no means a handsome horse himself, Top Ville proceeded to get stock who ran better than they looked, the Irish Oaks victory of his first-crop daughter, the lengthy, angular and unprepossessing Princess Pati, providing a good early advertisement. When the colts Saint Estephe and Shardari, from the second crop, began to develop high-class form, it seemed that a major new stallion might be emerging in Europe. The first hints of such an occurrence inevitably attracted interest from America, and the word was out that he was virtually on his way when Sheikh Mohammed moved in and bought him for £10 million to stand at Dalham Hall.

It is highly unlikely that Top Ville would have proved a suitable acquisition for America, although he has had one substantial earner there in Bello Horizonte. His stock are invariably late developers, and of his four Group 1 winners to date in Europe, only Shardari gained his victory at under a mile and a half; even he was probably more at home over the longer distance. Within a year of Top Ville's arrival in England he enjoyed splendid results from the second and third crops conceived in France, but he seemed awfully over-priced at a fee of £40,000, and in his fourth English season he was finally reduced to £30,000.

After such as Saint Estephe, Shardari and Darara departed the racing scene, his results became much less exciting and demand for the yearlings of 1988 and 1989 fell away. Although the first of his English-conceived crops was not due to race until 1990, by that time he had been returned to France. His departure will probably herald a second flurry of successes such as he had in 1986, but chances are that he is not quite the stallion that he once promised to be.

*Top Ville at Dalham Hall Stud before his return to France.*

## Racing record

| Year | Starts | Wins | 2nd | 3rd | 4th | FR |
|------|--------|------|-----|-----|-----|-----|
| 1978 | 5 | 3 | 1 | 1 | - | 302,400 |
| 1979 | 5 | 3 | - | - | 1 | 1,554,000 |
| | 10 | 6 | 1 | 1 | 1 | 1,856,400 |

## Principal wins

1978 Prix Saint Roman-Gr3
     Prix de Conde-Gr3
1979 Prix de Guiche-Gr3
     Prix Lupin-Gr1
     Prix du Jockey-Club-Gr1

## Principal progeny

**1981**

br f EULIYA (ex Eunomia, by Abdos)
    1984 Prix de Royallieu-Gr3
b c KIRMANN (ex Karmouna, by Val de Loir)
    1985 Jockey Club Stakes-Gr2
b f PRINCESS PATI (ex Sarah Siddons, by Le Levanstell)
    1984 Pretty Polly Stakes-Gr2
         Irish Oaks-Gr1

**1982**

b c SAINT ESTEPHE (ex Une Tornade, by Traffic)
    1985 Prix Maurice de Nieuil-Gr2
    1986 Prix d'Harcourt-Gr2
         Coronation Cup-Gr1
b c SHARDARI (ex Sharmada, by Zeddaan)
    1985 Cumberland Lodge Stakes-Gr3
         St Simon Stakes-Gr3
    1986 Princess of Wales's Stakes-Gr2
         York International Stakes-Gr1

**1983**

b c BELLO HORIZONTE (ex Euphorie, by Prudente)
    1989 Arcadia Handicap-Gr2
         New Jersey Turf Classic Handicap-Gr3

# TOP VILLE (bay, 1976)

| | | | Dante |
|--|--|--|--|
| High Top (br 1969) | Derring-Do | Darius | Yasna |
| | | Sipsey Bridge | Abernant |
| | | | Claudette |
| | Camenae | Vimy | Wild Risk |
| | | | Mimi |
| | | Madrilene | Court Martial |
| | | | Marmite |
| Sega Ville (b 1968) | Charlottesville | Prince Chevalier | Prince Rose |
| | | | Chevalerie |
| | | Noorani | Nearco |
| | | | Empire Glory |
| | La Sega | Tantieme | Deux pour Cent |
| | | | Terka |
| | | La Danse | Menetrier |
| | | | Makada |

b f DARARA (ex Delsy, by Abdos)
    1986 Prix de Psyche-Gr3
         Prix Vermeille-Gr1
b c UN DESPERADO (ex White Lightning, by Baldric)
    1986 Prix Eugene Adam-Gr2

**1985**

b f FLORIPEDES (ex Toute Cy, by Tennyson)
    1988 Prix de Lutece-Gr3
b c TOP SUNRISE (ex Marie de Russy, by Sassafras)
    1988 Prix Berteux-Gr3
    1989 Prix de Barbeville-Gr3
         Prix Kergorlay-Gr2
         Prix Royal-Oak-Gr1

**1987**

b c TOP WALTZ (ex Imperial Dancer, by Tudor Music)
    1990 Prix Hocquart-Gr2

# Vaguely Noble

THERE are certain safeguards for purchasers of Thoroughbreds at auction. They vary from company to company, but they generally relate to a few specific defects which are reckoned likely to detract from a horse's usefulness, and in certain cases an animal may be returned. Unfortunately, there are 1,001 other things which might be wrong for which there is no redress. The principle of *caveat emptor* applies, and in the bloodstock business that means: 'If you buy a horse in the belief that it will be fast, and it turns out to be slow, that is your hard luck.' No racehorse ever went for auction with a guarantee that it was of merchantable quality - unless it was Vaguely Noble.

Vaguely Noble did not go to the sales as an unbroken yearling who might or might not be able to perform the function for which he was bought. He came into the ring at the Newmarket December Sales on 7 December 1967 officially the second-best two-year-old in England, potentially the best three-year-old in the world. The first bid was 80,000gns, more than double the record price for a horse in training, which had stood since 1900. The bidding rose swiftly into six figures and beyond, halting momentarily at 125,000gns. 'He could still be cheap,' auctioneer Ken Watt insisted, and there were still two fellows on hand with money who agreed with him. On they went to 136,000gns before the hammer fell. The price was a world record for any Thoroughbred at auction, but Watt was right about him. He was the cheapest horse ever sold.

If Lionel Holliday had lived two more years, Vaguely Noble would not have gone to auction. That crusty Yorkshireman was the last of the old school of owner-breeders, with studs in England and Ireland, and a private trainer who could never count on an extended tenure of office. He died in December 1965 and it took years to wind up his estate. Vaguely Noble, in common with a lot of others from the last crop bred by the old man, was given a season in training by the executors before being sent to market.

He spent his campaign at Newmarket with Walter Wharton, who found him an impossible horse to assess. The colt would go just as fast as his company took him, never exerting himself, never asserting himself. He ran first in a six-furlong maiden at Newcastle at the end of August, and was beaten a neck. He tried again at Doncaster in September, over seven furlongs, and was beaten three-quarters of a length. He went to Ascot in October, for another maiden over the same distance, and won by 12 lengths. Everyone assumed that the ground was the cause. It resembled a bog, and Vaguely Noble was probably the only one who could handle it. Still, he had been entered in the Observer Gold Cup, the nation's top mile race for two-year-olds, and he might as well take his chance. That Doncaster race was a revelation. There were four or five who could win approaching the final furlong, but in a matter of strides there was only one. At the finish Vaguely Noble was seven lengths clear.

That was why Vaguely Noble was rated only 1lb from the top of the Free Handicap, and why he fetched 136,000gns at auction. He was a proven top-class galloper, yet one with the scope to be better still. There was no doubt he was of merchantable quality, but what could he win to be worth that amount? The entries for the English classics had closed, and Vaguely Noble's name was not among them. It looked as though he would just have to win the Prix de l'Arc de Triomphe.

The colt's buyers at Newmarket, Robert and Wilma Franklyn, had intended to send him to Paddy Prendergast in Ireland, but when under-bidder Nelson Bunker Hunt persuaded them to part with a half-share, he also induced them to agree to a switch to Etienne Pollet's stable in Chantilly. The 'Arc' would indeed be the target, and that trainer, who had already won the race with La Sorellina and Sea-Bird, would know how to go about it.

Vaguely Noble's second season opened at Longchamp in April with a comfortable win in the Prix de Guiche. That was good, but his victory in the Prix du Lys was better. In a race which took place an hour after the Prix du Jockey-Club, he upstaged the classic colts, forging clear in the last furlong to score by eight lengths. Then came a setback. The formality of a triumph in the Grand Prix de Saint-Cloud became a luckless third place, with jockey Jean Deforge overdoing his waiting tactics. Deforge had to go, and go he did, replaced by Australian Bill Williamson, the man who had guided Vaguely Noble

*Vaguely Noble, who stamped his stock with honesty and soundness.*

to his wins in England as a two-year-old. There were no further problems. Zeddaan, perceived as the only possible threat in the Prix de Chantilly, failed to stay and faded into fifth as the rampant Vaguely Noble registered a four-length win over Felicio. Last December's target did not seem so daunting now, and he started a warm favourite for the Arc de Triomphe in spite of the presence of eight individual classic winners among the opposition. He gave another majestic display, storming clear from two furlongs out and defying the rest to catch him. The best of those classic winners, Sir Ivor, gave chase and left the rest for dead, but he could not gain an inch on the superlative galloping machine who needed only hands-and-heels riding to win by three lengths.

Vaguely Noble was cheap all right. He had recovered all but £12,000 of his purchase price in five starts, and when John Gaines paid $1.25 million for a quarter-share in him shortly afterwards he became the highest-priced syndicated horse on record. That second deal seemed a far greater gamble than the first. Last time he had been bought to do a job he had already proved he could do; now he was switching to a completely different role, and he was a horse who flouted one of the oldest maxims in breeding lore. 'Never trust a horse to be a good sire if he is the son of a bad sire,' it runs, and it is no bad precept in the main. Vaguely Noble was a son of Vienna, and just about the only son of Vienna

anyone could name; that stallion had already been sold – out of Ireland and in disgrace – before his champion reached the racecourse. Nevertheless, Vaguely Noble was out of a Nearco mare, and American breeders would not penalize a horse of his stature, who had size and strength and an ideal temperament to boot.

He wasted no time in establishing himself as a great sire, and the support of Nelson Bunker Hunt was a key factor in making it happen. In 1972 he led the first-season sires' list in England, thanks to Hunt's Observer Gold Cup winner, Noble Decree. In 1973 and 1974 he topped the general sires' table, courtesy of Hunt's celebrated mare Dahlia. He was fifth in 1975, again with Dahlia's assistance, and in 1976 he was second, with the Derby victory of Hunt's colt Empery as the most significant contribution.

It was Dahlia who first spread her sire's fame, journeying back and forth across the Atlantic, recording a series of major triumphs until she was six years old and the world's leading stakes-earning mare, but she was to be only one of four Vaguely Noble products who surpassed the million-dollar mark in prize money. Exceller (bought by Nelson Bunker Hunt as a yearling for only $25,000), Lemhi Gold and Estrapade also achieved that feat, the first and third of them proving their merit in both Europe and the States.

Vaguely Noble's stock were never precocious. The

good juveniles emerged late in the year, and at three a mile was insufficient for them. With few exceptions they were stayers, the good ones often proving very good; they were also honest and remarkably sound, among them many who did not look it. They came in all shapes and sizes, often with faults which kept their sale prices down but with the courage and character to overcome them. The market to Europe was crucial, more so than to most of his era. Without an export outlet, and only dirt tracks to compete on, his stock would have done him little credit.

For the first four years of the 80s Vaguely Noble's fee stood at $100,000, then rose to $150,000 rather against the general trend and with no real justification. There has been little of note from his later crops to date, though there will still be three-year-olds to run for him in 1993. He collapsed and died, shortly after covering a mare, in April 1989, by which time his fee had been reduced to $50,000. Among his stallion sons only Exceller has had much success, and that not to the extent that he may be expected to wield a lot of influence; his virtue, for Americans, is that plenty of his runners can handle dirt tracks. Vaguely Noble's daughters have proved extremely good broodmares in both European and American environments.

## Racing record

| Year | Starts | Wins | 2nd | 3rd | 4th | FR |
|------|--------|------|-----|-----|-----|------|
| 1967 | 4 | 2 | 2 | - | - | 253,776 |
| 1968 | 5 | 4 | - | 1 | - | 1,544,150 |
| | 9 | 6 | 2 | 1 | - | 1,797,926 |

## Principal wins

| | |
|---|---|
| 1967 | Observer Gold Cup |
| 1968 | Prix de Guiche |
| | Prix du Lys |
| | Prix de Chantilly |
| | Prix de l'Arc de Triomphe |

## Principal progeny

### 1970

b c ACE OF ACES (ex Sofarsogood, by Revoked)
    1974   Prix du Chemin de Fer du Nord-Gr3
           Sussex Stakes-Gr1
           Oettingen Rennen-Gr3
ch f DAHLIA (ex Charming Alibi, by Honeys Alibi)
    1973   Prix de la Grotte-Gr3
           Prix Saint-Alary-Gr1
           Irish Oaks Stakes-Gr1
           King George VI & Queen Elizabeth Stakes-Gr1
           Prix Niel-Gr3
           Washington D.C. International Stakes-Gr1
    1974   Grand Prix de Saint-Cloud-Gr1
           King George VI & Queen Elizabeth Stakes-Gr1
           Benson & Hedges Gold Cup-Gr1
           Man o' War Stakes-Gr1
           Canadian International Championship Stakes-Gr2
    1975   Benson & Hedges Gold Cup-Gr1
    1976   Hollywood Invitational Handicap-Gr1
b f MANDERA (ex Foolish One, by Tom Fool)
    1973   Princess Royal Stakes-Gr3
b c NOBLE DECREE (ex Hidden Secret, by Promulgation)
    1972   Observer Gold Cup-Gr1
b c ROYAL AND REGAL (ex Native Street, by Native Dancer)
    1973   Dade Turf Classic Stakes-Gr3
           Bahamas Stakes-Gr3
           Florida Derby-Gr1

## VAGUELY NOBLE                                      (bay, 1965)

| | | | |
|---|---|---|---|
| Vienna (ch 1957) | Aureole | Hyperion | Gainsborough / Selene |
| | | Angelola | Donatello / Feola |
| | Turkish Blood | Turkhan | Bahram / Theresina |
| | | Rusk | Manna / Baby Polly |
| Noble Lassie (b 1956) | Nearco | Pharos | Phalaris / Scapa Flow |
| | | Nogara | Havresac / Catnip |
| | Belle Sauvage | Big Game | Bahram / Myrobella |
| | | Tropical Sun | Hyperion / Brulette |

### 1971

b c DUKE OF MARMALADE (ex Mock Orange, by Dedicate)
    1975   Premio Roma-Gr1 [dead-heat]
    1976   Premio Roma-Gr1
b c MISSISSIPIAN (ex Gazala, by Dark Star)
    1973   Grand Criterium-Gr1
    1974   Prix Niel-Gr3
gr c PASSIONATE PIRATE (ex Forgiving, by Fleet Nasrullah)
    1976   Stars and Stripes Handicap-Gr2

### 1972

ch f NOBILIARY (ex Goofed, by Court Martial)
    1975   Prix de la Grotte-Gr3
           Prix de Saint-Alary-Gr1
           Washington D.C. International Stakes-Gr1

### 1973

b c EMPERY (ex Pamplona, by Postin)
    1976   Derby Stakes-Gr1

b c EXCELLER (ex Too Bald, by Bald Eagle)
    1976   Prix du Lys-Gr3
             Grand Prix de Paris-Gr1
             Prix Royal-Oak-Gr1
    1977   Coronation Cup-Gr1
             Grand Prix de Saint-Cloud-Gr1
             Canadian International Championship Stakes-Gr1
    1978   Arcadia Handicap-Gr3
             San Juan Capistrano Handicap-Gr1
             Hollywood Invitational Handicap-Gr1
             Hollywood Gold Cup Handicap-Gr1
             Sunset Handicap-Gr1
             Jockey Club Gold Cup Stakes-Gr1
             Oak Tree Invitational Stakes-Gr1
b f PAINT THE TOWN (ex Belle de Nuit, by Warfare)
    1976   Prix de Royallieu-Gr3
    1977   Grand Prix d'Evry-Gr2

### 1974

br f HARTEBEEST (ex Sparkalark, by Cornish Prince)
    1977   Prix de la Grotte-Gr3
b c SPORTING YANKEE (ex Sale Day, by To Market)
    1976   Futurity Stakes-Gr1
ch c VAGARIES (ex Lindaria, by Sea-Bird)
    1978   Grand Prix d'Evry-Gr2

### 1975

ch f AMAZER (ex Sale Day, by To Market)
    1978   Prix de Royallieu-Gr3
b c GAY MECENE (ex Gay Missile, by Sir Gaylord)
    1978   Prix de Guiche-Gr3
             Prix Eugene Adam-Gr2
             Prix Niel-Gr3
    1979   Grand Prix de Saint-Cloud-Gr1
b c INKERMAN (ex Crimea, by Princequillo)
    1978   Gallinule Stakes-Gr2
             Joe McGrath Memorial Stakes-Gr1
    1980   Sunset Handicap-Gr1
b c REGAL AND ROYAL (ex Native Street, by Native Dancer)
    1978   Jamaica Handicap-Gr3
b f TRILLIONAIRE (ex Amerigo's Fancy, by Amerigo)
    1978   Princess Royal Stakes-Gr3
b c VALOUR (ex Louisador, by Indian Hemp)
    1978   Grosser Preis von Baden-Gr1
    1979   Prix Jean de Chaudenay-Gr2

### 1976

b c NOBLE SAINT (ex Santa Paula, by Santa Claus)
    1979   Great Voltigeur Stakes-Gr2
             Premio Roma-Gr1
    1980   Yorkshire Cup-Gr2
b f QUADRUPLER (ex Alota Calories, by Candy Spots)
    1979   Premio Legnano-Gr3
             Premio Principe Amedeo-Gr2
             St Leger Italiano-Gr2

### 1977

br c CORVARO (ex Delmora, by Sir Gaylord)
    1979   Prix Saint Roman-Gr3
             Prix de Conde-Gr3
    1980   Prix Eugene Adam-Gr2
b c GONZALES (ex Gazala, by Dark Star)
    1980   Gallinule Stakes-Gr2
             Blandford Stakes-Gr2
             Irish St Leger-Gr1

### 1978

b c EMINENCY (ex Minnetonka, by Chieftain)
    1982   Razorback Handicap-Gr3
             Oaklawn Handicap-Gr2
    1983   Razorback Handicap-Gr3
             Christmas Handicap-Gr3
    1984   Clark Handicap-Gr3
ch c LEMHI GOLD (ex Belle Marie, by Candy Spots)
    1982   San Juan Capistrano Handicap-Gr1
             Sword Dancer Stakes-Gr2
             Marlboro Cup Invitational Handicap-Gr1
             Jockey Club Gold Cup Stakes-Gr1
ch f NOBLE DAMSEL (ex Tender Camilla, by Prince Tenderfoot)
    1982   New York Handicap-Gr3
gr c TERRENO (ex Ileana, by Abernant)
    1982   La Coupe-Gr3
             Gran Premio di Milano-Gr1
    1983   Grand Prix de Vichy-Gr3

### 1979

b f FRIENDSWOOD (ex Summer Point, by Summer Tan)
    1982   Premio Lydia Tesio-Gr1
             Gran Premio del Jockey Club-Gr1
b f LAST FEATHER (ex Quill, by Princequillo)
    1982   Musidora Stakes-Gr3
br f VIDOR (ex Prestissimo, by Bold Reasoning)
    1982   Prix de Royaumont-Gr3
             E.P. Taylor Stakes-Gr2

### 1980

ch f ESTRAPADE (ex Klepto, by No Robbery)
    1984   La Coupe de Maisons-Laffitte-Gr3
    1985   Santa Ana Handicap-Gr1
             Gamely Handicap-Gr1
             Las Palmas Handicap-Gr2
             Yellow Ribbon Stakes-Gr1
    1986   Beverly Hills Handicap-Gr2
             Arlington Million Stakes-Gr1
             Oak Tree Invitational Stakes-Gr1
b f HAWAIIAN RAIN (ex Lullaby, by Hawaii)
    1984   N.E. Manion Cup Handicap-Gr3
b f REINE MATHILDE (ex Gay Matelda, by Sir Gaylord)
    1984   Prix de Malleret-Gr2
             Prix de l'Opera-Gr2
             E.P. Taylor Stakes-Gr2
b/br c TALAKENO (ex Katonka, by Minnesota Mac)
    1986   San Luis Obispo Handicap-Gr2
             Seneca Handicap-Gr3
    1987   Bernard Baruch Handicap-Gr2

### 1982

ch c NOBLE FIGHTER (ex Lindaria, by Sea-Bird)
    1985   Turf Classic Stakes-Gr1

### 1983

b c EL CUITE (ex Assez Cuite, by Graustark)
    1986   Gran Premio d'Italia-Gr1
             Prix Royal-Oak-Gr1
b c ROSEDALE (ex Ivory, by Riverman)
    1986   Premio Principe Amedeo-Gr2
    1987   San Juan Capistrano Handicap-Gr1

### 1985

b c WELKIN (ex Nina North, by Alleged)
    1988   Prix La Force-Gr3

# Index

## GENERAL INDEX

# HORSE INDEX